A FIELD BOOK OF
North American Snakes

Harmless and Poisonous Coral Snakes. The upper is a small Coral King Snake (*Lampropeltis elapsoides*), the lower a poisonous Coral Snake (*Micruroides euryxanthus*). While such ringed species have similar colors, and appear alike on gross examination, the red rings contact the black with harmless kinds, while with the dangerous Coral Snakes, both eastern and western, the red rings are margined with yellow.

A FIELD BOOK OF
North American Snakes

By RAYMOND L. DITMARS, Litt. D.

Curator of Mammals and Reptiles at the
NEW YORK ZOOLOGICAL PARK

ILLUSTRATED

Doubleday & Company, Inc.

GARDEN CITY, NEW YORK   1949

PRINTED AT THE *Country Life Press*, GARDEN CITY, N. Y., U. S. A.

TO MY WIFE

A Coast-to-Coast Companion
in the Field and in the
Laboratory

Acknowledgments

THE AUTHOR wishes to express his keen appreciation for courtesies extended by Dr. Thomas Barbour, Mr. Roger Conant, Dr. Howard K. Gloyd, Mr. L. M. Klauber, Mr. Marlin Perkins and Dr. Gordon L. Walls. Also in the acquiring of specimens particularly wanted for illustrations, thanks are extended to Mr. Ross Allen, Mr. Arthur Greenhall, Mr. A. H. King, Mr. Otto M. Locke and Mr. Paul Snyder. The work of producing the sectional photographs was done by Mr. Edward R. Osterndorff.

A series of photographs of western snakes is printed with the permission of Mr. L. M. Klauber, and another series was selected from the files of the New York Zoological Society. These are respectively acknowledged on the plates.

Contents

PAGE

Introduction ix

CHAPTER

Part One

THE SNAKES OF NORTH AMERICA

   I   A Reptile Survey of North America 3
  II   Habits of North American Snakes 10
 III   How to Identify Snakes 16

Part Two

THE SNAKES OF NORTHEASTERN NORTH AMERICA

 IV   Key to the Snakes of Northeastern North America . 23
  V   The Northeastern Nonpoisonous Snakes 33
 VI   The Northeastern Poisonous Snakes 63

Part Three

THE SNAKES OF SOUTHEASTERN NORTH AMERICA

 VII   Key to the Snakes of Southeastern North America . 73
VIII   The Southeastern Nonpoisonous Snakes 90
 IX   The Southeastern Poisonous Snakes 126

CHAPTER   PAGE

Part Four

THE SNAKES OF WESTERN NORTH AMERICA

X   Key to the Snakes of Western North America .   .   139

XI   The Nonpoisonous Western Snakes   170

XII   The Mildly Poisonous Rear-fanged Snakes   .   .   232

XIII   The Poisonous Snakes of Western North America   .   239

Part Five

XIV   Treatment of Snake Bites   267

XV   Classified List of the North American Snakes   .   .   276

BIBLIOGRAPHY   292

INDEX   295

Introduction

THE NEED FOR a field book on the North American snakes has become increasingly evident. There has been broad growth in the interest about reptiles, heightened by automobile touring and camping and accessibility to the vast wild areas of the national parks. Agriculturists are coming to consider the economic value of certain kinds of rodent-eating snakes. To many the use of a field book may be reduced to defining harmless reptiles from dangerous kinds—and that is a practical point of view which I have specifically considered.

Trend of inquiry has indicated the need for a clear and condensed identification book without technical details hard to diagnose. Such simplification is actually more difficult for a scientist to write than formal description. It represents an attempt at translation of technical terms which are only partial in definition. However, as this book stands, it is a general answer to a great number of queries which have come to me through correspondence, and to many questions from lecture audiences.

The study of this book will afford a fair introduction to the larger and formal works about North American reptiles, in which details regarding identification are carried to great length and where further problems about reptilian life may be solved.

Regarding distribution: When range is given, as for example, "Southeastern Virginia to Florida," it is meant that the kind of snake concerned occurs from a *section* of the former state to and *including* the latter-named state. If the description reads "Virginia to Florida," the range covers both states, including, of course, the states between the boundaries outlined. If the kind under consideration extends but a short distance into Florida, I have indicated the fact as follows: "to extreme northern Florida."

Throughout the text the ranges for the greater distances are approximate, without attempt at detailed definition of occurrences within states, except in particularly significant instances. Ranges as indicated by recent findings are brought up to date as far as possible.

Nomenclature: Zoological science undergoes constant changes as to scientific names. This comes about through intensive studies of the lists and deductions about priority of original descriptions. It thus sometimes happens that old names which have been buried in the lists of synonyms are lifted from such sources and take rank over those of long standing in the formal lists. Also, former full species are decided to represent nothing more than subspecies—connecting intergrades having been discovered. Changes of genera, or groupings, also take place, with further studies of relationship or, again, decided priority of former delineators of genera.

Such changes are confusing to younger students, who have become conversant with existing lists, only to find they must further master later ones. This was illustrated by a keen boy in high school, who had learned the scientific names of the snakes of his state, then was confronted with a list in which several of the names had been changed. He wanted to know why this had been done, and I explained that herpetology is undergoing constant change. His next question was embarrassing:

"Will it ever be right?"

I realized that from his point of view, in the changing of long-standing names, it may never be "right," as there is always the possibility of discovering in the interminable list of zoological descriptions a line here and there to indicate ultimately that one description may supersede another; that a genus has been named and stood for years, when it must fall and another be selected, as in preceding years, in some other branch, a similar name had been used. Quite recently I noted that a North American snake genus must be changed, as it was found that its name was preoccupied by a genus of fish.

To hold the manuscript in anticipation of such changes would be an endless procedure. It would never be published. As this manuscript proceeded towards completion, my scientific colleagues cordially sent me writings and notes of changes. These have been incorporated in the final proofs.

For the general reader of this field book, for general identification purposes and study of snakes, the preceding explanations relating to nomenclature may be regarded as rather superficial when compared to the scope of the serpent fauna of North America. Such understanding, however, is of interest as part of the background of North American reptiles.

List of Illustrations

Allen's Mud Snake, Fla. 19
Banded Rat Snake, Fla. 8
Banded Water Snake, Ga. 16
Blacksnake, N.Y. 3
Black-headed Snake, Fla. 20
Black Swamp Snake, Fla. 19
Blanchard's Water Snake, La. 17
Brown Water Snake, Fla. 15
Bull Snake, Tex. 9
Butler's Garter Snake, Ohio 23
California Black-headed Snake 41
California Boa 32
California Garter Snake 40
California King Snake (full) 36
California King Snake (mid-dorsal and abdominal sections) 11
California Lyre Snake 41
Cane-brake Rattlesnake, Ga. 28
Cane-brake Rattlesnake (rattles only) 31
Chaparral Flat-nosed Snake, Cal. 34
Coachwhip Snake, Ga. 33
Coachwhip Snake, Tex. 4
Common Water Snake (full), N.Y. 39
Common Water Snake (mid-dorsal and abdominal sections), N.Y. 16
Cope's Water Snake, Fla. 17
Copperhead Snake, N.Y. 27
Copperhead Snake (head) 42
Coral Snake (head and fangs) 43

Corn Snake, Fla. 6
Crotaline Snake (head and folding fangs) 43
Desert Leaf-nosed Snake, Cal. 34
Diamond-back Rattlesnake (full), Fla. 45
Diamond-back Rattlesnake (head), Fla. 27
Diamond-back Rattlesnake (section), Fla. 29
Diamond-back Rattlesnake (rattle), Fla. 30
Diamond-back Rattlesnake (rattles only) 31
Diamond-back Water Snake, Ark. 15
Eastern Garter Snake, N.Y. 40
Eastern King Snake, Ga. 37
Eastern Ribbon Snake, N.Y. 22
Flat-nosed Snake, Tex. 4
Flat-tailed Water Snake, Fla. 18
Florida Brown Snake 20
Florida Green Water Snake 14
Florida King Snake 12
Fox Snake, Ind. 7
Fox Snake, Ohio 35
Garter Snake, Fla. 21
Garter Snake, N.Y. 21
Green Water Snake, La. 14
Hog-nosed Snake, N.Y. 24
Hog-nosed Snake, Okla. 24
Horned Rattlesnake, Ariz. 48
Horn Snake, Fla. 1
Indigo Snake, Fla. 3

Keeled Green Snake, Fla.	2
Kirtland's Water Snake, Ohio	13
Lake Water Snake, Ohio	18
LeConte's Snake, Tex.	5
Lindheimer's Snake, Tex.	8
Marcy's Garter Snake, Tex.	23
Massasauga (full), Ohio	45
Massasauga (head), Ohio	28
Massasauga; Prairie Rattler, Ohio	27
Mexican King Snake, Tex.	12
Milk Snake, N.Y.	36
Milk Snake (abdominal), N.Y.	10
Northern Copperhead Snake, N.J.	25
Pacific Rattlesnake, Cal.	47
Pine Snake, N.J.	35
Pine Snake (head and mid-dorsal), N.J.	9
Pink Rat Snake, Fla. Keys	6
Prairie King Snake, Okla.	11
Prairie Rat Snake (head and abdominal), Okla.	7
Prairie Rat Snake (mid-dorsal), Okla.	8
Prairie Rattlesnake, Neb.	47
Prairie Rattlesnake (section), Neb.	31
Queen Snake, Ohio	13
Rainbow Snake, Fla.	1
Red and Black Ground Snake, Cal.	38
Red-bellied Snake, N.Y.	20
Red-bellied Water Snake, S.C.	39
Red Milk Snake, Ark.	10
Red Rattlesnake, Cal.	29
Red Rattlesnake (rattles only)	31
Ringed Ground Snake, Cal.	37
Ring-necked Snake, N.Y.	2
Rubber Boa, Cal.	33
Scarlet King Snake, Fla.	10
Scarlet King Snake, Va.	10
Scarlet Snake, Fla.	10
Short-tailed Snake, Fla.	5

Slender Gopher Snake, Tex.	5
Smooth Brown Snake, S.C.	20
Smooth Green Snake, N.Y.	2
Southern Copperhead Snake, Ga.	44
Southern Copperhead Snake, La.	25
Southern Hog-nosed Snake, Fla.	24
Southern Ribbon Snake, Fla.	22
Spotted King Snake, La.	12
Spotted Night Snake, Cal.	38
Spreading "Adder"	42
Storer's Snake, N.Y.	20
Striped Racer, Tex.	4
Striped Swamp Snake, Ohio	19
Tiger Rattlesnake, Ariz.	48
Timber Rattlesnake, N.Y.	28
Water Moccasin (full), Fla.	44
Water Moccasin (head), Fla.	27
Water Moccasin (mid-dorsal and tail), Fla.	26
Water Snake, Fla.	26
Western Blind Snake, Cal.	32
Western Copperhead Snake, Tex.	25
Western Diamond Rattlesnake (full), Tex.	46
Western Diamond Rattlesnake (section), Tex.	29
Western Diamond Rattlesnake (mid-section and rattles), Tex.	30
Western Diamond Rattlesnake (rattles only)	31
Western Diamond Rattlesnake (rattles of young snake)	31
Western Ribbon Snake, Tex.	22
Worm Snake, N.Y.	1
Yellow-bellied Racer, Ohio	3
Yellow-bellied Water Snake, La.	13
Yellow Lipped Snake, Fla.	2

PART ONE

The Snakes of North America

CHAPTER I

A Reptile Survey of North America

Brief study of the maps accompanying these chapters will show the method used in defining regional areas for grouping the snakes of North America.

The continent is divided into three "zones." While these are not highly distinctive in regard to the reptilian fauna, there is enough difference to warrant the groupings, treat chapters geographically and hence simplify identification by reference to locality.

As reptile life thins out in recession from warm latitudes, the smallest number of North American snakes occurs in southern Canada, north of which region reptiles disappear. In the United States, Maine has about the sparsest number of snakes and next come Vermont and New Hampshire. This area of New England is comparatively free of poisonous snakes. But one kind, the Timber or Banded Rattlesnake has ever been found there. While in the past it has been recorded from southern Maine, it now appears to have almost disappeared in that state. Thus of the whole United States, from coast to coast, Maine appears to be the only state almost devoid of poisonous reptiles. There are few rattlers in New Hampshire, and in Vermont they are seldom recorded except in the western portion. Every other state has its one or several kinds of poisonous snakes. They have their greatest number (rattlesnakes) in the Southwest. Three kinds of rattlesnakes get into Canada.

Where are snakes generally, nonvenomous and dangerous, most abundant in North America? That region is the southeastern United States. In its concentration of variety of species it geographically swings in crescentic form through the coastal states from North Carolina, South Carolina, Georgia, Florida, Alabama, Mississippi and

Louisiana to eastern Texas. In this region of low elevation, with winters short and tempered, in fact over much of it a near-subtropical background with long, hot summers and usually abundant rains, reptilian life flourishes. Over sixty kinds of snakes inhabit this region, of which six are poisonous. Three of these are rattlesnakes; also there are the Water Moccasin, Copperhead Snake and the slender Coral or Harlequin Snake.

In the northeastern United States, from New Jersey and Pennsylvania to Maine, there are about twenty species of snakes, of which the Copperhead, Massasauga or Swamp Rattlesnake and the Timber Rattlesnake are poisonous. The so-called "moccasin" of these states is not poisonous—the true Water Moccasin does not extend north of Virginia. In the extreme south of this area, if Maryland is included, there is encroachment of a few of the nonvenomous southern species.

In the central states, including the valleys of the Ohio and Mississippi rivers, there is an overlap of southern reptiles, with extension of several species up these valleys to points farther north than in the eastern coastal region—including the northern range of the true Water Moccasin and the Coral Snake, thus increasing the number of poisonous snakes in that area to two over the northeastern United States.

Canada has a moderate number of harmless snakes. The range of the Swamp Rattler or Massasauga swings into Ontario, in the region of the Great Lakes. In south-central Canada the Prairie Rattlesnake extends northward beyond the latitude of Medicine Hat, while the Pacific Rattler extends well into British Columbia. These are the only poisonous snakes of Canada—all rattlesnakes, and readily to be recognized as such.

Within the far-flung area of the United States west of the Mississippi, with terrain changing from fertile valley to great stretches of plains, the lofty Rockies, deserts, the chain of the Sierra Nevada and beyond an ocean-warmed coast, there is not the concentration of serpent species to be noted in the humid coastal region of the Southeast. However, owing to the far greater area, there is an imposing array of serpent life, and some of the species are very abundant. Some of the southern species extend well up the western side of the Mississippi Valley, their extension into the West covering a roughly triangular area with a broad western base in Texas and peak in Kansas and Missouri. Within this area are the poisonous Water Moccasin and the

Coral Snake, which otherwise might be designated as southeastern reptiles. Otherwise, in the entire western area the only poisonous serpents are rattlesnakes, with the exception of a Coral Snake in extreme southern New Mexico and Arizona. Every western state has its one or more kinds of rattlesnakes, with concentration in the Southwest, where there are a dozen. Summing up the typically western snakes, there are approximately 80 species (not including subspecies or varieties), and of these 13 are poisonous.

As a grand total of the snakes inhabiting the United States and southern Canada there are approximately 135 species, this number not including related forms listed as subspecies. Of the total enumerated, there are 20 poisonous species. There are 45 genera, 5 made up of poisonous snakes; a marine type of the southwestern region bringing the total to 6 genera. The aggregation is divided into 5 families. No species occur in Canada that are not to be found in the United States.

From the smallest to the largest of North American snakes, there is great difference in sizes. Species midway between extremes are in the majority, but there are more diminutive species than really large ones. As examples among the smallest are the Worm Snakes, *Carphophis* (average length 9 inches), the Brown Snakes, *Storeria* (average length 10 inches), the Smooth-scaled Brown Snakes, *Virginia* (average length 8 inches) and the Ring-necked Snakes, *Diadophis* (average length 15 inches). The average diameter of these little snakes is about a quarter of an inch. To establish a point of definition of "moderate" size for identification in coming chapters, a length of anywhere from $2\frac{1}{2}$ to $3\frac{1}{2}$ feet may be considered. Definite excess of this points to the really *large* North American snakes.

The largest species, figured from combination of bulk and length, are the Eastern Diamond-back Rattlesnake, with maximum length slightly in excess of 8 feet and weight up to 16 pounds; the Texas Diamond-back Rattlesnake, up to 7 feet and weight to 15 pounds; the Prairie Bull Snake, length about 8 feet, with approximately half the weight of the larger rattlers; the southeastern Indigo or Gopher Snake, length to about 8 feet and weight slightly inferior to the Bull Snake; the Pilot Blacksnake (of broad distribution in the East), length to about 8 feet, with weight similar to the preceding. All of these figures are considerably in excess of the average. Other particularly large snakes are the Rat Snakes and the Racers, among which lengths of 6 to 7 feet are not uncommon. Some of the harmless southern water snakes attain impressive bulk, but seldom exceed 5 feet in length. This is also the case with the poisonous Water Moccasin. It is a relatively thick-bodied species and in exceptional instances attains a weight of 10 pounds.

Among some snakes there are abnormal individuals that reach a length in excess of what may be rated large members of their respective kinds. These are equivalent to giants, and their extreme dimensions may result from glandular abnormalities or exceptionally rich feeding grounds. Thus we have occasional records of Garter Snakes in excess of 4 feet, while their average length is 2½ feet, or 6-foot "Milk" Snakes, among which normally large specimens are about 4 feet long. There was a recent authentic record of an Emory's Rat Snake, in Kansas, that was a few inches longer than 8 feet, while among most specimens few measure as much as 5 feet. Curiously enough, such abnormalities are not authentically recorded among the very largest of the North American snakes, or otherwise the Diamond-back Rattlesnake, Prairie Bull Snake and southern Gopher Snake would produce occasional huge members in excess of 10 feet. I have heard such allegations that were rather thrilling and traced them carefully. Skins that were located were found to be stretched, or if only sections remained, scale sizes showed the former owners to have been inferior to supposition. Photographs from such sources have never been convincing. Some of the declarations related to inference of size about huge snakes that "escaped." Once I thought I was on the way to measure the skin of an 11-foot Florida rattler. The skin was sent to my office at the Zoological Park for verification. On arrival it was carefully measured. It was slightly in excess of 11 feet; moreover it was not stretched. But it was the skin of a South American Boa Constrictor, which, without doubt, had escaped from a circus. Aside from brief mention of reptile abnormalities in this chapter of general review, I have not considered such dimensions in the chapters relating to description of species.

The largest, plus heaviest, North American snake ever personally examined by the author was a Diamond-back Rattlesnake in central Florida. It was 8 feet 3 inches long and 4½ inches in diameter. Its head was 3¼ inches wide. This snake weighed 16 pounds. The next-largest reptile was a Pilot or Mountain Blacksnake captured on a ledge at an elevation of about 2,000 feet, in Sullivan County, New York. This snake was 8 feet 4 inches long and slightly over 2 inches in diameter—hence of much less body bulk than the big Florida rattler. Occasional North American snakes may grow a few inches longer, but dimensions in excess of those given are extremely rare, as figured from the author's collecting experiences over a long period of years and checking of extensive series of specimens received at the Zoological Park during more than thirty-five years.

Diagnosis of the Poisonous Snakes: As the main idea of this field book is to simplify identification of snakes and answer the more frequently recurrent queries, an outline as to the *types* of poisonous snakes is of importance. Some readers' main thought in the use of this book, will be to distinguish dangerous kinds of reptiles from those that are harmless.

In the foregoing paragraph the word "types" of poisonous snakes is used. That is not a scientific definition, but employed for simplification. While there are 20 specifically different poisonous snakes in the United States, 3 of which extend into Canada, there are but *four types,* which the average observer would deduct as such without contact to formal descriptions, and these may be defined as follows:

1. **Coral Snakes.** (Two species. One in the Southeast and Mississippi Valley states; the other in the Southwest, but restricted to the boundary region.)
2. **Copperhead Snake.** (Central Massachusetts to northern Florida; westward in the North to Illinois and in the South to Oklahoma and Texas.)
3. **Water Moccasin.** (Virginia to Florida; westward to southern Illinois and in the south to Texas.)
4. **Rattlesnakes.** (There are sixteen distinct rattlesnakes, from small to very large. Also there are color varieties or subspecies. Every state has one or more kinds of rattlesnakes. They also inhabit southern Canada.)

From the outline it will be seen how it is possible to simplify a diagnosis of the North American snakes that are dangerous. Thus, when I have been asked the question, How many kinds of poisonous snakes are there in the United States? and the answer was expected to be devoid of technical deduction, the answer would be that *there are four "types"*—the **Coral Snake, Copperhead, Water Moccasin** and **Rattlesnake.**

Definition of the four is not complicated:

1. The **Coral Snake** type is of small to moderate size and slender, ringed with scarlet, yellow and black. There are harmless "mimics" but with different arrangement of color rings.

2. The **Copperhead** has vivid and rather characteristic pale and dark brown markings. Differing from harmless snakes, it has elliptic eye pupils instead of round, and a deep pit between eye and nostril.

3. The **Water Moccasin,** which is dull olive or brownish, is relatively thicker-bodied than the harmless water snakes. Like the Copperhead it has elliptic pupils and a deep pit between eye and nostril.

4. All **Rattlesnakes** may be readily told by the jointed caudal appendage or rattle.

The last three types bite with long, hollow teeth or fangs which have an orifice at the tip from which poison is forced forward from a gland on each side of the head. The fangs are long and fold backward into the mouth when the jaws are closed. They deeply inject poison like hypodermic needles. Coral Snakes have short, permanently erect fangs, but these carry a very dangerous, nerve-attacking poison. No species of snake "stings," hence the forked tongue is a harmless organ. While many snakes have a more or less sharp, spiny termination of the tail, none has any poisonous, stinging property in connection with this spine.

An illustration, among the plates, imparts better understanding of fang mechanism than written description. The pair of long, hollow teeth to be noted as characteristic among the rattlesnakes, Copperhead and Water Moccasin is attached to movable bones, enabling them to be folded backwards. Forward and backward motion of the fangs may be voluntarily employed independently of jaw motion, or alternately, in producing a hooking bite. Reserve fangs are constantly growing to replace the functioning pair. Thus if the functioning pair is broken off and the snake is temporarily unable to strike and inject its poison, a new pair of fangs soon grows into place.

Ordinarily, the Crotalids or Pit Vipers strike from a contracted, anterior loop. It is not necessary for them to be in a coil to strike effectively, nor is the loop necessary in producing an effective bite, as they can quickly turn and bite while the body is extended. The latter action is to be usually noted with the Coral Snakes.

The poison is carried in a pair of glands at the rear of the head and during the biting motion is forced forward and out of the fangs by muscular contraction against the glands. The poison of the Crotalids is of amber hue. Its composition may be summarized as a mixture, in variable proportions, of protein substance, mucus and debris of epithelial cells, some fatty matter, and salts such as calcium chloride and phosphate, also ammonia and magnesia. The density is somewhat greater than that of water, varying in specific gravity from 1.030 to 1.050. The proteins carry the various active toxins, which by certain methods can be removed or some of them inactivated, as has been demonstrated by research work in the New York Zoological Park.

CHAPTER II

Habits of North American Snakes

FROM HALF-BLIND, wormlike burrowers to six-foot racers which can glide as fast as a man can run, there is a wide difference in habits among North American snakes; but there are other diversities. With the range of form and size a variety of habits is inevitable.

The greater number of snakes are more or less secretive, timid and cautious. Relatively speaking, in comparison to their numbers, they are not commonly seen. During periods of digestion they seek hiding places, and as prey may be proportionately large and is swallowed entire, digestion, which even dissolves the bones of vertebrates, may continue for a week or more. Between unsuccessful prowls for food the same crevices or holes are sought. With exception of migration from hibernating places to summer feeding grounds, thence return in the autumn, but few snakes wander extensively. Thus the summer prowling grounds are restricted, with selected spots for hiding, and from these they may be lured to bask in the sun. Near these spots the same snakes may be intermittently seen, week after week, through the summer. Such habits are quite general among snakes in latitudes where there are cold winters.

As an example of the secretiveness of snakes, nonvenomous and poisonous, I can cite a mountainous area in central New York where I have done much collecting. Snakes are abundant, as evidenced by many specimens gathered during two weeks' time. An old mill dam was found to be infested with Water Snakes; Striped Snakes hidden under stones; "Milk" Snakes secreted under the top stones of the old foundation; and smaller kinds under the loose bark of fallen trees. Yet, to wander through meadows or scant timber (particularly favored by snakes) brought to view only an occasional specimen in the open.

To the uninitiated, snakes would have seemed to be scarce. An occasional blacksnake might be seen, but to me there was no doubt of a goodly population of these lithe reptiles in the weedy meadows, for in a spring hunt a blacksnake den had been visited while its denizens still basked near the crevices, though soon to scatter for summer feeding. There were many blacksnakes there, and on some higher ledges or rocky shelves a congregation of rattlers. Yet the near-by farmers spoke of only an occasional blacksnake or rattler to be seen during the summer.

Snake dens, or hibernating shelters, are specific places. There are crevices or holes that lead in deep enough to be safe from penetration by frost. The activity of snakes is contingent to temperature of environmental air. Having no body temperature, all snakes, as with most reptiles, are unable to endure freezing conditions. There may be sheltered ledges along many parts of a slope, or south-facing pockets with indicated labyrinth of crevices, but none are populated in the autumn; the crevices are not deep enough. Snake dens are often unlikely-looking spots, from an amateur student's point of view. But the reptilian clan knows what provides deep ingress. Return to a specific spot year after year has been going on for centuries, as indicated by crevices worn smooth by successive generations. A populous copperhead den was located at the base of a hill where no snakes were to be found after the late spring. The unique thing about this den was its situation in a railroad cut close to the vibration of the trains. Snakes remained congregated at the den until settled spring weather was established.

There is much sun-basking on clear days at the dens, if the temperature is mild and there is no wind. Emergence from the den is also made at the annual breeding period. During den congregation there is no search for food. By middle May, in average seasons, the dens are depopulated, and by the beginning of June the snakes have scattered to summer feeding grounds. There are not many dens where more than a few individuals remain through the warm months. This may be accounted for by lack of sufficient food to support a congestion of individuals. It has been established that snakes may travel as far as two miles from the dens to summer feeding grounds.

Hibernation by concentration of individuals does not appear to occur in parts of the United States where the winters are short and mild. In the extreme southern states a few snakes may gather at the base of an old tree where there are fairly deep crevices among the roots or they may make their way individually into the burrows of rodents. In most of California, one does not hear of snake dens, as reptiles seek shelter in such small groups that there are no main congregating spots to attract human attention. In the mountains to the north, however, in Washington and Oregon there are snake dens where hundreds of reptiles congregate.

The snakes of North America breed in the spring, and a little earlier in the southern latitudes. Some snakes lay eggs; others produce the young alive. With both types the young, upon emergence, are able to shift for themselves and receive no parental care. Poisonous snakes are born with perfectly formed fangs and are able to use them at once in subduing prey. There is rather a mixture of egg-laying and viviparous kinds. Among nonpoisonous snakes that lay eggs are the Blacksnake and other Racers, the Green Snakes, "Milk" and King Snakes, Hog-nosed Snakes and the big Rat Snakes. Snakes' eggs are white, with soft but tough leathery shell. They are hidden under stones or in debris where they may remain moderately damp. Clutches of eggs vary from half a dozen to a couple of dozen. They are laid in midsummer, and incubation differs according to species. The time ranges from two to eight weeks. As a rule the clutches of eggs are of lesser number than live-born litters. Among nonpoisonous snakes that produce living young are the Striped or Garter Snakes, Water Snakes and the little Brown Snakes. With Garter and Water Snakes there may be as many as fifty in a litter, and in exceptional instances a greater number. In the northern latitudes snake litters are born in late summer. In the South they are born earlier, owing to the earlier breeding season.

All of the North American poisonous serpents with the exception of the Coral Snakes produce living young, and fortunately their litters are relatively small—infrequently much over a dozen.

In general habits North American snakes conduct their lives in a variety of ways. Roughly separated into habit groups, snakes may be defined as strictly burrowing (mostly of warm latitudes), ground-roving or terrestrial, arboreal, and semiaquatic. There are variations among the burrowing kinds. The minute southwestern Worm Snakes are half blind and rarely come to the surface, boring their way through loose soil in search of insects. Other so-called worm snakes of wide distribution spend much of their time burrowing, but have good eyes and cannot be classed as really degenerated types. The Mud Snakes of the Southeast are large, strong and handsome and do much burrowing in damp soil. Their small eyes show adaptation for a life largely underground. A number of small snakes have sharp or scoop-shaped snouts for intermittent burrowing in sand, although such actions are also used in seeking temporary shelter.

In defining terrestrial snakes, such kinds may be listed which are not fitted for boring or burrowing into soil or sand. They mostly prowl on the ground, and while some are comparatively stout-bodied and seldom or never climb into bushes or trees, others are agile climbers and at times ascend to considerable heights, as are the habits of the Racers and Rat Snakes. While thus partially arboreal, for sake of simplification they may be grossly rated among terrestrial kinds. Specifically, they are not tree snakes; in fact there is but one really specialized tree snake in the United States, an extremely slender species of the boundary region of the Southwest. The next nearest to it as a North American arboreal type is the Keel-scaled Green Snake, of wide range in eastern, central and southern United States.

Semiaquatic habits have become so definitely developed as to be noted with the genus of nonvenomous Water Snakes, with most of the Striped or Garter Snakes; also the poisonous Water Moccasin. Such snakes live along streams or lakes, are agile swimmers, are adept in pursuing fish, and dive when frightened, to hide on reedy bottoms.

In northern latitudes snakes are rare in heavy timber where little sun strikes through. I have investigated such spots in Pennsylvania, New York and New Jersey in which I have seldom seen any snakes. In the southern states, where heat of the summer sun is intense, snakes may often be seen in heavy woods. Scant timber, with open patches traversed by old stone walls and alternating with weedy meadows, are favorite resorts of many kinds of snakes. Next in selection are ledgy slopes with abundance of shelving rocks. These are particularly frequented by rattlesnakes and copperheads. A fair number of species inhabit desert areas and are adapted to live in such places by modification of gait on the surface or sharp snout for burrowing in sand. Such types even appear to be so specialized that they obtain their liquid nourishment by absorption of dew. Deserted, tumble-down buildings in remote places are often a rendezvous for snakes. Streams or ponds with dense margin of bushes are the lurking places of Water Snakes, as are old mill dams where stonework is "dry" laid, without cement. Sufficient food and water to drink—even though the latter is supplied by underground springs—provide lures for summer congregation of many species.

The food of North American snakes ranges from small insect larvae, crickets, spiders and earthworms among the smaller kinds, to frogs, toads, salamanders and fishes among the moderate-sized species, thence through the smaller rodents to kinds as big as squirrels and rabbits with the larger snakes. A number feed upon birds, and some seek their eggs. Some snakes are cannibalistic. Among all of the kinds, however, there are specific preferences for food. Few of the insect eaters will feed upon anything else. There are kinds that will take nothing but cold-blooded food (frogs, toads and salamanders), and others nothing but warm-blooded food. A few of the larger kinds, although in the minority, take both cold- and warm-blooded food. The nonvenomous, rodent-eating species are of economic value and should not be killed.

Methods of subduing prey differ according to classified groups. With prey that is relatively small, rapid motion of the loosely constructed jaw bones, forward extension and pulling back, quickly draw the quarry into the mouth and elastic throat. Nonconstricting frog and toad eaters have elongate rear teeth to hold the prey firmly as well as pierce its body and expel air. There are semiconstricting kinds which press the prey to the ground under a fold while the engulfing process goes on. The typical constrictors, of which there are several genera, seize the quarry and throw several coils around it, so tightly squeezing it that it quickly dies from strangulation. The long-fanged poisonous snakes strike their prey from a lateral loop, and the prey is overwhelmed by the large amount of venom compared to its body weight. This is a natural process of poisonous snakes in obtaining food; the venom has no deleterious effect in the snake's stomach during digestion.

In answer to two recurrent questions, How fast do snakes grow? and How long does a snake live? the author would say:

The average North American snake requires about three summers' growth to become what might be called a young adult or of fair size for its species. After that time it may slowly increase in size for several years.

For authentically recorded length of life, an eastern Timber Rattlesnake tops the record by having lived in captivity nearly twenty years, having been two years old when received. A Copperhead received when half grown lived for thirteen years, when it was killed by an accident, and a tropical snake, related to kinds found in the United States, received when nearly full grown, has lived in the Zoological Park for seventeen years and is still thriving. It seems safe to say that the larger North American snakes may live at least as long as twenty-five years, and that the smaller kinds probably have a shorter life span.

CHAPTER III

How to Identify Snakes

THERE IS A COMMON but mistaken idea that poisonous snakes may be recognized by the shape of their heads; that their heads are wide and flat, hence very distinct from the neck. It is well to correct this impression and clarify the reason for its origin.

It is true that rattlesnakes, the Copperhead and Water Moccasin have wide heads, but such is the case with a large number of harmless kinds, like the Water Snakes (*Natrix*), the Rat or Chicken Snakes (*Elaphe*) and the Hog-nosed Snakes or Hissing "Adders" (*Heterodon*). Members of the latter genus, in particular, have stout bodies and head outlines that suggest the common idea of a poisonous snake, and these reptiles intensify the impression by flattening the body and the head until this member bulges in triangular outline. Many snakes when frightened have such habits, producing relatively wider head outlines than those of the poisonous snakes of the Pit Viper family, the *Crotalidae*.

The dangerous Coral Snake (*Micrurus*) of the Southeast and its near-ally of the southwestern boundary region have outlines covering the popular conception of nonvenomous snakes. They are slender-bodied and with head barely wider than the neck. They are members of quite a different family from the Pit Vipers, the *Elapidae*, which has a large number of Old World species, such as the Cobras and Mambas. The Coral Snakes of temperate and tropical America are the only New World representatives. Most of the members of this large family are slender-bodied and have narrow heads.

It might be said that all snakes in North America that have a relatively slender body and heads not accentuated by a bulge at the neck may be identified at a glance as nonpoisonous; that is, if occurring outside the range of the two Coral Snakes. While such definition is of some help and may satisfy an observer where simple definition or occurrence is all that is wanted, this leaves out of consideration the large number of harmless snakes that may appear as having bulging heads, or which voluntarily flatten and produce such outlines. It will thus be seen that points for identification must be regarded with detail.

To revert to separation of poisonous snakes in gross terms, a key may be outlined, as follows:

A. Definition of crotaline snakes by structural characters: **Rattlesnakes, Copperhead** and **Water Moccasin.**
   1. Species with elliptic pupils.*
   1a. A deep cavity or "pit" between the eye and nostril. Scales keeled.
   (*a*) Tail ending in a series of loosely connected segments (a rattle) or with the very young a swollen "button":
   Rattlesnakes.
   (*b*) No rattle. Greater number of crossplates under tail in a single row. Body moderately stout:
   Copperhead and **Water Moccasin.**
B. Definition of the Elapine snakes by structural characters and color pattern:
   Body slender, head not distinct. Scales smooth and lustrous. Pupil round. Color pattern in rings of red, black and yellow, *the yellow rings the narrower and bordering the black:*
   Coral Snakes.

Now let us analyze this "key" to further differentiate its members from harmless snakes:

1. It will be noted that all snakes with a rattle are poisonous.

2. That the only other poisonous crotaline snakes of North America—the Copperhead and Water Moccasin have a marked pit between the eye and nostril, elliptic pupil and most of the plates under the tail in a single row. In this combination they differ from all other nonvenomous snakes in the regions they are to be found, which have round pupils, no facial pits, while the plates under the tail are in two rows.†

---

*North American nonvenomous snakes, with exception of a few small western species, have round pupils.

†With exception of the western Pygmy Boas and the genus *Rhinocheilus,* with plates under the tail in a single row; but such species will not be confused with the Crotalids.

3. With the deceptive Coral Snakes *pattern* should be carefully noted. Several kinds of nonpoisonous snakes have similar colors, but the arrangement of the rings or bands is different. With the poisonous kinds the yellow rings are on the outside of the black or may be said to border the black at anterior and posterior margins. With nonvenomous kinds of similar color combinations the black *encloses* the yellow or whitish rings.

General points for identification: The suggestions presented indicate points of identification among all North American snakes, nonvenomous and venomous. Mention has been made of *keeled* scales and *smooth* scales. Here is a point of particular significance, and illustrations among the plates bring out its importance. Snakes have either perfectly smooth scales or a longitudinal keel on the greater number of scales. The keel is a linelike ridge on the scale. With some the keels are coarse and very apparent, producing a longitudinally serrated appearance of the body. With others the keels are faint and may be confined to the rows of scales along the back. Whatever the combination is, smooth-scaled, faintly or roughly keeled, diagnosis of this character is of importance in identification. Smooth-scaled snakes, viewed close or a few feet away, appear either polished or satiny, according to their kinds. Roughly keeled snakes are dull on the back or if freshly shed may look velvety.

The underside of the reptile also warrants diagnosis. With North American nonvenomous snakes, except some miniature Boas of the Pacific region and the single genus *Rhinocheilus,* the plates under the tail are in a *double row,* but a plate immediately anterior to these, where the body ends and tail begins is of importance in identification. This is the ventral or anal plate. It may be single or double, and such difference may figure in detailed description for identification.

The plates or shields of the head may also figure in diagnosis. While this field book is being held to as readable terms as are practicable head scalation may be referred to in descriptions. An understanding of the names of head plates is important, if specific identification is desired. Where mention is made, there is definition of character, or location.

Relative thickness—stout or slender—and mention of large, moderate or small size will occur with all species described. Another point in "running down" identification relates to locality where the specimen is found, this checked against description of species occurring in the region concerned. That is the reason for grossly sectioning the species treated.

Consideration of color and pattern is of much importance, but may be confusing, owing to unrelated kinds being similarly marked and variation of pattern among individuals of a species. The keys will help, plus checking points brought out in the detailed descriptions.

Patterns may be roughly classified as striped or banded *lengthways*. (The Garter Snakes are examples.)

Transversely banded across the back and down the sides. (Examples are the Water Snakes, Copperhead and others.)

Symmetrical ringlike arrangement of colors which may completely encircle the body and in which pattern a bright red is often present. (Coral King Snakes, the poisonous Coral Snakes and others.)

A blotched pattern, composed of a row of large saddles along the back usually in alternation with a row of smaller saddles on each side. (Some of the Rat Snakes, the "Milk" Snakes, etc.)

Small spots arranged in tessellated or "checkerboard" fashion or irregularly scattered spots. (A number of the smaller species.)

A uniform, dark body hue, with a yellow ring around the neck. (The genus of Ring-necked Snakes.)

A symmetrical series of rhombs or "diamonds" along the back. (Some of the Rattlesnakes.)

No pattern. The body black, brown, gray, olive or bright green.

In addition to such definitions of pattern, abdominal hues and markings are of importance. They are characteristic with some species.

The young of some snakes are quite different in color and pattern from adults.

The actions of certain snakes are cited, in some of the descriptions of the chapters that follow, as helpful in indicating a grouping to which they belong. Such are the swift movements of the Racers, the plunging into ponds or streams of species of the aquatic groups, burrowing or climbing habits, manifestations when angry, and indicated power of construction. These are points that help and add to the interest in observing snakes.

A glance at a reptile may be fleeting, as snakes as a rule seek to escape from the presence of human observers. Yet a glance may reveal a great deal when it comes to diagnosis. Form, size, color and markings may be deducted in a few seconds. The actions and kind of place where the snake was seen help to determine a species or its immediate kin.

Encroachment of intensive farming, land drainage and the like materially change reptilian fauna. The poisonous species disappear; next the larger nonvenomous kinds. "Milk" Snakes, Garter and Water Snakes, as well as the little Brown Snakes, remain. "Milk" Snakes and Water Snakes may be mistaken for Copperheads owing to some similarity of coloring, but as I have noted descriptions in correspondence about snakes, it has been possible to provide identification from brief details; the poisonous kinds are in the minority.

PART TWO

The Snakes of Northeastern North America

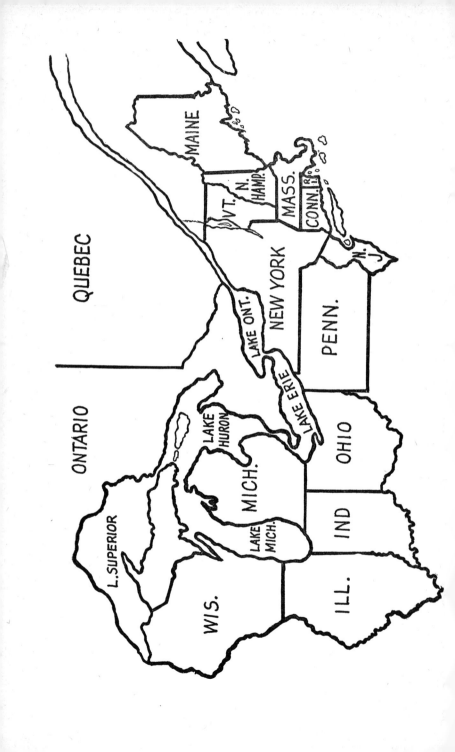

CHAPTER IV

Key to the Snakes of Northeastern North America

Wᴴɪʟᴇ ʙᴏᴜɴᴅᴀʀɪᴇs ᴏꜰ sᴛᴀᴛᴇs have no effect in regulating the distribution of snakes, there is enough difference in occurrence of species to divide the map of North America into three sections. It should be understood, however, that this arrangement is for the convenience of the student, rather than of zoogeographical significance. A fair number of species are approximately confined within the continental divisions indicated in the following chapters. Many overlap a moderate distance, and others extend far outside the zones defined. In considering the northeastern region as an example, southern and western species may extend but slightly into the zone outlined.* Such are points for deduction in furthering identification.

The reader of the field book who is particularly interested in the reptiles of northeastern North America will find identification comparatively easy, owing to moderate number of species and little of confusing similarity among them.

Following is a key or deductive listing:

NONVENOMOUS SNAKES

I. Pᴜᴘɪʟ ᴏꜰ ᴇʏᴇ ʀᴏᴜɴᴅ

*Several typically southern snakes, which but slightly encroach into the section of the map outlined—in extreme southern Illinois—are not included in this chapter. The Horn Snake, *Farancia abacura reinwardtii,* is an example. Southern forms extending up the Mississippi Valley are treated in Chapters VII, VIII and IX.

A. *Scales smooth*

Size—small

Brown to purplish black above; pink beneath:
Worm Snake, *Carphophis amoena amoena.*
Distribution: Connecticut and New York; westward into the Appalachians and southward to Florida.

Brown to gray above with minute black dots; pale yellow or white beneath:
Smooth Brown Snake, *Virginia valeriae valeriae.*
Distribution: New Jersey to South Carolina; westward to Ohio.

Pale green above; white beneath:
Green Snake, *Liopeltis vernalis.*
Distribution: Southern Canada through eastern and central North America to the Mexican boundary.

Dark gray with a yellow ring around neck; yellow beneath:
Ring-necked Snake, *Diadophis punctatus edwardsii.*
Distribution: Southern Canada to the Carolinas; westward to Wisconsin.

Wide spaces of scarlet, separated by ringlike spaces of yellow or white margined with black; white beneath:
Scarlet Snake, *Cemophora coccinea.*
Distribution: Southern New Jersey to Florida; westward to Louisiana.

Size—moderate

Gray with chestnut, reddish (sometimes olive) blotches margined with black. Spaces between blotches sometimes narrowed and ringlike. White beneath with square black spots:
"Milk" Snake, House Snake, Checkered "Adder,"
Lampropeltis triangulum triangulum.
Distribution: Southern Canada to Virginia; westward to Iowa.

Grayish brown with dark brown blotches along back. A row of smaller alternating blotches on sides. Yellow beneath with dull square blotches. (Young with more intense pattern):
  Yellow-bellied King Snake, *Lampropeltis calligaster.*
Distribution: Indiana to Wisconsin; southward to Texas.

Size—large

Black with narrow yellow or white crossring or chainlike markings; black and white beneath:
  King Snake, Chain Snake, *Lampropeltis getulus getulus.*
Distribution: New Jersey to northern Florida.

Satiny black above; black or dark gray beneath; chin white. (Young gray with dark blotches on back):
  Blacksnake, Black Racer, *Coluber constrictor constrictor.*
Distribution: The entire eastern United States.

Form and size like the preceding. Olive to greenish or bluish green; yellow beneath:
  Blue Racer, *Coluber constrictor flaviventris.*
Distribution: Ohio and Michigan to the western states.

B. *Scales feebly keeled*

Size—large

Grayish or yellow with vivid crimson blotches along back; black and white beneath. (Distinguished from the similarly marked "Milk" Snake by its feebly keeled scales):
  Corn Snake, *Elaphe guttata.*
Distribution: New Jersey to Florida; westward to Missouri and Louisiana.

Brown or yellowish with large, dark brown blotches along the back and series of smaller, alternating blotches on each side:
  Fox Snake, *Elaphe vulpina.*
Distribution: Michigan and Indiana to Iowa and Minnesota.

Polished black above; white beneath blotched with gray. Some scales of the sides show white edges. Distinguished from the Blacksnake by its polished scalation and feebly keeled scales. (Young gray with dark blotches):

Pilot Blacksnake, Mountain Blacksnake, *Elaphe obsoleta obsoleta.*

Distribution: Southern Canada to Florida; westward to Michigan and Louisiana.

C. *Scales strongly keeled*

Size—small

Brown above; pink beneath; snout blunt:
DeKay's Snake, *Storeria dekayi.*
Distribution: Southern Canada to Mexico.

Brown or dark gray above; bright red beneath; snout blunt:
Storer's Snake, *Storeria occipitomaculata.*
Distribution: Southern Canada to Mexico.

Brown above; yellowish beneath; snout sharp:
Small-eyed Brown Snake, *Haldea striatula.*
Distribution: Virginia to Illinois; southward to the Gulf states.

Size—small to moderate

Uniform pale green above; yellow beneath:
Keeled Green Snake, *Opheodrys aestivus.*
Distribution: Connecticut to Florida; westward to Illinois and in extreme south to New Mexico.

Brown or black above, with vivid yellow stripe on back and similar stripe on each side on 3rd and 4th rows of scales from underside. Form very slender:
Eastern Ribbon Snake, *Thamnophis sauritus sauritus.*
Distribution: Southern Canada to Georgia; westward to Mississippi.

Pale brown with upright blackish brown blotches on sides. Obscure alternating blotches on back:

Kirtland's Water Snake, *Natrix kirtlandii.*
Distribution: New Jersey and Pennsylvania to Wisconsin.

Size—moderate

Brown to black. A yellow stripe on back and less intense stripe on each side on 2nd and 3rd rows of scales:
Common Garter Snake, Striped Snake, *Thamnophis sirtalis sirtalis.*
Distribution: Southern Canada; the eastern and southern United States.

Brown to black. Three yellow stripes, those on the sides on 3rd and 4th rows of scales. Form moderately stout:
Plains Garter Snake, *Thamnophis radix.**
Distribution: Illinois to Great Plains and Canadian Northwest.

Brown to black. Three yellow stripes. Those on the sides on 2nd, 3rd and 4th rows of scales. Head relatively small:
Butler's Garter Snake, *Thamnophis butleri.*
Distribution: Western New York and Pennsylvania to Illinois and Wisconsin.

Brown, with three black stripes on back, a yellow stripe on each side and two dark stripes on abdomen—seven stripes in all. (Young more vivid—stripes more distinct):
Queen Snake, *Natrix septemvittata.*
Distribution: Eastern and central United States.

Brown, a pale stripe on back and a broad yellowish band on side, the latter bordered with black stripes:
Graham's Water Snake, *Natrix grahamii.*
Distribution: Illinois to Louisiana and Texas.

Gray to brown. A pale stripe on back bordered with black dots; a similar stripe on side on 2nd and 3rd rows of scales. Two rows of black dots beneath:
Striped Swamp Snake, *Tropidoclonion lineatum.*
Distribution: Ohio to South Dakota; southward to Texas.

*The Plains Garter Snake encroaches slightly from the West.

Size—moderate to large

Brown above with more or less distinct dark or reddish trans-verse bars; whitish beneath spotted with red. (Young pale gray with strong blackish bands) :
Common Water Snake, *Natrix sipedon sipedon.*
Distribution: Maine to Alabama; westward to Minnesota and Colorado.

Grayish to pale brown. Pattern obscure with adults. Abdomen white and lacking the red spots of *N. s. sipedon* (preceding) :
Lake Water Snake, *Natrix sipedon insularum.*
Distribution: Islands of Lake Erie and the Ohio shore.

Medium to pale brown with indistinct darker crossbands. *Abdomen uniform red:*
Red-bellied Water Snake, *Natrix erythrogaster erythrogaster.*
Distribution: Northward into Michigan in the central region. Virginia to Florida in the East.

Brown or olive with narrow, dark bars on sides, which fork and unite on back to form rhombs or "diamonds" :
Diamond-back Water Snake, *Natrix rhombifera.*
Distribution: Southern Illinois and Indiana to Mexico.

Dark green or olive brown with numerous black bands crossing the back, these about one scale wide and two scales apart. Alternating dark blotches on sides :
Green Water Snake, *Natrix cyclopion.*
Distribution: Southeastern states and up the Mississippi Valley to southern Illinois.

Brown, gray or olive with about 20 – 30 darker, angular blotches. Body very stout. Head broad; snout upturned and sharp :
Hissing "Adder," Flat-headed "Adder," Hog-nosed Snake, *Heterodon contortrix.*
Distribution: Massachusetts to Florida; westward to Texas.

Gray or brown with about 22 – 26 large dark blotches. Snout more sharply upturned than with preceding :

Southern Hissing "Adder," Sand "Adder," Hog-nosed Snake, *Heterodon simus.*

Distribution: The southeastern United States with extension into southern Indiana.

Size—large

White, with strong blackish blotches; abdomen marble white. Snout conical and pointed:

Pine Snake, *Pituophis melanoleucus melanoleucus.*

Distribution: Pine barrens of southern New Jersey to Florida.

Yellow with a row of large, square blotches, dark brown or blackish, along back and smaller series on side. Abdomen yellow:

Bull Snake, Western Gopher Snake, *Pituophis sayi sayi.**

Distribution: Western states to the Rockies, but herein listed, as it crosses the Mississippi into Illinois and Wisconsin.

VENOMOUS SNAKES

II. PUPIL OF EYE ELLIPTIC

C1. *Scales strongly keeled*

Size—moderate to large

Light brown or pinkish gray with dark brown transverse bands, narrow on back and much wider on sides:

Northern Copperhead Snake, *Agkistrodon mokasen cupreus.*

Distribution: Central Massachusetts to the Carolinas; westward to Illinois, with related forms in South and West.

Dull brown, olive or blackish, with broad transverse **bands** which are obscure except on sides:

*The Bull Snake encroaches slightly from the West.

Water Moccasin, *Agkistrodon piscivorus.*
Distribution: The Dismal Swamp of Virginia to Florida in coastal region. Northward to Illinois and southern Indiana in the Mississippi Valley; westward to Texas.

D. *Tail with a rattle*

Gray or brown with a series of dark blotches on the back. Top of head with symmetrical shields:
Massasauga, Swamp Rattlesnake, *Sistrurus catenatus catenatus.*
Distribution: Western New York and Pennsylvania to Nebraska. Extends northward into Canada and southward to Kansas.

Size—large

Yellow, tan or gray, with dark transverse bands, usually angulate in backward point. Some examples almost black. Head with small scales:
Timber Rattlesnake, Banded Rattlesnake, *Crotalus horridus horridus.**
Distribution: Southern Maine to northern Florida; westward to Iowa and Texas.

Examination of the preceding key will point to several phases of diagnosis. The following should be considered:

While the list covers the snakes of northeastern North America, it will be noted that but few kinds are really confined to that region—the range of the greater number extending far outside of it. Also, that several species come but slightly within the area from other "zones" indicated by sectioning the map of North America. The poisonous Water Moccasin may be particularly noted as an extreme variant from the southern fauna. They should be almost foreign to consideration in the northeastern region, but must be listed owing to records of occurrence. Two species in the list, the Plains Garter Snake and Bull Snake, encroach slightly from the West.

*The Canebrake Rattlesnake, *C. h. atricaudatus,* ranges up the Mississippi Valley to Illinois.

Referring back to Chapter III, which outlines points for identification, several are to be noted in the key. There are *size,* and character of scales, whether *keeled* or *smooth.* And there are coloration and *pattern.* What is the method of most clearly diagnosing the latter? This can be shown by listing the species under a gross grouping for pattern deduction, as follows:

Worm Snake
Smooth Brown Snake
Keeled Brown Snake
DeKay's Snake (with some a faint band on
    back and black dots)
Storer's Snake (with some a faint band on
    back and black dots)
Smooth Green Snake
Keeled Green Snake
Ring-necked Snake (a yellow ring on neck)
Black Snake
Blue Racer

} No body pattern

"Milk" Snake
Corn Snake
Fox Snake
Pine Snake
Bull Snake
Yellow-bellied King Snake
Common Hog-nosed Snake
Southern Hog-nosed Snake
Massasauga

} Blotched pattern

Common Water Snake
Red-bellied Water Snake
Diamond-back Water Snake (bands split-
    ting into rhombs on back)
Green Water Snake
Kirtland's Water Snake
Copperhead Snake
Water Moccasin
Banded or Timber Rattlesnake

} Transverse bands

King Snake	} Pale, chainlike pattern
Scarlet Snake "Milk" Snake (more southern and central examples may appear ringed above)	} Symmetrical, ringlike pattern
Pilot or Mountain Blacksnake	} Scales narrowly edged with white to form tracing when body is distended
Ribbon Snake Common Garter Snake Butler's Garter Snake Plains Garter Snake Graham's Water Snake Queen Snake Striped Swamp Snake	} Striped lengthwise

Description of Species: Treatment of species in the northeastern section is comparatively simple, owing to limited number. The descriptions are listed in the following chapter.

In all descriptions the scientific name will be in trinomials if varieties or subspecies are associated with the typical form. Thus, the forms of the Ribbon Snake are technically designated as *Thamnophis sauritus sauritus* or *Thamnophis sauritus proximus,* as the case may be. When binomials are used, as with the Hog-nosed Snake, *Heterodon contortrix,* but one form is recognized. There may be color variants, but they are not consistent enough to warrant subspecific names.

Scientific names are in italics, followed by the name of the authority in parentheses if the name has been modified since the original description, and without parentheses if the scientific name has remained unchanged.

CHAPTER V

The Northeastern Nonpoisonous Snakes

Dᴇsᴄʀɪᴘᴛɪᴏɴs ꜰᴏʟʟᴏᴡ in continuity of formal listing, which, in some instances indicate linking relationship.

Worm Snake, *Carphophis amoena amoena* (Say)

Size: Seldom exceeding 10 inches, diameter of ¼ inch. One of the smallest snakes of the Northeast.

Form and scalation: Scales smooth, lustrous, opalescent. Relatively, the body is moderately stout; head not distinct and terminating in pointed snout. Eyes very small.

Coloration: Chestnut brown above. Pink on the lower sides and abdomen. There is range of body hue to lustrous black, but brown examples are more common. Young specimens are much darker.

Distribution: The typical form inhabits Connecticut and New York, thence southward to Florida. In the Mississippi Valley and states closely eastward there is a subspecies, *C. amoena helenae* (Kennicott). It differs only in form of the head shields.

Habits: This little snake may be found beneath stones that set close to the ground. Under these it makes channels like those of an earthworm. It also may be exhumed from loose soil or forest debris. It is a true burrower and seldom to be seen on the surface except after warm rains, and then on soft soil amongst litter of dead vegetation. It appears to feed largely upon the soft-bodied larvae of small insects and earthworms. Its occurrence is spotty, common in some places, rare in others. I found it common at the western base of the Palisades, near Tenafly, in northern New Jersey. Most of the specimens were burrowing under rounded stones.

This species will not endure captivity unless provided with medium in which to burrow and hide. A mixture of dead leaves and wood pulp, kept moderately damp (not wet), was used successfully as a hiding medium for some specimens that were maintained for several years.

Northern Ring-necked Snake, *Diadophis punctatus edwardsii* (Merrem)

Size: Average length is 10 – 12 inches, with body thickness slightly in excess of ¼ inch. Occasional specimens are larger. The largest example I have examined was 19½ inches long and nearly half an inch in diameter, but the species may be listed as among the smallest snakes of the Northeast.

Form and scalation: Moderately slender, the head flat though not very distinct from the neck. The scales are smooth and of satiny luster.

Coloration: Coloration is so unique that this snake may be identified at a glance. It is gray to bluish black, with brilliant yellow ring around the neck, immediately behind the head, in vivid contrast to body coloration. The abdomen is orange yellow, and there is often a row of black dots in the center.

Distribution: In its extension into southern Canada this species may be rated as one of the most northern of American reptiles. It occurs throughout the New England states, then southward to the Carolinas. Westward its habitat extends to Wisconsin. Related forms extend the distribution southward and westward.

Habits: The Northern Ring-necked Snake is a secretive species, but not a burrower. It is more commonly found in mountainous or hilly places, living in stone piles or under the loose bark of fallen trees. As its favorite food consists of small salamanders, it is more frequently found in damp places. Flat stones on the tops of old mill dams are favored hiding places, and under one of these as many as a half-dozen specimens may be found. The species also feeds upon earthworms. It is oviparous, or egg-laying, but embryos are well developed before the eggs are laid, and hatching usually occurs within a month's time, which is shorter than with other oviparous snakes.

Captive specimens do well if kept under terrarium conditions and provided with strips of bark so they may hide. They may be maintained on a diet of earthworms.

Hog-nosed Snake, Flat-headed "Adder," Hissing "Adder," Puffing "Adder," Spreading "Adder," *Heterodon contortrix* (Linnaeus)

Size: A fair-sized, relatively heavy-bodied snake, commonly 2½ feet long and over an inch in diameter. Specimens a yard long are not uncommon, and occasional examples slightly exceed this length. A 3-foot specimen is about 1½ inch in diameter.

Form and scalation: In proportion to length this is the thickest-bodied snake of the Northeast. The head is wide and distinct, the snout sharp and upturned—hence one of its names, Hog-nosed Snake. When it is angry, the head and neck are excessively flattened, producing a sinister aspect. The scales are keeled.

Coloration: Colors and markings are variable, but the commoner hues are yellowish or brown with dark brown or black irregular blotches, which may assume the form of crossbands, or broken into three rows of blotches. Some specimens have bright shades of yellow or brick red, the latter being particularly evident on the forward parts. Occasional examples are dark slaty gray or entirely black.

Distribution: Not occurring northward of Massachusetts in the Atlantic states, but in its western extension ranging to Minnesota. South of the southern New England region the range is through all of the states to Florida, with general distribution to the Mississippi Valley.

Habits: This is a particularly interesting snake. No other species among the northeastern harmless serpents exhibits such marked and eccentric habits. When frightened it flattens the neck, by means of elongated ribs which are spread laterally; its head also becomes broad and flat and is moved in threatening fashion, while the snake exhales the breath in sharp hisses. As these actions produce a formidable aspect, it is natural that this harmless snake has a bad reputation and acquired the title of "Adder."

As a rule these snakes are slain during their harmless bluffing, hence have no opportunity to exhibit a final resort to delude the intruder. This is in feigning death. The hissing ceases, the body writhes as though in pain, and the jaws drop open. The snake then rolls on its back with the appearance of having died; but there is one inconsistent part of the performance. If turned over with a stick to its crawling surface, the reptile returns with agility to its former position. Apparently it has the conviction that the only position for a dead snake is on its back.

Specimens or fragments of specimens are frequently sent me from country places, or from camps, with supposition that this is a very dangerous snake. With its thick body and wide head, it is mistaken for the poisonous Copperhead, from which it differs in irregular pattern, shovel-shaped snout, *round pupils,* and double row of plates under the tail. Moreover, the Copperhead never puts on such a show.

This species is more commonly to be seen in sandy places. There are parts of Long Island, immediately back of the sea beach, where it is abundant; and such is also the case in sandy parts of Connecticut and New Jersey. However, it is not confined to sandy regions, as it is also to be found in mountainous areas, though more sparingly. Most of the uniform black specimens occur in elevated districts.

It appears to feed altogether upon toads and frogs, and mostly the former. Captive specimens become very tame and live best in a plain wooden case, with glass front. They will seldom take other food than toads.

The species is oviparous, laying about two dozen eggs during the latter part of July.

Southern Hog-nosed Snake, Hissing "Adder," Sand "Adder," *Heterodon simus* (Linnaeus)

Size: Smaller than the preceding—attaining maximum length of about 20 inches.

Form and scalation: Relatively stouter than *H. contortrix.* The shovel-like plate on the snout is more prominent and very sharply upturned. Scales strongly keeled.

Coloration: Grayish or brownish with a series of large patches or blotches of blackish brown along the back. Between these blotches the body hue is usually paler than on the sides. On each side is a row of smaller spots in alternation with the dorsal series. Abdomen pale, and without spots or blotches, which is in contrast to *H. contortrix.* Also, there is a greater number of dorsal blotches, usually 22 – 26 as against 16 – 19 with the species widely distributed in the Northeast.

Distribution: A southeastern reptile but ranging northward into Indiana.

Habits: Wild specimens feed mostly upon toads, but, quite unlike the common Hog-nosed Snake, are difficult to induce to take such food when captive.

Smooth Green Snake, *Liopeltis vernalis* (Harlan)

Size: Greatest length about 20 inches, but average size is not much over a foot, with diameter of ¼ inch.

Form and scalation: Of relative, moderate thickness. The scales are smooth, with satiny luster.

Coloration: Readily identified by its uniform grass-green color above and whitish beneath. Just before shedding, the body hue may appear grayish green or bluish. Very young examples are olive or bluish green.

Distribution: One of the species extending farther north than most of the northeastern snakes. The habitat includes southern Canada, all of New England and the states southward to Florida. It also ranges far to the westward. It is most frequently found in wild meadows, but occurrence is erratic, common in some areas, but not to be found in others that appear equally favorable.

Habits: Insectivorous snakes, which are not specialized burrowers, are much in the minority, but the Smooth Green Snake appears to feed mostly upon insects, preferring soft-bodied larvae, crickets, grasshoppers and spiders. I have not been able to induce captives to feed upon anything else.

Keeled Green Snake, *Opheodrys aestivus* (Linnaeus)

Considerably longer than the Smooth Green Snake, but very slender. Length is from 2 to 3 feet, but a specimen of the latter size would be less than half an inch in diameter.

Form and scalation: Slenderness of form is indicated by the great length of the tail, which is in excess of a third of the total length. The scales are distinctly keeled.

Coloration: Uniform green above and bright yellow beneath. The keeled scales and yellow (instead of white) underside readily distinguish this species from the other Green Snake occurring in the Northeast. Both stand out distinctly from all the other serpents of the North American area under consideration, as they are the only uniformly green species.

Distribution: A southern snake and not to be found over the greater part of the area inhabited by the Smooth Green Snake in the Northeast. It ranges into New Jersey from the South and has been recorded in Connecticut and Pennsylvania, but the latter occurrences are unusual and out of the zone of general distribution. Like some other southern reptiles it ranges up the Mississippi Valley to southern Illinois.

Habits: A semiarboreal reptile, climbing into low bushes and among vines. Specimens were found in a heavy growth of old grapevine attached to a farmhouse. It was at a spot where the collector had stood morning after morning to have a smoke after breakfast, and the snakes had been but a few feet from us, remaining undiscovered owing to their leaf-green bodies twined through the vines. Discovery came about through one of them trying to swallow a caterpillar, which writhed so vigorously that it made the snake slip downward, to hang by little more than its tail. We looked through the vine and found two more, one nearly a yard long. Simulation of the slender bodies among leaves and green tendrils was quite remarkable.

Blacksnake, Black Racer, *Coluber constrictor constrictor* (Linnaeus)

Size: A large Blacksnake is about 6 feet long and slightly over 1 inch in diameter. Specimens 4 – 5 feet long are the more commonly seen.

Form and scalation: Relatively slender, with head but little distinct from neck. Body scales are smooth, with luster like a new gun barrel. The smooth scales, with dull sheen, form an important point in separating this large snake from an equally important species, the Pilot or Mountain Blacksnake, which may occur in areas inhabited by the Black Racer. The Pilot Blacksnake has faintly keeled scales, and its body appears polished or glossy.

Coloration: Satiny black above, black or dark slaty gray beneath. There is a more or less evident patch of white on the chin. Young examples are gray, with brownish blotches, these more prominent anteriorly. The young usually become quite black when about two feet long.

Distribution: The entire eastern United States.

The **Blue Racer,** *Coluber constrictor flaviventris* (Say), of similar proportions to the Black Racer, but olive to bluish green above and yellow beneath is recorded from Ohio and Michigan, thence westward, where it assumes a more pronounced difference from the typical form. Juveniles are blotched.

Habits: The Blacksnake is swift and nervous, usually gliding quickly away at the approach of an intruder. If cornered, however, it will double the anterior part into lateral loops and strike, part of its show of defense being to vibrate its tail, which, if among dried leaves, produces a buzzing sound. It should be noted that this vibrating of the tail is also the habit of the Pilot Blacksnake, Corn Snake, Fox Snake, Pine Snake, "Milk" Snake, King Snakes and poisonous Copperhead—all listed within this chapter or section. The habit has brought about many errors in flash deductions of observers who have seen such reptiles and heard the buzzing sound, to figure that such serpents were rattlers. Thus we often hear of allegations of "rattlesnakes" where such poisonous reptiles are never to be found.

In the spring, some Blacksnakes exhibit tactics which may be alarming to persons who lack knowledge in distinguishing harmless snakes from poisonous ones. These antics occur near the hibernating ledges, where mating takes place before the snakes scatter for the summer. While most of the snakes on such ledges will glide away at the approach of a human, an occasional specimen will deliberately attack. This is not done with a rush, but the snake deliberately glides up to the intruder and strikes repeatedly.

The author had an experience with such a bellicose Blacksnake, while seeking to locate a rattlesnake den. The snake came gliding up. I was stooping to peer under a shelving rock. It was necessary to stand to avoid being struck in the face. This snake deliberately followed me from spot to spot and became such a nuisance that it was captured, taken to the edge of a cliff and dropped down to a growth of sumac, where it landed without injury. From its actions it was indicated that if there were not a precipitous wall, it would have been back again.

The Blacksnake is not an enemy of the Rattlesnake, nor is it a constrictor, as its scientific name implies. Blacksnakes and rattlers may often be noted in close proximity, coming from the same hibernating crevices or basking in spring sunshine apparently in quite normal, fraternal association.

This species may be rated as of economic value owing to a large part of its food consisting of small rodents. It also eats birds and frogs, but its more pronounced rodent-destroying habits warrant its preservation.

As captives, the adults seldom thrive, being too nervous to accept food. As with all of the species thus far described, the Blacksnake is oviparous, depositing from one to two dozen eggs, covered with a tough white, leathery integument. The eggs are usually hidden under flat stones. For study purposes clutches of eggs may be incubated in sphagnum moss of the kind that may be obtained in florists' shops. The moss should be kept damp, but not wet, and in ordinary room temperature. The eggs are laid in early July and require about two months for incubation. Very young Blacksnakes do fairly well if fed on small frogs.

Pilot Blacksnake, Mountain Blacksnake, *Elaphe obsoleta obsoleta* (Say)

Size: The largest snake of northeastern North America, attaining a length in excess of 8 feet and diameter of 2 inches.

Form and scalation: The scales of the back are feebly keeled, but with polished surface. The body is relatively stout, with indication of strength and weight; the head quite wide and distinct from the neck, rather flattened and blunt at the snout, in fact heavier and much more distinct than the cylindrical head of the Black Racer.

Coloration: Shining black, but with tendency of scales to show narrow white edges, which, when the body is distended, may indicate a pattern of obscure tracery. Greater part of abdomen gray, blotched with white. Some specimens dark gray above, blotched with black.

May be confused with the Blacksnake or Black Racer, but the faintly keeled scales of the back, the polished scalation with white edges and blotched gray-and-white underside are clear characters for separation.

Distribution: Attains the most northern range of any of the really large snakes of northeastern North America. In the Atlantic states it ranges as far north as central Massachusetts, thence southward to Florida. Farther inland, however, it ranges much farther north. In "Notes of the Snakes of Leeds and Frontenac Counties, Ontario," G. C. Toner says:*

"*Elaphe obsoleta obsoleta* (Say)—Lindsey (1931) summarized the records for Ontario, to which I have added others (Toner, 1934). The pilot blacksnake is common in the rocky lands of Leeds County and has several times been noted on the islands of the St. Lawrence River. A number of specimens were taken during 1934. Two live ones from Gananoque Lake were sent to Mr. Logier. There is a small area near this lake which has never been burnt or cut over, with a talus slope close to the water that makes an ideal wintering den. Farmers in the vicinity have told me that they have seen as many as 15 or 20 blacksnakes in the spring, sunning themselves near this talus slope."

Copeia, 1935, No. 1, p. 42.

This snake ranges to Florida and westward to Texas. In the South it is commonly known as the Black Chicken Snake. The largest specimens occur in the northeastern section, where it favors the hills and mountains, though not invariably. The largest specimen I have examined (8 feet 4 inches long) was found in Sullivan County, New York. A 7-foot specimen was captured in Westchester County, New York, in the reservoir district, not far from the city of White Plains. Other localities are the Kittatinnies of New Jersey, the Hudson Highlands, the Ramapo Mountains and parts of Connecticut, where it appeared to be particularly abundant.

Habits: Often climbs trees and shelters in hollow places formed by disintegration of rotted knots. It is to be found hibernating in the same dens with rattlesnakes, copperheads and black racers.

The food consists of rodents and birds, apparently never cold-blooded prey. While alleged to commit depredations among small birds, the species' rodent-destroying habits should be considered. It is oviparous, and the young are very different from the parent, being pale gray with a dorsal row of square blotches which disappear under black suffusion during the second year.

As captive the species is phlegmatic and hardy, subsisting upon small rodents.

Corn Snake, Red Rat Snake, *Elaphe guttata* (Linnaeus)

Size: Up to 6 feet in the South, but the few specimens recorded as far north as New Jersey have averaged $3\frac{1}{2} - 4$ feet long.

Form and scalation: Strong-bodied, the scales of the back faintly keeled.

Coloration: Colors and pattern are very striking. The body hue is gray, tan or reddish. On the back is a row of large, crimson blotches, bordered with black. There is a row of similar blotches, though smaller, on the sides. The abdomen is white, with large black squares. The pattern is rather similar to that of the "Milk" Snake, but the Corn Snake has faintly keeled scales.

Distribution: A southern reptile and seldom found north of Maryland but recorded in the pine barrens of southern New Jersey in the vicinity of Chatsworth. It ranges southward to Florida and is common in the southern states, thence westward to Louisiana.

Habits: The food consists of rodents and small birds. This very handsome snake—one of the most brilliantly colored in North America—is a hardy captive. It is an egg-laying species.

Fox Snake, *Elaphe vulpina* (Baird and Girard)

Size: Up to 6 feet in length. An average measurement is 4 feet long and slightly over 1 inch in diameter.

Form and scalation: The body is quite stout, tapering rather abruptly to a sharply pointed tail. The scales are distinctly, though not heavily, keeled.

Coloration: Pale brown or yellowish, with row of large, rich brown blotches along the back, and a series of smaller, alternating blotches on each side. Beneath the latter and at the edges of the abdominal plates is a yet smaller row. The underside is yellow with numerous dusky spots.

Distribution: Indiana, Iowa and Illinois to Michigan, Wisconsin and Minnesota; western Ohio.

Distribution alone points to identification of adult examples of this large and readily definable snake.

Habits: Compared with other kinds of *Elaphe,* this is a ground species, seldom ascending trees or bushes. Its food consists of rodents and birds. It is hardy as a captive, but when first captured emits a strong-smelling secretion from glands at the base of the tail. The odor is like that of a fox, hence the common name.

Pine Snake, *Pituophis melanoleucus melanoleucus* (Daudin)

Size: The second-largest snake of northeastern North America, attaining a length in excess of 7 feet and close to 2 inches in diameter.

Form and scalation: The body appears strong and quite heavy. The head is of curious form, resembling that of a turtle. It is small in proportion to the snake's size and sharply pointed at the snout, which protrudes over the lower jaw. The scales of the back are keeled and lusterless; those of the sides, highly polished.

Coloration: Dull white on the back, becoming pure white on the sides. Along the back is a series of large black blotches, quite close together on the forward portion but posteriorly much more separated and in vivid contrast with the whitish body. A row of small blotches on each side, and beneath these a row of large black spots, in sharp contrast to the marble white of the abdomen.

The first impression on seeing this serpent is of a *white* reptile, boldly blotched with black. No other snake of its habitat imparts this pattern effect.

Distribution: A southern reptile, but extending into the pine barrens of New Jersey, where it is common. Subspecies extend into Florida and westward to the Mississippi.*

Habits: The Pine Snake has an alarming habit of taking a deep breath, opening the mouth slightly and, by means of a voluntarily erectile appendage in front of the breathing passage or glottis, is able to eject the air, in a loud hissing sound. The effect is much like holding a card in front of one's mouth and blowing forcibly upon it. When thus bluffing, it vibrates its tail.

A powerful constrictor, feeding upon rodents and birds—sometimes the eggs of ground-nesting birds. It lays from 15 – 24 eggs. The young are similar to adults. As a rule this snake does not thrive as a captive, although occasional individuals feed fairly well.

Bull Snake, Western Gopher Snake, *Pituophis sayi sayi* (Schlegel)

Size: 6 – 8 feet.

Form and scalation: Similar to the preceding, with pointed snout.

Coloration: Pale yellow to orange or ruddy hue. A series of large dark blotches, rather square in outline, along the back and a smaller row of blotches on side. Abdomen yellow.

Distribution: Western, but concisely listed in this chapter as it crosses the Mississippi into Illinois and Wisconsin. For detailed description and habits see Chapter XI.

"Milk" Snake, House Snake, Checkered "Adder," *Lampropeltis triangulum triangulum* (Lacépède)

Size: Average length is 3 feet, with diameter of slightly over ½ inch. Occasional 4-foot specimens are to be found, and an exceptional specimen over 6 feet long was authentically recorded in New England, but in a long period of years this was by far the largest example the author has ever heard mentioned.

Form and scalation: Moderately slender and cylindrical, with small head, but little distinct from neck. The scales are smooth and of satiny luster. The anal plate is undivided (entire).

Coloration: Yellowish brown or pale gray, with a series of irregu-

*The closely related Bull Snake, *Pituophis sayi,* appears to cross the Mississippi into the prairies of Illinois and Wisconsin. See key, Chapter X.

lar chestnut-brown or reddish blotches, edged with black. With occasional old specimens the blotches are dark olive. With most young examples they are quite bright red. On the sides are smaller blotches in alternation with those on the back. White beneath, with oblong spots of black, sometimes imparting a "checkerboard" effect. Examples in the latitude of Maryland have particularly red, close-set dorsal blotches with the paler spaces between them of ringlike form.

Specimens of this brightly marked snake often come to me for verifying identification, with supposition that they are Copperheads. The species may be immediately separated in identification from the poisonous snake, however, by its smooth scales and round pupils.

A subspecies designated as *L. triangulum syspila* (Cope), occurring in Iowa, Illinois and Indiana, has very bright red blotches, extending well downward on the sides and, being quite close-set, imparting a ringed appearance. This form is smaller than the more eastern ally.

Distribution: The entire northeastern area, including southern Ontario, the New England states to the Carolinas and westward to Iowa. Subspecies extend the range southward and westward.

Habits: The term "Milk" Snake comes from habits of prowling into stables, where this reptile is alleged to steal milk from cows. This theory is but one of many fallacies associated with snakes. Actually this species prowls about old buildings in search of small rodents—its favorite food, which it subdues by constricting power. Hence it is of economic value and should not be destroyed. It is oviparous. Few captive specimens can be readily induced to feed.

While "Milk" Snakes occasionally prowl during daylight, they are more inclined to hide under large, flat stones. The common prowling places of this snake are among stones of old foundations; this is evidenced by fragments of shed skins.

King Snake, Chain Snake, *Lampropeltis getulus getulus* (Linnaeus)

Size: While of the same genus as the preceding, this is a longer and heavier-bodied reptile. In the South it reaches a length of 6 feet, but southern New Jersey specimens (that being the area of encroachment in the coastal, northeastern region) are seldom much over 4 feet, though over an inch in thickness.

Form and scalation: Form is cylindrical, with but little taper over the greater part of the body; the head distinctly small and thus slightly distinct from the neck. The scales are smooth and rather glossy. The anal plate is entire.

Coloration: Lustrous black with narrow white or yellow crossbands, which fork on the sides and connect in chainlike fashion. Black beneath with large patches of white or yellow.

A subspecies, the **Black King Snake,** *L. getulus nigra* (Yarrow), ranging northward into southern Ohio and Indiana, has very narrow or obscure crossbands and may appear almost uniform black.

Distribution: A southern species, the typical form ranging from southern New Jersey to northern Florida. The form with but faintly discernible crossbands, the Black King Snake, ranges southward from southern Ohio and Indiana into the Gulf states.

Habits: This reptile is unique from marked cannibalistic habits. While all of the members of the genus *Lampropeltis* are more or less inclined to eat small snakes of other kinds, the King Snake attacks and kills snakes of dimensions closely approaching its own, and kills and devours Copperheads, Water Moccasins and Rattlesnakes. It is immune to the bites of these poisonous species. Rodents form a considerable part of its food, and it may be regarded as of economic value. It is a constrictor and, like all the snakes previously listed, oviparous.

This handsome snake is docile and quickly tamed. It is hardy as a captive, feeding readily upon small rodents. It is particularly free from parasitic skin troubles to be noted with some of the other larger snakes, hence a very satisfactory type for study in a collection, living for years in a simple wooden case with glass front and water dish—and doing best without imitative accessories of soil or plants.

Yellow-bellied King Snake, *Lampropeltis calligaster* (Harlan)

Size: Up to 4 feet long and about ¾ inch in diameter.

Form and scalation: Moderately stout with smooth scales of dull luster; anal plate entire.

Coloration: Grayish brown with row of dark, fairly symmetrical brown blotches along the back, which are transversely wider than long. They are narrowly bordered with black. There is a smaller, alternating row of blotches on the sides and a smaller row at the edges of the abdominal plates. The underside is yellowish, with square, dull blotches, usually of reddish hue. Head markings are usually strong, a dark band across the forward part of the head and an arrowheaded mark on the central and rear part. From the eye to angle of the mouth is a dark band. On the neck there are usually two parallel bands touching the base of the head.

There is considerable variation in intensity of the body blotches. They may be partially blocked out by a smoky band of about their width extending along the mid-dorsal region. With young specimens the dorsal blotches are strongly defined.

Distribution: Locality should be duly noted in consideration of this species. Its habitat is the central states. Its eastern extension is to Indiana, whence it ranges to Minnesota, southwestward through Kansas and Oklahoma and to Texas.

Habits: Feeds upon small rodents, birds and lizards and appears to be less inclined to cannibalism than others of its genus. The author has not been successful in maintaining this snake as a captive.

Scarlet Snake, *Cemophora coccinea* (Blumenbach)

Size: Average length 16 inches, with diameter of ¼ inch. Exceptional examples (but southern) may be as much as 24 inches long and ½ inch in thickness.

Form and scalation: Rather slender and cylindrical, not tapering until near head and tail. Head not distinct from neck; snout sharply pointed. Scales smooth; lustrous; anal plate entire.

Coloration: This small but very beautiful snake is characteristic among the species listed in this chapter. It barely enters the northeastern region.

From above it appears encircled with wide scarlet bands, separated by pairs of black rings enclosing a white or yellowish one. These markings do not cross the abdomen, however, which is pale and unmarked. The head is reddish with a black bar across the eyes.

Distribution: Mostly the southeastern United States, but extending northward into southern New Jersey;* westward to Oklahoma and Louisiana.

Habits: The brilliant little Scarlet Snake resembles the species of *Lampropeltis* in habits. It is oviparous and a constrictor. It feeds upon other small snakes and lizards, and searches for immature rodents in their nests. Its habits are secretive, and it may be looked for under the

---

*Two specimens collected in the pine barrens of Burlington County in 1934. See *Copeia*, 1935, No. 4, p. 191; and another, more recently.

loose bark of fallen trees. In captivity, if given slabs of bark, under which to hide, it does fairly well if provided with very young rodents ("pink mice") and small snakes such as *Storeria* and *Diadophis*.

Common Water Snake, Banded Water Snake, "Moccasin,"
Natrix sipedon sipedon (Linnaeus)

Size: 3 – 4 feet long and from 1¼ to 1¾ inch in diameter.

Form and scalation: Form quite stout; head distinct from neck and rather flattened. Scales roughly keeled and without luster on dorsal surface. The anal plate is divided (double, like the undertail plates).

Coloration: Dull brown, with broad irregular crossbands of reddish brown, which are seldom plainly evident except on the sides. *The underside is yellowish, brightly marked with red spots or blotches.* These undermarkings form a strong point for identification. Large or old examples may look uniform dull brown or almost black, but the underside is always brightly colored. Very young specimens are pale gray with the crossbands blackish and very distinct.

Distribution: Southern Quebec and southern Ontario, thence throughout the eastern United States to North Carolina; westward to Wisconsin and Colorado. Subspecies carry the range into Florida and westward to Texas.

Habits: The Common Water Snake of northeastern North America, improperly called "Moccasin," lives along streams, ponds, frequents old mill dams and the foundations of country bridges where masonry is of "dry" construction, with crevices for hiding. While there are allegations about the Water Snake being harmful in destroying game fish, this condition is not likely. Game fish, as a rule, are too active for Water Snakes to catch them. This species pursues the slower-moving fish, as well as frogs and toads.

This is the first species so far listed which produces its young alive, in as many as three dozen or more in a litter. It should not be confused with the poisonous Water Moccasin, which, in the Atlantic region, does not extend northward of Virginia. There are no poisonous Water Snakes in the northeastern region.

For laboratory observation the Water Snake is hardy and a voracious feeder. Despite its semiaquatic habits when wild, as a captive it does best in dry quarters with nothing more than a small dish containing water for drinking

Lake Water Snake, *Natrix sipedon insularum* Conant and Clay

Size: Appears to average about the same as the typical form.

Form and scalation: Similar to *N. s. sipedon.*

Coloration: Described as differing from the typical form in reduction of the dorsal pattern and absence of abdominal spotting with red. The dorsal surface is gray, greenish gray or pale brown, with faint traces of pattern in adult examples. The abdomen is usually whitish and practically unmarked except clouding along margins of the shields posteriorly.

Distribution: In the original description it is explained:

"*N. s. insularum* inhabits the islands of Lake Erie lying between Point Pelee (south of Leamington) Essex County South, Ontario, and Catawba and Marblehead peninsulas, east of Port Clinton, Ottawa County, Ohio. . . . Specimens showing intergradation with *N. sipedon sipedon* have been examined from the Catawba and Marblehead peninsulas and certain of the islands. . . ."

Habits: Common along the shores of the islands, particularly in rocky places. "In some instances as many as 12 and 14 large individuals were found hiding under a single rock." (Conant and Clay.)

Red-bellied Water Snake, *Natrix erythrogaster erythrogaster* (Forster)

Size: Smaller than the Common Water Snake.

Form and scalation: Form and keeled scalation similar to the preceding; eyes relatively larger.

Coloration: Rusty, to rather dark brown above with indistinct crossbands. *Abdomen immaculate reddish, varying from coppery red to crimson hue.* The young are vividly marked with crossbands of dark brown or black.

Distribution: While this is a southeastern form, not occurring north of Virginia in the coastal area, it extends into Michigan in the central United States.

Its habits are similar to those of the Common Water Snake.

Kirtland's Water Snake, *Natrix kirtlandii* (Kennicott)

Size: Smallest of the water snakes, seldom attaining a length of 20 inches. A fair-sized example is 14 inches long and ⅜ inch in diameter.

Form and scalation: Moderately stout in proportion to length, head fairly distinct. Scales strongly keeled.

Coloration: Brown with upright blackish-brown bars on sides, separated by narrow spaces of ground color. Two rows of rather obscure rounded blotches on the back. The blotches of the back and the sides are in alternation. Lip plates yellowish. Middle of abdomen brick red, with a row of dark spots on each side.

Distribution: Northern part of the Mississippi Valley, including Ohio, Indiana and Illinois, with northern extension into Wisconsin and Michigan. There is eastern extension into Pennsylvania and New Jersey.

Habits: Not so aquatic as the larger water snakes. It may be found in damp woods and swampy places, hiding under logs or loose bark. If frightened, when near the edge of water, it dives in, but is not so commonly seen swimming as with other species of *Natrix.*

It feeds upon salamanders, small frogs, toads and fishes and is fairly hardy as a captive, but must be given opportunity to hide. As with all the water snakes, the young are produced alive.

Diamond-back Water Snake, *Natrix rhombifera* (Hallowell)

Size: 4 – 5 feet; diameter $1\frac{3}{4}$ to 2 inches.

Form and scalation: Body very stout; head distinct from neck; lip plates swollen and protruding (with adults). Scales roughly keeled. Anal plate divided.

Coloration: Olive or brownish with a narrow chain of dark markings along the back, enclosing diamond-shaped areas of the ground color. From the lower angle of each "diamond" or rhomb is a band of black, about two scales wide, extending down the side. Seen from the side, the snake appears to be symmetrically marked with upright bars, their width about equal to the interspaces.

Distribution: This big and savage-looking Water Snake—abundant in the lower Mississippi Valley—extends northward into southern Illinois and Indiana.

Habits: This species has a common habit of climbing into bushes which overhang the water and plunging in at the slightest alarm. The food consists mostly of fishes and frogs, but the author has found that these snakes will also eat crawfish. Adults do not take well to captivity; most of the larger specimens refuse food. The best chance of inducing them to feed is to provide them with a fair-sized tank containing living fish. They are sullen and inclined to bite if handled.

Green Water Snake, *Natrix cyclopion* (Duméril and Bibron)

Size: One of the larger water snakes, often reaching a length of 4 feet. A measured specimen, 43 inches long, had a body diameter of 1½ inch.

Form and scalation: Stout and heavy, although the tail is long and tapering. The head is rather elongate but distinct from the neck. The upper lip is swollen, and the eyes are placed rather high and forward, toward the snout. *There is a unique character in arrangement of a ring of small plates around the eye, thus separating the eye from the lip plates or labials.* Body scales strongly keeled; anal plate divided.

Coloration: Dark green or olive brown, with numerous narrow black and wavy bands crossing the back. The bands are about the width of one scale and separated by width of two scales. There are narrow, alternating blotches on the sides. Abdomen uniform yellowish with exception of grayish tinge at edges of the plates.

Distribution: Ranging into southern Illinois from the southeastern region.

Habits: A typical water snake, taking refuge in aquatic shelter when frightened. It is a sullen captive, usually refusing food.

Queen Snake, Striped Water Snake, *Natrix septemvittata* (Say)

Size: Of moderate size, from 2 to 2½ feet long. A 2-foot specimen is ⅝ inch in diameter.

Form and scalation: Relatively more slender than the other water snakes. The scales are roughly keeled.

Coloration: Adults dark brown, with three narrow dark stripes on the back, which may be indistinct. A yellow stripe on the lower side, covering one half of the first and second rows of scales. Abdomen yellow with dark stripes in the center. The name *septemvittata* means seven stripes; thus, with 3 dark stripes on the back, one on each side and two in the central part of the abdominal area, the technical name indicates the pattern.

In examining the pattern, which varies in strength of delineation of the striping or longitudinal banding, it should be noted that some specimens, particularly when young, look like brown garter snakes without a central (dorsal) stripe, but retaining a bright yellow stripe on each side. The dark stripes on the abdomen, however, readily separate this species from the striped snakes (*Thamnophis*). The two close and parallel dark bands in the central part of the abdomen may, in some examples, be almost fused. If the narrow area of ground color beneath the yellow stripe on the side may be considered a band, such specimens might be figured as having three dark bands beneath. Unless closely examined, this small water snake appears dull brown, with a pale stripe on each side.

Distribution: Western Pennsylvania to Wisconsin and southward to the Gulf of Mexico.

Habits: Lives along the margins of quite clear, flowing streams, climbing into bushes that overhang the water, dropping in and diving when disturbed. Food consists of small frogs, toads and fishes. But few captive specimens can be induced to take food.

Graham's Water Snake, *Natrix grahamii* (Baird and Girard)

Size: Similar to the preceding.

Form and scalation: Similar to preceding.

Coloration: Another of the small, striped water snakes. The back is dull brown with an indistinct, pale band down the center, this band narrowly bordered with black. On each side is a broad band of yellow, in strong contrast to the dark hue above it. This pale band covers the first three rows of scales. Along its lower margin is a narrow black stripe. The abdomen is yellowish, and a dark stripe or band is generally present on the central portion.

Distribution: Valleys of the Mississippi and Missouri rivers. Extends into southern Illinois, thence to Louisiana and Texas. Habits similar to *N. septemvittata.*

Striped Swamp Snake, *Tropidoclonion lineatum* (Hallowell)

Size: Rather small, seldom as long as 20 inches. A 16-inch specimen is slightly under ½ inch in diameter.

Form and scalation: Moderately stout for its size. Head small, rather pointed and not distinct from neck. Scales distinctly keeled.

Coloration: Grayish brown with whitish or yellowish stripe along back, usually bordered with black dots. A less prominent stripe on each side on the 2nd and 3rd rows of scales. Abdomen yellowish white with two rows of black spots.

At first glance this species looks like a Garter Snake. Its head, however, is smaller, more pointed and less distinct. The rows of black dots on the abdomen provide a point for identification.

Distribution: Ohio, Indiana and Illinois to South Dakota; southward to Texas.

Habits: While allied to the Water Snakes, this small species is not semiaquatic. It prefers rather low, damp places, though not invariably in the immediate vicinity of water. It is commonly to be found hiding under flat stones or loose debris. The food consists partially of earthworms, and captive examples will subsist upon such diet. When picked up, it has a habit of tightly coiling about one's finger.

DeKay's Snake, Brown Snake, *Storeria dekayi* (Holbrook)

Size: One of the smallest of the North American snakes. Average length is 12 inches, with diameter slightly exceeding ¼ inch. The largest specimen the author has measured was 15 inches long.

Form and scalation: Moderately stout; head fairly distinct. Eyes relatively large. Scales heavily keeled.

Coloration: Dull brown above, or grayish brown. A band of paler tint on the back, bordered with blackish dots. The pale band on the central area of the back is sometimes pronounced. Top of the head dark. *Abdomen pinkish.*

The color of the underside should be deducted as an identifying character among the several kinds of small brown snakes of northeastern North America.

Distribution: Southern Canada and the entire eastern United States. The range extends westward to Kansas and southward into Mexico.

Habits: This unobtrusive species still holds its own in many places where other kinds of snakes have been exterminated. It still occurs in parts of Central Park in New York City, hemmed in on all sides by the bustle of a great metropolis. Occurrence in the northeastern United States is general, except in elevated areas, where it is usually replaced by the allied Storer's Snake.

The little Brown Snake, or DeKay's Snake, is commonly to be found hiding under flat stones. In such places it can find its food, which consists largely of earthworms. Such a simple diet enables it to exist where other serpents, even the Common Garter Snake, have long disappeared. Its secretive habits, diminutive size and dull coloration aid in its protection. It is viviparous. The young are very dark, with a whitish ring around the neck. They thus resemble the young of the Ring-necked Snake, but may be recognized by their keeled scales. This snake does fairly well as a captive, under terrarium conditions, with earth, bark or stones under which to hide. Small earthworms form sufficient diet.

Storer's Snake, Red-bellied Brown Snake, *Storeria occipito-maculata* (Storer)

Size: Slightly smaller than the preceding; seldom exceeding a length of 12 inches. An average example is 10 inches long and ¼ inch in thickness.

Form and scalation: Similar to preceding.

Coloration: Brown or gray above, with or without a pale longitudinal band on the back. *Coral red beneath.* Gray examples have the more brilliant red undersurface.

Distribution: Widely distributed. Southern Ontario and the United States from the Atlantic coast to North Dakota. Southward into Mexico.

Habits: Inhabits the same general regions as DeKay's Snake (the preceding species), but appears to prefer elevated areas and to be more "spotty" in occurrence than the more commonly distributed Brown Snake (*S. dekayi*).

Habits are similar to DeKay's Snake. With a number of eastern specimens, the average number of young (born alive) was 10, the litters appearing during the latter half of August. One of these young snakes could readily coil upon a dime. The body was dark with a pale collar.

Small-eyed Brown Snake, *Haldea striatula* (Linnaeus)

Size: Very small—seldom as much as 12 inches. The measurement of an adult female was 11 inches long and ¼ inch in diameter.

Form and scalation: This is the smallest of the *keel-scaled,* little Brown Snakes and may be readily told from the two species of *Storeria* (preceding) by its elongate, pointed head and very small eyes. Both species of *Storeria* have a blunt head and proportionately large eyes. The scales of all three are similarly keeled.

Coloration: Uniform grayish brown or reddish brown above; yellowish white beneath. Often a pale, indistinct band across the top of head.

Distribution: The range is wide, but mostly southern, from Virginia to Indiana and Illinois in western distribution. Southward the range is into Florida and Texas.

Habits: The author has found this little snake abundant in southern pine forests, where it hides under litter of bark that has slipped from dead trees or under loose bark that may be readily peeled from fallen trees. No specimens were seen prowling on the surface. The situations in which it is to be found indicate an abundance of soft-bodied insect larvae and earthworms. Such forms of life would thus appear to form the diet of this diminutive reptile. It gives birth to living young.

Smooth Brown Snake, *Virginia valeriae valeriae* Baird and Girard

Size: Smallest of the little Brown Snakes—usually under 10 inches. The measurement of an average adult is $7\frac{1}{4}$ inches long and $\frac{1}{4}$ inch in diameter.

Form and scalation: Moderately stout and short, with abruptly tapering tail. Head rather pointed. *Scales of satiny smoothness.* While there may be faint keels on the posterior portion, these are not apparent unless a specimen is examined with a strong glass. On gross examination, the appearance indicates a perfectly smooth-scaled surface, quite different from the strongly keeled *Storeria* and *Haldea.*

There may be confusion in separating this species from the Worm Snake (*Carphophis*), but the head of the latter is of the same width as the neck, the scales are polished and lustrous, while the color of the undersurface is *pinkish.* With *Virginia,* the head is perceptibly wider than the neck, the scales of dull or satiny surface, while the underside is *yellowish.*

Coloration: Chestnut or grayish above, usually with two rows of minute black dots along the back. Abdomen yellowish.

Distribution: New Jersey* and Maryland, southern Pennsylvania to Ohio; southward to Georgia.

A subspecies, *V. valeriae elegans,* extends the range to southern Illinois and southward to Texas. On gross examination both forms appear alike. If the rows of scales across the body are counted, 15 rows will be found in *V. valeriae valeriae,* while in *elegans* there are 17 rows.

Habits: Secretive and similar to the other Brown Snakes. Earthworms and the larvae of insects that burrow into decaying trees appear to form the principal food. The species produces its young alive. The young are not as thick as a wooden match.

Ribbon Snake, *Thamnophis sauritus sauritus* (Linnaeus)

Size: Up to a yard (the maximum), but appearing smaller owing to very slender outlines. An example of average length is 2 feet 2 inches in length, with diameter of $\frac{3}{8}$ inch.

*Recorded from the Watchung Mountains, near Plainfield (Pope).

Form and scalation: Very slender, with long, gradually tapering tail a third or more the total length. Scales strongly keeled, imparting a velvety look to the upper surface.

Coloration: Dark brown or black above with a vivid yellow stripe down the back and a similar stripe on each side *on the 3rd and 4th rows* of scales above the abdominal plates. The dorsal stripe is very sharply outlined, producing a ribbonlike aspect. Abdomen yellowish white, without markings.

Distribution: Southeastern Canada and the United States generally east of the Mississippi to Georgia and Alabama.

Habits: Seldom found except in damp places, in fact more generally along the grassy banks of ponds and streams or in wet meadows. For escape it will take to the water, and it dives and swims with agility of the water snakes. Food consists of small frogs, toads and fishes. It is hardy and feeds readily as a captive. It produces living young, but seldom to the number of over a dozen.

Common Garter Snake, Striped Snake, *Thamnophis sirtalis sirtalis* (Linnaeus)

Size: A large specimen is a yard in length, but this is well above the average. A fairly large example from Sullivan County, New York, was 31 inches long and ⅝ inch in diameter at the thickest part.

Form and scalation: Moderately stout; head quite distinct. Scales coarsely keeled; as is usual with snakes of such carination, the area of the back is dull and lusterless.

Coloration: Subject to much variation, but the average is blackish or brownish with a yellow stripe along the back and a similar stripe on each side. *The side stripe is on the 2nd and 3rd rows of scales.* Here is a point of definition from the Ribbon Snake, on which the lateral stripe is on the 3rd and 4th rows of scales. The color beneath is greenish yellow.

The skin along the sides, between the scales, has numerous white or pale greenish spots, which are often so arranged that a checkerboard or tessellated effect is produced when the scales are separated after eating, or if the snake is angry and flattens its body. With many specimens there may be a double row of black spots on the scales themselves, between the stripes, the two rows arranged alternately or in checkerboard pattern. When the spots are strong and the dorsal stripe weak or absent, the subspecies *ordinatus* is indicated.

In the varying of pattern and hues, the stripes may be more or less distinct. With some specimens the central stripe may be ragged or broken, and with others, from mountainous areas, the dorsal stripe may be faint or absent. With these the tessellated pattern of the skin invades the scale coloration, producing a checkered effect, and the side stripes remain to aid in identification.

Distribution: Of all the northeastern snakes this is the most commonly seen. While given to considerable hiding under flat stones and the like, it is not of particularly secretive nature and is commonly found prowling the surface. The range of the typical form is wide, including southeastern Canada and all of the central and eastern United States.

Habits: The Garter Snake is to be found over practically all kinds of terrain. It is common in the extensive salt meadows of the coastal states, the inland, fresh-water swamps of the interior, and is equally abundant in the elevated, mountain regions. This is in variance to most members of the striped snake genus, which prefer wet places; in fact some of the western species might be quite properly called water snakes.

Next to the little brown snakes, which are not readily to be seen owing to combination of hue and secretiveness, the Garter Snake, in northeastern North America, makes the best showing of holding its own near reclaimed or improved areas where other reptiles have long since disappeared. Another factor in its perpetuation is the large number of young that may be produced in a litter. The young are born alive, and there is great variance among the broods, from one to six dozen in a litter, and the higher numbers are in the majority. The young are marked similarly to the parents.

Garter Snakes subsist upon cold-blooded prey such as frogs, toads, salamanders and earthworms. They can thrive upon the latter, alone, which accounts for their persistence in areas which have undergone human-made changes in reclamation from wild tracts.

Butler's Garter Snake; *Thamnophis butleri* (Cope)

Size: Smaller than the common (preceding) species. An average measurement, from a series of fifteen specimens, is as follows: Length $17\frac{3}{4}$ inches; greatest diameter $\frac{1}{2}$ inch.

Form and scalation: Moderately stout and but gradually tapering to the neck, with small head. The reduced head size is an important character for diagnosis. The scales are strongly keeled.

Coloration: The yellow stripes are sharply defined. The stripe on the side places this species midway between those garter snakes having the lateral (side) stripes on the 3rd and 4th rows of scales and members with the lateral stripes on the 2nd and 3rd rows.

Ground color is brown or blackish, with a strong and ribbonlike stripe on the back and *a stripe on the side covering the upper half of the 2nd, the entire 3rd, and the lower half of the 4th rows of scales.* The underside is greenish white with black dots on the edges of some of the plates.

Distribution: Western New York and western Pennsylvania, with extension through Ohio, Indiana and southern Michigan, Illinois and Wisconsin. Particularly common in Ohio, Indiana and southern Michigan.

Habits: Captives feed readily upon small frogs, toads, fishes and earthworms.

Plains Garter Snake, *Thamnophis radix* (Baird and Girard)

Size: One of the larger striped or garter snakes. An adult in my collection is 32 inches long and ¾ inch in diameter at thickest part.

Form and scalation: Rather stout, with head quite distinct. (Note diameter of body in relation to length in preceding paragraph.) Scales strongly keeled.

Coloration: Dark brown, olive or blackish with three yellow stripes —one in the center of back and one on each side. *The side stripe is on the 3rd and 4th rows of scales.* There are usually two distinct rows of square, black spots between the stripes, as with the common eastern Garter Snake, which the present species overlaps in distribution.

Although this species resembles the eastern garter snake in form, it may be separated by the lateral stripes being on the 3rd and 4th rows of scales, instead of the 2nd and 3rd rows, as with *T. sirtalis.*

The higher-placed stripes on the side might confuse it with the Ribbon Snake, *T. sauritus,* but that is a very slender species as compared with the heavy-bodied *radix.*

Distribution: If it were not for this snake occurring in Illinois, into which state it extends from the West, it would be excluded from this chapter. It is a western reptile, common in the central-western states, its habitat extending through the Great Plains to the Canadian Northwest.

Habits: Found in both dry areas and along streams and lakes. Specimens living in the latter conditions may be as semiaquatic as water snakes, as they take to the water, dive to the bottom and hide among aquatic plants. Large litters of living young are produced during August or early in September.

ADDITIONAL KINDS ENTERING OR AT MARGIN OF THE NORTHEASTERN SECTION

It is, of course, understood that boundaries of states cannot be used in defining reptile distribution and have little or no effect upon such unless attended with marked physical differences in terrain. In consequence, the technical reptile student might take exception to my "zoning" the map of North America into regions, or, more properly speaking, sections. But as previously and successively explained, this has been done to simplify identification of species according to interest or requirements of the reader of this field book. Instead of interminable listing of the species of the continent, the section, according to the location of the reader, cuts down grouping or listing of species to deductive keys and descriptive chapters that are not too lengthy.

In selection of block of states to define a gross northeastern quadrant, the southern point of Illinois, extending into the Mississippi Valley, creates a contact with southern kinds. If the southern spearhead of that state and adjacent extreme southern Indiana were included in strong emphasis, the southeastern fauna would be too highly emphasized. Indications of northward extension of southern kinds have already appeared in deductive key and text, but there has been restraint in their listing. Students of the reptilian fauna of the mid-Mississippi water basin are referred to Chapters VII, VIII and IX, covering the snakes of southern and southeastern North America.

As defining conditions in southern Illinois, a letter from my friend R. Marlin Perkins, is clearly explanatory:

"The mixing of southern, western and northern species in the Mississippi Valley south of St. Louis is indeed an interesting thing, and because of this, hunting in this locality is full of surprises. The spot we took you to when you were hunting with us a few years ago is about ten miles south and a little west of Murphysboro, Illinois. The sandstone rocks of the great bluff overlooking the dens was worn down by the actions of the waters of the Big Muddy River, which you will remember flows near the dens today. The narrow, heavily wooded valley between the river and the bluff is from a quarter to a half mile wide, and about two and a half miles long. With the bluff on one side and the river on the other this little spot is set apart from the rest of the country. *A. piscivorus*" (the true Water Moccasin) "is very numerous in this whole section, being found along the Big Muddy River and north a distance of fifteen or twenty miles, but always associated with the bluff of brown sandstone. At this den section I have seen one hundred and five snakes in one day. At one time it was thicker with snakes than any other place I have ever seen. In the past few years the natives have killed great numbers and have burned over the dens and this little valley.

"We have collected the following near Murphysboro, Illinois:

Worm Snake	*Carphophis amoena*
Ring-necked Snake	*Diadophis p. arnyi*
Spreading Adder	*Heterodon contortrix*
Rough Green Snake	*Opheodrys aestivus*
Black Racer	*Coluber c. constrictor*
Pilot Black Snake	*Elaphe o. obsoleta*
Gray Coluber	" " *confinis*
Evan's King Snake	*Lampropeltis calligaster*
Say's King Snake	" *g. holbrooki*
Southern Milk Snake	" *t. syspila*
Graham's Water Snake	*Natrix grahamii*
Diamond-back Water Snake	" *rhombifera*
Common Water Snake	" *s. sipedon*
Banded Water Snake	" " *pleuralis*
Yellow-bellied Water Snake	" *e. transversa*
DeKay's Snake	*Storeria dekayi*
Virginia Snake	*Virginia elegans*
Little Brown Snake	*Potamophis (Haldea) striatulus*
Common Garter Snake	*Thamnophis s. sirtalis*
Ribbon Snake	" *proximus*
Copperhead Snake	*Agkistrodon m. mokasen*
Cotton-mouth Moccasin	" *piscivorus*
Canebrake Rattlesnake	*Crotalus h. atricaudatus*

"The section between here and Memphis is intergrade territory for many species, among which is the *Elaphe obsoleta obsoleta* and *confinis* group. An individual snake picked nearly anywhere around here could be either."

In the succeeding chapter, relating to the poisonous snakes of the northeastern section, all species which may enter even a marginal portion from the South are considered in detail.

Summary: It is of interest to summarize some points that crop up in frequent queries about the nonpoisonous species.

The following kinds lay eggs:

Worm Snake	*Carphophis amoena amoena*
Ring-necked Snake	*Diadophis punctatus edwardsii*
Common Hog-nosed Snake	*Heterodon contortrix*
Southern Hog-nosed Snake	" *simus*
Smooth Green Snake	*Liopeltis vernalis*
Keeled Green Snake	*Opheodrys aestivus*
Blacksnake; Racer	*Coluber constrictor constrictor*
Pilot Blacksnake	*Elaphe obsoleta obsoleta*
Corn Snake	" *guttata*
Fox Snake	" *vulpina*
Pine Snake	*Pituophis melanoleucus melanoleucus*
"Milk" Snake	*Lampropeltis triangulum triangulum*
King Snake	" *getulus getulus*
Yellow-bellied King Snake	" *calligaster*
Scarlet Snake	*Cemophora coccinea*

The preceding are scientifically designated as being *oviparous.*

The following produce living young:

Common Water Snake	*Natrix sipedon sipedon*
Red-bellied Water Snake	" *erythrogaster erythrogaster*
Kirtland's Water Snake	" *kirtlandii*
Diamond-back Water Snake	" *rhombifera*
Green Water Snake	" *cyclopion*
Queen Snake	" *septemvittata*
Graham's Water Snake	" *grahamii*
Striped Swamp Snake	*Tropidoclonion lineatum*
DeKay's Snake	*Storeria dekayi*
Storer's Snake	" *occipitomaculata*

Smooth Brown Snake	*Virginia valeriae valeriae*
Small-eyed Brown Snake	*Haldea striatula*
Ribbon Snake	*Thamnophis sauritus sauritus*
Common Garter Snake	" *sirtalis sirtalis*
Butler's Garter Snake	" *butleri*
Plains Garter Snake	" *radix*

The preceding are designated as *viviparous,* or more formally, as *ovo-viviparous.*

Without repetition of scientific names further summarization may be noted.

The following are constrictors, their food including rodents:

> Pilot or Mountain Blacksnake
> Corn Snake
> Fox Snake
> Pine Snake
> "Milk" Snake
> King or Chain Snake
> Yellow-bellied King Snake
> Scarlet Snake

The following is not a constrictor, but diet includes rodents:

> Blacksnake or Racer

The following are not constrictors and confine diet to cold-blooded prey, including frogs, toads and fish:

> Common Water Snake
> Kirtland's Water Snake
> Diamond-back Water Snake
> Queen Snake
> Graham's Water Snake
> Striped Swamp Snake
> Ribbon Snake
> Common Garter Snake
> Butler's Garter Snake
> Plains Garter Snake
> Common Hog-nosed Snake
> Southern Hog-nosed Snake

Nonconstrictors feeding mostly upon worms, insects and small salamanders:

> Worm Snake
> Ring-necked Snake
> Smooth Green Snake
> Keeled Green Snake
> DeKay's Snake
> Storer's Snake
> Small-eyed Brown Snake
> Smooth Brown Snake

Among the species enumerated, the Blacksnake or Racer, Pilot or Mountain Blacksnake, Corn Snake, Fox Snake, Pine Snake, "Milk" Snake, King Snake, Yellow-bellied King Snake, or Prairie King Snake and Scarlet Snake should be rated as of economic value because of rodent-reducing habits. While the other nonvenomous snakes are not of specifically useful habits, they are not harmful, and their destruction is no more nor less than an exhibition of malice prompted by unreasonable hatred of snakes. Despite allegations to the contrary, the harmless water snake is not a menace to streams stocked with game fish. It may catch a few trout, but is not active enough to feed largely upon such lively prey. Its common food consists of the slower fish, frogs and crawfish.

To prospective students I would suggest that, among the larger species listed, the Blacksnake or Racer, the Pine Snake, the "Milk" Snake, Yellow-bellied or Prairie King Snake may prove difficult to maintain, as they are reticent in feeding, although individual Blacksnakes may prove to be exceptions. The Water Snakes and Striped Snakes are hardy and good feeders. The smaller kinds, with sympathetic care and provisions for hiding, offer interesting possibilities for observations on captive longevity. Poisonous snakes, with proper diet, may live for years, but the maintenance of venomous reptiles should not be attempted without keen realization of the danger involved and unless every precaution is taken to prevent accident to the student and to visitors who may inspect a collection.

CHAPTER VI

The Northeastern Poisonous Snakes

THE THREE TYPES occurring in the region under consideration belong to one family. They are to be noted, as follows:

The Family *Crotalidae:*

This is the grouping of the Pit Vipers, so called from a deep pit between the eye and the nostril. The larger number of species are New World. Rattlesnakes, Moccasins, the Fer-de-lance group (*Bothrops*) and the big tropical Bushmaster are among the Crotalids. These snakes are stout-bodied, but with reduced neck and wide, distinct, even bulging head. Their fangs are long, fixed to movable bones, and fold against the roof of the mouth when the jaws are closed. The venom is mostly hemolytic, or blood-and-tissue-destroying. Four of these snakes, two rattlers, the Copperhead and the Water Moccasin occur within the northeastern section of the North American map. For simplification we may regard them as representing three "types." Detailed descriptions follow:

Northern Copperhead Snake, Chunkhead, Highland Moccasin, Pilot Snake, Rattlesnake Pilot, *Agkistrodon mokasen cupreus* (Rafinesque)

Sizes: 2 – 4 feet, the latter length rare. A specimen from Pennsylvania that may be considered fairly large is 33 inches long, $1\frac{1}{4}$ inch in diameter, with head 1 inch in width.

Form and scalation: From comparison of length and diameter, this will be noted to be a stout-bodied snake. The neck tapers, and the head thus appears broad and distinct, being nearly as wide as the greatest diameter of body. The scales are very distinctly keeled, though not to the extent to impart a rough surface, as with the larger Water Snakes. Most of the plates under the tail in a single row. A deep pit between eye and nostril. Pupil of eye elliptic. Top of head with symmetrical plates.

Coloration: Pale hazel brown to brownish gray with quite widely spaced, large crossbands of rich chestnut brown. These bands are narrow on the back and very broad on the sides and when seen from above resemble the outline of a thick-stemmed hourglass or spoollike form. From the sides, most of the bands look like thick Y's with the stems directed upward. On the average specimen several of the bands are broken on the back, forming inverted V- or Y-shaped blotches on the sides. All of the bands are darker at their borders and may enclose light patches similar to the general hue of the body. Top of head usually of a coppery hue.

The abdomen is pale pinkish brown with a row of dark spots on each side.

With northeastern specimens there is not much color variation. Occasional examples have a duller or dark body hue, rendering the transverse blotches less vivid.

Two of the harmless species are often mistaken for the Copperhead. These are the Common Water Snake and Hog-nosed Snake, which are stout in form and have dark transverse markings, though not of close similarity.

The Copperhead carries its points of ready separation in having elliptic pupils (round with the harmless species), pit between eye and nostril, and greater number of plates under the tail in a single row—in place of double row. The "Milk" Snake is also confused with the Copperhead, but the former is slender and has smooth scales.

Distribution: Central Massachusetts, thence southward through all of the eastern states to northern Florida; westward to Illinois, thence southwestward to Oklahoma and Texas. Particularly common in Connecticut, eastern New York, Pennsylvania, New Jersey, Maryland, the Virginias and the Carolinas. Its greatest abundance is in mountainous and ledgy regions, but its domain is not limited to elevated districts, as it occurs in swampy districts and in the South is to be found in the low-lying stretches of cypress growth.

Habits: Owing to protective coloration, like fallen leaves and debris of the forest floor, this serpent has held its own in persistent occurrence over the larger and more dangerous Rattlesnake. Copperheads are still found along the top and base of the Palisades of the Hudson River, while rattlesnakes have been exterminated from that area for fifty years. It is still fairly common in parts of Westchester County, New York, where some of the larger kinds of nonvenomous snakes have disappeared. As it does not extend northward of central Massachusetts, it may be eliminated from consideration in Vermont, New Hampshire and Maine.

In the northeastern United States, ledgy, wooded hills, with base of wild, damp meadows, form the favorite prowling places where this species searches for small rodents, birds and frogs. Old stone walls are prowling places, and such spots should be negotiated with caution in use of hands by summer picnickers.

In the northern states copperheads return to specific hibernating dens, often in company with rattlers and blacksnakes. It is close to such locations that the young are born in late August or early September, from six to a dozen in a litter, the tails of the infant snakes a bright sulphur yellow.

The Copperhead likes light and air but is not promiscuous in its prowling or resting intervals. It has a habit of tucking itself under the edge of a shelving rock so that it cannot be seen from a glance directly downward. To detect such snakes it is necessary to bend low and peer beneath the rocks. Here is a source of danger to the human traversing ledgy terrain, with no protection to ankles or legs. There is the chance that the snake may be alarmed by an approaching foot and strike at it, although most copperheads, under such conditions, remain motionless to escape detection. Another trait is to coil among dead leaves, so arranging the body folds that parts of them are hidden. The pale and dark brown hues of the snake furnish a fine example of protective resemblance.

The author remembers an occurrence when he was lunching during reconnoiter of an extensive copperhead den. Seated on a rock, he at first concentrated attention on the luncheon, but after lighting a pipe and glancing among patches of dead leaves that had drifted over the ledge, he saw the protruding snout of a Copperhead not more than six feet away. Closer inspection disclosed half a dozen others, all within a radius of about twenty feet. These snakes had remained motionless, half covered with leaves, for a full half-hour during the siesta.

That would have been a bad spot for an incautious human without protective attire!

If met while prowling, Copperheads will usually try to escape. If cornered, they will coil and vibrate the tail. As a rule it is not an irritable snake and not nearly so bold in putting up a show of defense as the Timber Rattlenake, with which it often dens up for the winter.

Water Moccasin or Cotton-mouth Snake, *Agkistrodon piscivorus* (Lacépède)

Size: Large—up to five feet. An adult 4 feet long measured $2\frac{1}{2}$ inches in diameter at thickest part. Its width of head was $2\frac{3}{8}$ inches.

Form and scalation: Stout and heavy-bodied in appearance, with very distinct head. A deep pit between eye and nostril. Pupil elliptic. Top of head with symmetrical plates; body scales distinctly keeled; most of the plates under tail in a single row.

Coloration: Dull olive or brown on the back; lighter on the sides, where there are more or less distinct wide, dark bands enclosing an area of the body color and darker blotches. Abdomen dull yellow blotched with brown or black, which becomes solid toward the tail.

The young are quite vividly colored and might be mistaken for copperhead snakes, as the blotches are reddish and strongly defined as they cross the back. While they are narrowed on the back, they are not so markedly constricted as with the Copperhead. Moreover, with the Water Moccasin, the bands are markedly margined with white, making the pattern very striking.

Distribution: This is a southeastern snake, but must be listed in consideration of the northeastern section, as it extends up the Mississippi Valley into southern Illinois. In the Atlantic region it occurs as far north as the Dismal Swamp, in Virginia.

While there is frequent mention of water "moccasins" in the northeastern United States, it should be understood that all semiaquatic serpents found north of the two points of limit of northward range of the Water Moccasin are harmless water snakes.

Habits: The habits of the Water Moccasin will be noted specifically under the area where this dangerous snake is to be more broadly found. It may be looked for along waterways or in swampy spots, where it may take refuge, when disturbed, in reedy vegetation in shallow water. Its tendency is to coil, partially hidden, along marginal spots in such places. In the chapter on the southeastern region, which is its typical home, it will be considered in detail.

Massasauga or Swamp Rattlesnake, *Sistrurus catenatus catenatus* (Rafinesque)

Size: One of the smallest of the rattlesnakes, as length of a yard is exceptional. An adult, as indicated by segments of rattle of uniform width, was 26 inches long. Its greatest diameter was $1\frac{1}{8}$ inch.

Form and scalation: From the Timber or Banded Rattlesnake (the only other rattler of the northeastern region) the Massasauga may be recognized by the top of the head having symmetrical shields. The body is quite stout, the head distinct, scales strongly keeled, rattle well developed.

Coloration: Grayish brown to rather dark brown, with a row of chestnut-brown, symmetrical oval blotches on the back narrowly outlined with pale hue. There is a smaller row of blotches on each side and sometimes smaller, alternating blotches or spots beneath. Some of the dorsal blotches sometimes fuse into the larger blotches of the sides. The light and dark hues assume a ringed pattern on the tail. The abdomen is gray, marbled with black—with some examples entirely black.

Distribution: Central New York, from Onondaga and Madison counties, also western Pennsylvania westward through Ohio, Michigan, Indiana, Illinois and Iowa to Nebraska and southern Minnesota. The range extends northward into Ontario and southward to Kansas, whence a subspecies extends the habitat.

Habits: The Massasauga frequents swampy places and damp meadows, although it prowls into near-by farmlands during midsummer. It is particularly common in Ohio and Michigan, where it is rated as a reptile of swampy places. There is a fair-sized area in the state of New York known as the Cicero Swamp, between Oneida and Onondaga lakes, where this species persists in fair numbers. This swamp is about 14 miles long and 7 miles wide. There is an abundance of mice, small birds and frogs in this area, hence abundance of food for a Rattlesnake, which takes both warm- and cold-blooded prey.

Timber Rattlesnake or Banded Rattlesnake, *Crotalus horridus horridus* (Linnaeus)

Size: Large, from $3\frac{1}{2}$ – 5 feet (exceptionally 6 feet). An adult from Pennsylvania is 3 feet 8 inches long, $1\frac{5}{8}$ inch in diameter, width of head $1\frac{3}{8}$ inch.

Form and scalation: Heavy-bodied with wide and very distinct head. Body scales strongly keeled. Top of head with small scales—the only northeastern snake with such head scalation. Rattle well developed.

The rattle is represented by a black, bulbous knob with very young examples, this also being the case with the young of the Massasauga (preceding).

Coloration: Color and pattern are in considerable variety. The commoner phase is sulphur yellow or pale tan, with wide dark brown or black crossbands, usually wavy or pointed at the rear and sometimes broken into three longitudinal rows of blotches, the central or larger ones being rather rhomblike. With darker example the blotches may be intensified by being margined with yellow. Rear part of the body darker; tail black. Some specimens almost entirely velvety black.

Distribution: All of the United States (in suitable areas) east and inclusive of the Mississippi Valley states, with exception of the greater part of Maine, northern New Hampshire and the Florida peninsula. The author has no records from southeastern Canada, where, it appears, there is no poisonous snake except the smaller swamp rattler— the Massasauga.

In the northeastern United States the distribution of the Timber or Banded Rattlesnake is more commonly associated with the wilder, wooded, mountains of moderate height on which there are broken ledges, with large, loose fragments of rock on the slopes and top. These flat fragments may be a foot or more in thickness and from a yard to six or eight feet in length, sloping back into a fissure, the bottom of which may be covered with soil or leaves, and which provides shelter during storms. It is the habit of rattlesnakes to coil under the edges of these rock masses, protected from the too hot summer sun, and prepared to retreat if disturbed. If the intruder goes his way, the snake may lie in motionless coil, without sounding the rattle, thus seeking to escape notice.

Also, near these shelters are specific crevices or "dens," where rattlers that have roamed over a considerable area during the summer congregate each fall preparatory to deep penetration and hibernation, beyond the frost line. During the late summer the females return to such places, and here the young are born, with natural instinct to return to this specific place each year for winter shelter. From the areas of the ledges, rattlesnakes prowl through the forests for food, and often into the farmlands, sheltering in old stone walls. Variations of weather produce difference in numbers observed. During particularly dry summers, rattlers may come into the low grounds for water. Their natural prey—small rodents and birds—sometimes shift their feeding grounds, and this also affects summer distribution. If a farm is infested with rats and mice, and a rattlesnake den is not far distant, it will not take the reptiles long to discover such favorable feeding ground.

While a very dangerous snake, owing to its large fangs and amount of venom it is able to inject at a bite, this northern rattlesnake is rather inoffensive as compared with its larger allies in the southern states. It usually gives warning of its presence by sounding the rattle, if disturbed when out of contact with sheltering crevice. If closely approached, it will strike, but the striking distance of the average specimen is barely eighteen inches—and usually shorter. There are records of fatalities from the bite of this species, but generally considered, there is a surprisingly small number reported. In the southern Berkshires, where rattlesnakes are frequent, the author has records of but three bites during a period of about twenty years. One was fatal.

As far as the author is aware, no Rattlesnake has ever been recorded from the Adirondack Mountains proper, although the species is common on Tongue and Black mountains, in the vicinity of Lake George. Likewise, the only recent Catskill records come from the vicinity of Tremper and Slide mountains, at the edge of the higher Catskills, near Phoenicia, New York. The species is abundant in the Ramapos (where accidents are extremely infrequent), the Kittatinnies of New Jersey and Pennsylvania, and the Shawangunk range in New York. In central New Jersey it occurs in conditions rather curious. There is considerable flat, forested country back of the central coast, quite damp in spots and with large sections covered with heavy sphagnum moss. In these locations the species attains a larger average size than the mountain type and exhibits a slightly different coloration. It is grayish, with strongly contrasted black bands, and faint rusty dorsal stripe. There is resemblance to the southern race known as the Canebrake Rattlesnake, which, in the coastal area of the Southeast and the lower Mississippi Valley attains a length of close to eight feet.

Rattlesnakes are extremely rare in the state of Maine, and that area is thus unique among all the states in the virtual absence of poisonous serpents. The Boston Society of Natural History has been unable to obtain an authentic record specimen for its collection from Maine over a number of years. There appear to be few records from New Hampshire, although specimens have been reported from an island in Lake Winnepesaukee. Vermont seems to have few rattlers except along the western slopes of the Green Mountains and in the southern portion.

Both the Copperhead and Rattlesnake appear to be extinct on Long Island, although that the latter was formerly found there is evident from skins and rattles among the trophies of old farmhouses. I have been unable to verify the occurrence of a specimen of either species during the past thirty years.

PART THREE

The Snakes of Southeastern North America

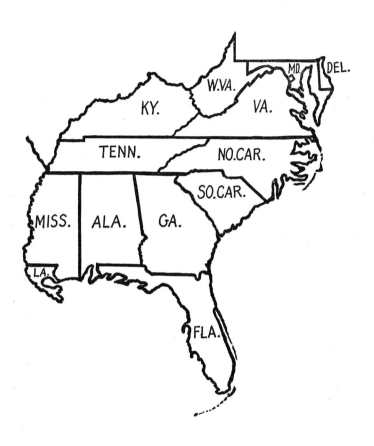

CHAPTER VII

Key to the Snakes of Southeastern North America

R EPTILE LIFE picks up in number of kinds, variety of form and size with approach to warm latitudes. This marked difference of fauna within the boundaries of a continent may be noted by glance at the sections defined on the maps preceding Part One and Part Two. In the preceding chapters some three dozen species are listed, with but a small number of associated subspecies. In the present chapter there is an additional dozen species, with the number of subspecies or related forms far surpassing those of the North. Large and showy kinds dominate in comparison with snakes of the northeastern section.

It should be understood that the majority of snakes described in the preceding chapters extend into the Southeast, and a fair number range completely through it. Of the typically southern reptiles, a few extend northward into southern New Jersey, but more particularly up the valley of the Mississippi into southern parts of Illinois and Indiana.

In preparing a simplified key, all of the species occurring in the Southeast will be grouped according to size, form, type of scale covering and coloration. In the detailed descriptions that follow, more critical diagnostic characters will be listed for all species of the region or section, but to conserve space the reader will be referred back to preceding chapters for descriptions of habits, if such species have already been thus described.

The lower or coastal regions of southern North Carolina, South Carolina, Georgia, Florida, Alabama, Mississippi and Louisiana have a particularly rich reptile fauna. Such river systems as the Pedee, the Santee and the Savannah offer a wealth of fascinating reconnoiter for the student of reptiles, as does a great part of Florida, but the latter state is undergoing changes from accessibility by motor roads and spread of fires, the latter devastating to fauna and flora.

Following is a key or deductive listing:*

NONVENOMOUS SNAKES

I. PUPIL OF EYE ROUND (all plates under tail in double row)

A. *Scales smooth*

Size—small

Brown to purplish black above; pink beneath:
Worm Snake, *Carphophis amoena amoena.*
Distribution: New England states southward through the southeastern region.

Brown above with minute black dots; pale yellow or white beneath:
Smooth Brown Snake, *Virginia valeriae valeriae* (and *V. v. elegans*).
Distribution: New Jersey to Georgia; westward to Texas.

Pale green above; white beneath:
Smooth Green Snake, *Liopeltis vernalis.*
Distribution: Southern Canada to Florida; westward to Texas.

Gray or lustrous blue black above. A bright orange ring around neck. Orange yellow beneath:
Ring-necked Snake, *Diadophis punctatus punctatus.*
Distribution: North Carolina to Florida. Similarly marked subspecies of the Ring-necked Snakes extend the range throughout the southeastern section.

Pale brown; head black followed by a whitish collar, thence a band of black 3 – 4 scales wide:
Crowned Snake, Miter Snake, *Tantilla coronata coronata.*†

---

*Subspecies quite evidently different from typical forms are entered in the listing.

†Rear-fanged, but so small it should be listed among harmless kinds.

Distribution: Virginia to Florida; westward to Tennessee.

Pale brown; head black, whitish collar indistinct:
   Wagner's Miter Snake, *Tantilla coronata wagneri.*
Distribution: Peninsula Florida.

Reddish brown; paler on sides. Upper lip bright yellow;
abdomen yellow:
   Yellow-lipped Snake, *Rhadinaea flavilata.*
Distribution: North Carolina to Florida; westward to the
Mississippi Valley.

Lustrous blue black, most scales with a fine, pale line imparting effect of being keeled. Brick red beneath crossed by black
bars:
   Black Swamp Snake, *Seminatrix pygaea.*
Distribution: Coastal states, South Carolina to Florida.

Ringed with scarlet, yellow and black, the scarlet the widest,
the yellow rings bordered with black. Snout red:
   Scarlet King Snake, "Coral Snake," *Lampropeltis
   elapsoides elapsoides.** (Compare with *Lampropeltis triangulum amaura* in text.)
Distribution: Greater part of the southeastern region; westward to Louisiana.

·Dorsal pattern similar to preceding; *abdomen whitish and
unmarked:*
   Scarlet Snake, *Cemophora coccinea.**
Distribution: Southern New Jersey to Florida; westward to
Louisiana.

Size—moderate

Gray, with brownish to reddish blotches which are black-
bordered, the spaces between sometimes ringlike. White beneath with square black spots:
   "Milk" Snake, House Snake, *Lampropeltis triangulum
   triangulum.*

*Check patterns against the poisonous Coral Snake, *Micrurus fulvius,* in
latter part of list. Colors are similar, but combination in contact of rings is
different.

Distribution: Southern Canada to Virginia and further south inland. A subspecies, *amaura,* with redder blotches extending to the abdomen and imparting a ringed pattern, extends to the Gulf. (Check *L. triangulum amaura* and *L. elapsoides* in text.)

Pale brown with obscure, rounded, darker dorsal blotches. (Young with more intense blotches):
> **Brown King Snake, Mole Snake,** *Lampropeltis rhombomaculata.**
Distribution: Maryland to Georgia; westward to Alabama.

Silvery gray, with 60 – 70 irregular brown, black-bordered blotches along the back. Spaces between the blotches may be mottled with pale red. Abdomen grayish white, blotched with black.
> **Short-tailed Snake,** *Stilosoma extenuatum.*
Distribution: Known only from Marion, Orange and Lake counties, Florida.

A broad longitudinal band of brown about 5 scales wide; a paler band on each side about 2 scales wide, and beneath this a band of darker hue about $2\frac{1}{2}$ scales wide. Abdomen yellow:
> **Allen's Snake, Swamp Snake, Mud Snake,** *Liodytes alleni.*
Distribution: Georgia and Florida.

Size—large

Lustrous blue black above, with three reddish stripes; abdomen red with rows of black dots:
> **Rainbow Snake,** *Abastor erythrogrammus.*
Distribution: Virginia to Florida; westward to Alabama.

Lustrous blue black above; vermilion bars on sides. Abdomen vermilion:
> **Horn Snake, "Stinging" Snake, "Hoop" Snake,** *Farancia abacura abacura, F. a reinwardtii.*
Distribution: Virginia to Florida; westward to Louisiana.

---

*The similarly marked Yellow-bellied King Snake, *L. calligaster* (Harlan) may extend slightly eastward of the Mississippi in the central valley region. Its description is included in Chapter V.

Lustrous black above and beneath; chin and throat usually reddish:

> **Gopher Snake, Indigo Snake,** *Drymarchon corais couperi.*

Distribution: Southern North Carolina to Florida; westward to Texas.

Lustrous black above with narrow yellow or white transverse, ringlike marks forking into chainlike pattern on sides; black and white beneath:

> **King Snake, Chain Snake,** *Lampropeltis getulus getulus.*

Distribution: Southern New Jersey to northern Florida; westward to the Mississippi Valley.

(Subspecies of *getulus* follow.)

> Chainlike markings very indistinct:
>> **Black King Snake,** *Lampropeltis getulus nigra.*
>> *Distribution:* West Virginia to Indiana, Kentucky, Tennessee and Alabama.
>
> Brown or olive, with narrow yellow crossbands (45 – 80), these ending at seventh row of scales:
>> **Florida King Snake,** *Lampropeltis getulus floridana.*
>> *Distribution:* Florida, from Orange County to the vicinity of the Miami River.
>
> Brownish or yellowish, with dark spot at tip of each scale. Crossbands similar in number to preceding, but barely discernible:
>> **Brook's King Snake,** *Lampropeltis getulus brooksi.*
>> *Distribution:* Southeastern portion of Dade County, Florida.
>
> Blackish, with bright green or yellow spot in center of most of the scales:
>> **Holbrook's King Snake,** *Lampropeltis getulus holbrooki.*
>> *Distribution:* Mississippi Valley region.

Above dull satiny black; black beneath; chin white. (Young gray with dark blotches):

> **Blacksnake, Black Racer,** *Coluber constrictor constrictor.*

Distribution: The entire eastern United States; westward to the Great Plains and Texas.

Satiny bluish green, olive or grayish above; yellow beneath:

> **Blue Racer,** *Coluber constrictor flaviventris.*

Distribution: Mississippi Valley region and westward.

Forward portion black or dark brown, becoming pale brown or gray on posterior half. Abdomen usually dull white and unspotted. Scales of upper surface with dull, satiny luster:

> **Eastern Coachwhip Snake,** *Masticophis flagellum flagellum.*

Distribution: Southern Virginia to Florida; westward to the Rocky Mountains.

B. *Scales of back feebly keeled*

Size—large

Lustrous (polished) black above, some of the scales on sides narrowly white-edged. When scales are separated by body distension, skin coloring may indicate large blotches along sides or back. Abdomen white, blotched with gray. (Young gray with dark H-shaped blotches):

> **Black Chicken Snake, Pilot Blacksnake, Mountain Blacksnake,** *Elaphe obsoleta obsoleta.*

Distribution: Southeastern Canada to Florida; westward to Texas.

Pale gray with large dark brown or blackish saddles along back, the anterior ones usually sending out extensions to assume H-shaped formation. Smaller blotches on sides:

> **Gray Rat Snake, Gray Chicken Snake,** *Elaphe obsoleta confinis.*

Distribution: Virginia to Florida, but more frequent in the Carolinas. Westward to Kansas and eastern Texas.

Tan to bright yellow with four dark brown or blackish stripes —two on the back and one on each side. Large, but rather obscure blotches may extend along the back between the dorsal stripes. (Young grayish with strong dorsal blotches):

Chicken Snake, Banded Chicken Snake, Yellow Rat Snake, Magnolia Snake, *Elaphe quadrivittata quadrivittata.*

Distribution: Southeastern North Carolina to Florida and westward to the Mississippi River.

Orange red with four longitudinal bands and about 40 dark blotches extending along the back between the two upper bands or stripes. Abdomen unspotted:

Deckert's Rat Snake, *Elaphe quadrivittata deckerti.*
Distribution: The upper Florida Keys.

Pale brown with a series of transverse blotches of deep pink, these approaching vermilion with some examples. Four dark but faint longitudinal bands. Abdomen unspotted:

Pink Rat Snake, *Elaphe rosacea.*
Distribution: The lower Florida Keys.

Grayish or yellowish (sometimes pale reddish) with deep crimson blotches along the back. White, with square black markings beneath. (Distinguished from the similarly marked "Milk" Snake by the feebly keeled scales):

Corn Snake, Red Rat Snake, House Snake, *Elaphe guttata.*

Distribution: Southern New Jersey to Florida; westward to Missouri and Louisiana.

C. *Scales of back strongly keeled*

Size—small

Brown above; pink beneath. Sometimes a pale dorsal band. Snout blunt:

DeKay's Snake, *Storeria dekayi.*
Distribution: Southern Canada and the greater part of the eastern United States; westward to Kansas and into Mexico.

Brown above; bright red beneath. Sometimes a pale dorsal band. Snout blunt:

Storer's Snake, *Storeria occipitomaculata.*
Distribution: Southern Canada and the greater part of the eastern United States in elevated regions.

Brown above; pinkish or white beneath with row of black spots on each side of abdomen:

Florida Brown Snake, *Storeria victa.*
Distribution: Southeastern Georgia and Florida.

Brown above; yellow to pinkish beneath. Snout pointed:

Small-eyed Brown Snake, Ground Snake, *Haldea striatula.*
Distribution: Virginia to the Gulf states; westward to Oklahoma.

Size—small to moderate

Uniform pale green above; yellow beneath:

Keeled Green Snake, *Opheodrys aestivus.*
Distribution: Connecticut to Florida; westward to Illinois and in the South to New Mexico.

Brown or black above with vivid yellow stripe on back and similar stripe on each side on 3rd and 4th rows of scales above abdomen:

Eastern Ribbon Snake, *Thamnophis sauritus sauritus.*
Distribution: Southern Canada to Georgia; westward to Mississippi.

Similar striping to preceding, but the dorsal stripe orange or reddish and the side stripes pale yellow or greenish:

Western Ribbon Snake, *Thamnophis sauritus proximus.*
Distribution: Mississippi Valley states, westward to Texas thence to Central America.

Dark brown or olive. Dorsal stripe faint or absent. Side stripes similar to the preceding:

Southern Ribbon Snake, *Thamnophis sauritus sackenii.*
Distribution: Coastal regions of South Carolina, Georgia and Florida.

Size—moderate

Blackish, brown or olive. A yellowish stripe on back and less intense stripe on each side on 2nd and 3rd rows of scales above abdomen. A more or less apparent checkerboard or tessellated dotting between dorsal and lateral stripes:
Common Garter Snake, Striped Snake, *Thamnophis sirtalis sirtalis.*
Distribution: Southern Canada and the entire eastern United States.

Brown, with a broad yellowish band on each side bordered with black. Abdomen yellow, usually with a central black band:
Graham's Water Snake, *Natrix grahamii.*
Distribution: Illinois and the Mississippi states to Texas.

Brown with three more or less evident black stripes above, a yellow stripe on each side and two stripes on abdomen—seven stripes in all:
Queen Snake, *Natrix septemvittata.*
Distribution: Pennsylvania to Wisconsin; southward to the Gulf states.

Brown or olive, paler on sides, with two narrow black stripes along the back. Abdomen yellow with two rows of black spots, often fusing to produce bands:
Striped Water Snake, *Natrix rigida.*
Distribution: The Carolinas to northern Florida and westward to Louisiana.

Brown to olive with three paler bands, the dorsal about 3 scales wide, those on the sides covering the 3rd, 4th and portion of 5th rows of scales above abdomen. Beneath yellowish in center and darker on side:
Clark's Water Snake, *Natrix clarkii.*
Distribution: Northwestern Florida to Texas.

Greenish gray or ashy gray with obscure and irregular darker bands, sometimes with alternating blotches on sides. Beneath, gray or brown with central yellow spots. (*Base of tail slightly compressed, vertically*) :

Flat-tailed Water Snake, *Natrix compressicauda.*
Distribution: Extreme southern Florida and the Keys.

Brown, gray or olive with about 20 – 30 darker transverse, usually broken blotches. Body very stout; head very broad; snout sharp and upturned:

Hissing "Adder," Spreading "Adder," Hog-nosed Snake, *Heterodon contortrix.*
Distribution: Massachusetts to Florida; westward to Texas.

Form similar to preceding. Gray or brown with about 22 – 26, usually rounded blotches:

Southern Hissing "Adder," Sand "Adder," Hog-nosed Snake, *Heterodon simus.*
Distribution: Southeastern states with extension north to Indiana.

Form similar to preceding. Not more than 20 transverse blotches:

Brown's Hog-nosed Snake, *Heterodon browni.**
Distribution: Extreme southern Florida.

Size—large

Rusty brown with large, *square* blackish blotches on back which are separated by about 4 – 5 scales. A similar, alternating row of blotches on each side:

Brown Water Snake, *Natrix taxispilota.*
Distribution: Maryland to Florida; westward to Louisiana.

Rounded blackish or brownish blotches along back, separated by narrow lines of ground hue about 1 scale wide. *Alternating blotches on sides.* Abdomen yellow, each plate narrowly clouded:

---

*See supplementary key of the Hog-nosed Snakes in text of Chapter VIII.

Yellow-bellied Water Snake, *Natrix erythrogaster transversa.*
Distribution: Lower Mississippi Valley and westward to Oklahoma.

Medium to pale reddish brown, sometimes with indistinct blotches like preceding. Abdomen uniform red. (Young strongly blotched):
Red-bellied Water Snake, *Natrix erythrogaster erythrogaster.*
Distribution: The Carolinas to Florida and westward to the Misissippi Valley. Northward to Michigan in the Central States.

Brown above with more or less distinct dark transverse bars narrowly separated on back and broken *posteriorly into alternating blotches.* White beneath, spotted with bright red:
Common Water Snake, *Natrix sipedon sipedon.*
Distribution: Maine to Alabama; thence to central western states.

Pattern similar to *N. sipedon sipedon* with exception of the transverse blotches being unbroken the entire length of body. Whitish beneath, spotted with bright red:
Southern or **Banded Water Snake,** *Natrix sipedon fasciata.*
Distribution: Virginia to northern Florida; westward to Louisiana.

Banded as with *N. sipedon fasciata,* but the underside is margined with brown and encloses yellow blotches and less red than *fasciata:*
Cope's Water Snake, *Natrix sipedon pictiventris.*
Distribution: The Peninsula of Florida.

Pairs of bands along body nearly fusing (in twos), producing effect of very wide bands of about half the number of the preceding (related) forms of *sipedon:*
Blanchard's Water Snake, *Natrix sipedon confluens.*
Distribution: The lower Mississippi Valley.

Dark green or olive brown with numerous *narrow* black bands crossing the back, these about 1 scale wide and 2 scales apart. Alternating dark blotches on sides. Abdomen yellow and clouded:
> **Green Water Snake,** *Natrix cyclopion cyclopion.*
Distribution: Southeastern states and the Mississippi Valley.

Similar to preceding, with little clouding beneath:
> **Florida Green Water Snake,** *Natrix cyclopion floridana.*
Distribution: Florida peninsula.

Brown or olive with narrow bars on sides which fork and unite on back to form a chain of small rhombs:
> **Diamond-back Water Snake,** *Natrix rhombifera rhombifera.*
Distribution: Mississippi Valley; westward to Texas and southward into Mexico.

White, with strong blackish blotches; these most prominent posteriorly; abdomen marble white:
> **Pine Snake,** *Pituophis melanoleucus melanoleucus.*
Distribution: Pine barrens from southern New Jersey to Georgia; westward to the Mississippi.

Dull white with suffusion of brown. Large, dark brown blotches, most prominent posteriorly:
> **Southern Pine Snake,** *Pituophis melanoleucus mugitus.*
Distribution: Georgia and Florida.

Mostly pale brown, mixed with white. 40 – 50 obscure darker blotches. Abdomen whitish:
> **Ruthven's Pine Snake,** *Pituophis melanoleucus ruthveni.*
Distribution: Louisiana.

Body suffused with black, but with white specklings; mostly blackish beneath:
> **Black Pine Snake,** *Pituophis melanoleucus lödingi.*
Distribution: Southern Alabama.

POISONOUS SPECIES

Ia. PUPIL OF EYE ROUND
  A1. *Scales smooth*
    Size—moderate (form slender)

> Broad rings of deep scarlet and black, the latter margined with narrow rings of yellow:
>> **Coral Snake, Harlequin Snake,** *Micrurus fulvius fulvius.*
>
> *Distribution:* In coastal region from southern North Carolina to Florida; the Gulf states; Mississippi Valley states.
>
> Check above with similar color combinations of the following nonvenomous snakes:
>> *Lampropeltis triangulum amaura*
>>   "   *elapsoides   elapsoides*
>>   "   "   *virginiana*
>
> *Cemophora coccinea*
> With these harmless species there are similar colors, *but the black rings are the narrower and form margins for the yellow.*

II. PUPIL OF EYE ELLIPTIC
  C1. *Scales strongly keeled* (most of plates under tail in single row)
    Size—moderate to large

> Light brown, reddish brown or pinkish gray, with dark brown transverse bands, narrow on the back and much wider on the sides. Abdomen usually pinkish brown. Pattern always strongly defined:
>> **Copperhead Snake, Chunk-head, Highland Moccasin, Pilot Snake,** *Agkistrodon mokasen mokasen.*
>
> *Distribution:* The Carolinas to northern Florida; westward to Texas. Intergrades with the northern Copperhead in north portion of the southeastern section.
>
> Dull brown, olive or suffused with black. Broad transverse bands, often obscure except on side. (Young reddish with strong bands):

Water Moccasin, Cotton-mouth Snake, *Agkistrodon piscivorus.*

Distribution: Virginia to Florida in coastal region; northward to Illinois in Mississippi Valley; westward to Texas.

D. *Tail ending in a rattle*
  (a) *Rattle very small*
  Size—moderate (top of head with shields as with harmless snakes)

Ashy gray with large, rounded black blotches on the back, sometimes separated by reddish on anterior part. Smaller blotches on sides. Abdomen white, marbled with gray or black:
Pygmy Rattlesnake, *Sistrurus miliarius miliarius.*
Distribution: The typical form occurs from central North Carolina to northern Georgia and westward to the Mississippi Valley. Two subspecies, *barbouri* and *streckeri,* not markedly different, extend the range into Florida and westward through the Gulf states to Oklahoma and southern Texas.

  (b) *Rattle large*
  Size—large (top of head with small scales)

Yellow or brown with dark crossbands, usually angular at the rear—sometimes broken into three rows of blotches. Occasionally blackish, with obscure markings:
Banded Rattlesnake, Timber Rattlesnake, *Crotalus horridus horridus.*
Distribution: New England to Georgia; westward to Iowa and Texas. In the southeastern region the typical form occurs inland in the more elevated districts.

Gray, pinkish gray or grayish brown, with wavy black crossbands which are angulate at the rear. A dull yellow or reddish band on anterior part of back:
Canebrake Rattlesnake, *Crotalus horridus atricaudatus.*
Distribution: Southeastern coastal region and the lower Mississippi Valley.

Olive or brown with symmetrical chain of large, yellow-edged rhomboid or "diamond" markings:
Diamond-back Rattlesnake, *Crotalus adamanteus.*

Distribution: Southern North Carolina to Florida and westward to the Mississippi Valley.

Diagnosis of the preceding key will follow suggestions offered in the grouping of the northeastern reptiles. Points of guidance, for identification, in Chapter III should be carried in mind. Several are to be deducted from the preceding key in "running down" the naming of a snake. *Size* is to be considered, and character of scales, whether *keeled* or *feebly keeled*. Consideration of coloring and pattern is a big help; both dorsal pattern and abdominal hue and markings. One point stands out as of prime importance: *Any snake of the southeastern section having elliptic (catlike) pupils is poisonous.*

In gross viewing, to be checked against the key, consider groupings from standpoint of coloration and pattern markings (without repetition of scientific names and inclusion of all the subspecies):

Worm Snake
Smooth Brown Snake
Keeled Brown Snake
DeKay's Snake (with some a pale band along back)
Storer's Snake (with some a pale band along back)
Florida Brown Snake
Smooth Green Snake
Keeled Green Snake
Ring-necked Snake (a yellow ring on neck)
Crowned Snake, Miter Snake (head black, whitish collar)
Yellow-lipped Snake
Black Swamp Snake
Blacksnake
Blue Racer
Coachwhip Snake
Gopher or Indigo Snake
Brook's King Snake (centers of scales paler)
Holbrook's King Snake (each scale with yellowish spot)
Black Pine Snake

No body pattern

Short-tailed Snake
"Milk" Snake, House Snake
Brown King Snake
Corn Snake
Gray Rat Snake
Pink Rat Snake
Pine Snake
Florida Pine Snake
Ruthven's Pine Snake
Common Hog-nosed Snake
Southern Hog-nosed Snake
Brown's Hog-nosed Snake
Pigmy Rattlesnake

} Blotched pattern

Common Water Snake
Southern Banded Water Snake
Blanchard's Water Snake
Cope's Water Snake
Red-bellied Water Snake
Yellow-bellied Water Snake
Green Water Snake
Brown Water Snake
Diamond-back Water Snake (bands splitting into rhombs on back)
Flat-tailed Water Snake
Horn Snake, Mud Snake
Copperhead Snake
Water Moccasin
Timber Rattlesnake
Canebrake Rattlesnake

} Transverse bands; or vertical bars on sides

King Snake, Chain Snake
Black King Snake

} Chainlike pattern

Scarlet Snake
Southern "Milk" Snake
Scarlet King Snake
Florida King Snake (effect of close, ring-like marks across back)
Coral Snake

} Symmetrical, ringlike pattern

Pilot Blacksnake, Black Chicken Snake   } Scales narrowly edged with white

Diamond-back Rattlesnake   } Symmetrical chain of large, dorsal rhombs

Ribbon Snake
Southern Ribbon Snake
Western Ribbon Snake
Common Garter Snake
Graham's Water Snake
Queen Snake
Clark's Water Snake
Striped Water Snake
Allen's Swamp Snake
Rainbow Snake
Chicken Snake, Magnolia Snake
   (sometimes both striped and blotched)
Deckert's Chicken Snake (sometimes both
   striped and blotched)

} Striped or banded lengthwise

CHAPTER VIII

The Southeastern Nonpoisonous Snakes

IT IS THE AIM to make the chapters of this field book practically complete booklets by themselves. That is the reason for sectioning the far-flung map of North America, thus splitting the continent in areas specifically interesting to separated readers. Thus, also, the approximately 136 species of North American snakes and the large number of subspecies may be grouped in reduced and more definable keys than would be possible in an interminable listing of the grand total. Thus descriptions of *all* the snakes occurring in the southeastern region will be presented in this chapter, to make it complete, as its heading signifies. There will be reiteration of descriptions carried in Chapter V, as distribution of a number of species is broad.

Where *Habits* are concerned with species figuring in both this and preceding chapters, reference will check back to former chapters.

Descriptions follow in continuity of formal listing, which, in some instances, indicates relationship.

Worm Snake, *Carphophis amoena amoena* (Say)

Size: Seldom exceeding 10 inches; diameter of ¼ inch. One of the smallest snakes of the Southeast.

Form and scalation: Scales smooth, lustrous, opalescent. Relatively, the body is moderately stout; head not distinct and terminating in pointed snout. Eyes very small.

Coloration: Chestnut brown above. Pink on the lower sides and abdomen. There is range of body hue to lustrous black, but brown examples are more common.

Distribution: Connecticut and New York to Florida and westward to the Appalachians.

Subspecies: C. amoena helenae (Kennicott) is technically defined as having the plates immediately above the nostrils (internasals) united with the prefrontals (the pair immediately behind them), imparting the effect of two large shields. *C. a. helenae* occurs in the valleys of the Mississippi and Tennessee rivers; West Virginia and southward to Alabama.

C. amoena vermis (Kennicott) is a form denoted by opalescent purplish black above and bright pink beneath. It occurs in the Mississippi Valley southward to Louisiana.

Habits: See **Worm Snake,** Chapter V.

Southern Ring-necked Snake, *Diadophis punctatus punctatus* (Linnaeus)

Size: The average length of this southeastern form is 10 – 14 inches with body thickness slightly in excess of ¼ inch. Exceptional specimens may be as long as 20 inches, with diameter of approximately ½ inch.

Form and scalation: Moderately slender, the head flat though not very distinct from neck. The scales are smooth and of satiny luster.

Coloration: The coloration is so unique that this snake can be readily identified. It is gray to bluish black with a brilliant yellow ring around the neck immediately behind the head. Abdomen brilliant orange, usually with row of black dots.

Distribution: The typical form, *D. punctatus punctatus,* occurs in the lower elevations of the southeastern United States from North Carolina to Florida. It may be distinguished from the northern form, *D. punctatus edwardsii,* by indicated breaking of the yellow collar at top center of neck, *edwardsii* having an unbroken collar and often lacking abdominal black dots. *Edwardsii* occurs in Maryland, Virginia and the mountains of the Carolinas.

Another subspecies, *D. punctatus stictogenys* Cope, has thickly massed abdominal black dots, sometimes fusing into a longitudinal band. It inhabits the Mississippi Valley.

Habits: The southern forms are abundant among the debris of pine forests, particularly under slabs of loose bark. For general habits see **Northern Ring-necked Snake,** Chapter V.

Hog-nosed Snake, Flat-headed "Adder," Hissing "Adder," Puffing "Adder," Spreading "Adder," *Heterodon contortrix* (Linnaeus)

Size: Of fair size and heavy-bodied. Commonly 2½ feet long and over an inch in diameter. Occasionally a yard long and 1½ inch in diameter.

Form and scalation: In proportion to length this is one of the thickest-bodied snakes of the southeastern region. The head is wide and distinct; the snout sharp and upturned, hence one of its names —Hog-nosed Snake. When angry the head and neck are excessively flattened. The scales are keeled, dull and lusterless.

Coloration: Colors and markings variable, but the common hues are yellowish or brown with dark brown or irregular blotches inclined to transverse markings, or broken into three rows. Some examples have particularly bright hues of yellow or red on the anterior portion. Occasional specimens are slaty gray or entirely black.

Distribution: Massachusetts to central Florida and westward to Texas.

Habits: Assumes alarming airs, in flattening the anterior portion, weaving the head and neck and hissing. (See general habits under **Hog-nosed Snake,** Chapter V.)

Note: As three species of Hog-nosed Snakes or Hissing "Adders" occur in the southeastern region, a supplementary key, based on head plates, is helpful:

> Internasals separated by a small scale (the azygous); prefrontals in contact:
> > *Heterodon contortrix.*
> Internasals and prefrontals in contact, no azygous scale:
> > *Heterodon browni.*
> Prefrontals and internasals separated by small scales:
> > *Heterodon simus.*

Descriptions follow:

Brown's Hog-nosed Snake, *Heterodon browni* Stejneger
Size: Similar to *H. contortrix.*

Form and scalation: Similar to preceding, but lacking an anterior head plate (the azygous).

Coloration: Similar to preceding, but with lesser number of transverse markings, thus: *H. contortrix* 20 – 30; *H. browni* 16 – 19.

Distribution: Southern Florida.

Habits: Typical of the Hog-nosed Snakes.

Southern Hog-nosed Snake, *Heterodon simus* (Linnaeus)
Size: Smaller than the preceding species—attaining maximum length of about 20 inches.

Form and scalation: Relatively stouter than the preceding, with more sharply upturned snout.

Coloration: Grayish or brownish with large dark dorsal blotches, about 22 – 26. The spaces between these blotches on the back are paler and thus more accentuated than on the sides. Beneath the dorsal blotches, on each side, is a smaller row, in alternation with those above. The abdomen is pale and immaculate, in contrast to *H. contortrix,* in which the edges of the abdominal plates are spotted or blotched with black.

Distribution: North Carolina to Florida and westward to the Mississippi. Particularly common in South Carolina, Georgia, Florida and Alabama.

Habits: Typical of the Hog-nosed Snakes. See Chapter V.

Smooth Green Snake, *Liopeltis vernalis* (Harlan)

Size: Greatest length about 20 inches, but average not much over a foot and diameter of $\frac{1}{4}$ inch.

Form and scalation: Of relative, moderate thickness. Scales smooth, with satiny luster.

Coloration: Readily identified by its uniform grass-green hue above; whitish beneath. Just before shedding, it may appear grayish green or bluish. Very young specimens are olive or bluish green.

Distribution: The entire southeastern region. Also northward and westward.

The Keeled Green Snake, occurring over much the same area, (description following) may be readily distinguished from the preceding by its sharply keeled scales and yellow abdomen.

Habits: See **Smooth Green Snake,** Chapter V.

Keeled Green Snake, *Opheodrys aestivus* (Linnaeus)

Size: Considerably longer than the Smooth Green Snake, but very slender. Length is from 2 – 3 feet, but an example of the latter size would be less than $\frac{1}{2}$ inch in diameter.

Form and scalation: Slenderness of form is indicated by the considerable length of tail, which is usually well in excess of a third the total length. Scales strongly keeled.

Coloration: Uniform pale green above and bright yellow beneath. With exception of the Smooth Green Snake, there are no uniformly bright green snakes (without spots or markings) occurring in the southeastern region.

Distribution: This may be rated as a southern reptile. It inhabits the entire southeastern region westward to the Mississippi Valley. It occurs along the chain of Florida Keys, among the southernmost of which it reaches its greatest length—in excess of a yard.

Habits: See **Keeled Green Snake,** Chapter V.

Blacksnake, Black Racer, *Coluber constrictor constrictor* (Linnaeus)

Size: While in the more inland and elevated areas of all the southeastern states the Blacksnake approaches the size of examples in northern states, or a length up to 6 feet and diameter of an inch, the tendency for specimens in the coastal regions—namely, in South Carolina, Georgia, Florida and Alabama—is to be smaller and of lighter build. With a number of South Carolina examples, examined and turned loose again, none exceeded a length of 5 feet, and the greater number were not much over 4 feet. The district hunted was mostly pine country. Similar results were checked in Florida. This form occurs over the entire southeastern region, where it is more abundant than in the North.

Form and scalation: Relatively slender, with head but moderately distinct (more so with southern examples than northern ones). Body scales smooth and with luster like a gun barrel. The smooth scales, with dull sheen, form an important point in separating this snake from the less common Black Chicken Snake (as known in the coastal Southeast) or Pilot Blacksnake, and Mountain Blacksnake, as frequently referred to in higher country. This latter species, while often pitch black, differs from the Black Racer in having feebly keeled scales which appear glossy.

Coloration: Satiny black above, black or dark slaty gray beneath, with patch of white more or less evident on the chin. Very young specimens are pale gray, with brownish blotches, these more prominent anteriorly. The young usually become quite black when two feet long.

The white patch on the chin of southern adult Blacksnakes is much more evident than with northern specimens. With specimens in South Carolina, Georgia and Florida the white may cover the entire upper labials, thus indicating a fairly well-defined southern race.

Distribution: All of the southeastern United States, with extension northward and westward.

Habits: See **Blacksnake, Black Racer,** Chapter V.

Blue Racer, Green Racer, Yellow-bellied Racer, *Coluber constrictor flaviventris* (Say)

Size: This subspecies of the Blacksnake is usually inferior in size to the black form. The largest specimen I have examined was $4\frac{1}{2}$ feet long. Central western examples are larger.

Form and scalation: General form similar to the preceding. Scales smooth, with satiny luster.

Coloration: Bluish green, pale or dark olive. The abdomen is pale yellow, the chin and throat lighter. Upper labials yellow. Very young specimens have strong dorsal blotches. In the lower Mississippi Valley there is a color variant, with which adults have a sparse and irregular sprinkling of white or yellow scales.

Distribution: The Mississippi states and westward, in rather dry, open districts.

Habits: Similar to the typical form—the Blacksnake.

Coachwhip Snake, *Masticophis flagellum flagellum* (Shaw)

Size: Attains a maximum length of 8 feet, but such length is unusual. A Florida specimen measures 7 feet 1 inch in length, with greatest diameter of $1\frac{1}{4}$ inch.

Form and scalation: The preceding paragraph showing length of approximately 7 feet and diameter of $1\frac{1}{4}$ inch indicates the very slender outlines of this large snake. The scales are smooth and almost lusterless.

Coloration: The most frequent coloration is blackish anteriorly, becoming pale brown or gray on the posterior half. Some specimens are thus very striking, being sooty black anteriorly and very pale posteriorly. The abdomen is dull white, with some clouding toward the neck. Very young specimens are blotched.

Distribution: The entire southeastern region from Virginia to Florida. Westward to the Rocky Mountains.

Habits: More frequent in the pine or sandy areas of the coastal regions. Habits are similar to those of the Blacksnake, but the present species is even more speedy, its wonderful agility made possible by extremely slim body. Its gait on the ground is particularly graceful, and a well-grown specimen can travel about as fast as a man at a run. It feeds principally upon small rodents, birds and eggs and is also inclined toward cannibalism. It is not a constrictor. While an excellent climber it is not commonly to be seen in trees or bushes.

When cornered, the Coachwhip Snake will make sweeping strikes and vibrate its tail. Captives remain nervous, and the greater number refuse food. The species lays from one to two dozen eggs, the period of incubation being 6 – 8 weeks.

THE RAT SNAKES
Elaphe and allied Genera

The Genus *Elaphe* is made up of a fair number of large, strongly constricting snakes which feed almost entirely upon warm-blooded prey, rodents and birds. Some of the species are called Chicken Snakes, owing to their occasional raids upon poultry houses, where they eat young chicks and swallow eggs entire, dissolving the shell by powerful gastric juices. Despite allegations that they are highly destructive to bird life, they should be rated as of economic value as a balancing factor in the reduction of the smaller, injurious rodents. Several are of brilliant and handsome coloration. Six forms inhabit the southeastern region, concisely defined in the key of the preceding chapter. The body scales of most are but feebly keeled, and among all the anal plate is divided.

Black Rat Snake, Black Chicken Snake, Pilot Blacksnake, Mountain Blacksnake, *Elaphe obsoleta obsoleta* (Say)

Size: Attains a length of 8 feet and diameter of 2 inches; 5 feet is an adult average length.

Form and scalation: Scales of back feebly keeled, but with polished surface. The body is relatively stout, the head quite wide and distinct, rather flattened, and blunt at the snout.

Coloration: Shining black, but with tendency of scales to show narrow white edges, which, when the body is distended, may indicate a blotchy pattern of obscure tracery. Abdomen gray blotched with white.

Young specimens are pale gray, with large dark blotches on the back, rather square in form, with linelike extensions from their corners running lengthwise.

This species might be confused with the common Blacksnake or Black Racer, but the faintly keeled scales, the polished (instead of satiny) scalation, the white edges of the scales and blotched under-surface are characters for distinction. It is also a much stouter snake.

Distribution: The entire southeastern region with extension northward and westward.

Habits: See **Pilot Blacksnake,** Chapter V.

Gray Rat Snake, Gray Chicken Snake, *Elaphe obsoleta confinis* (Baird and Girard)

Size: Like the preceding, or typical, form.

Form and scalation: Like the preceding.

Coloration: With this subspecies the markings of the young are retained to maturity. The body hue is gray with a series of large dark brown or blackish saddles on the back. On the neck these are elongated and send out extensions from their corners, assuming H-shaped formation. On each side is a series of smaller blotches and beneath another smaller series at edges of the abdominal plates. Numerous scales along the sides show white edges when body is distended.

Distribution: Virginia to Florida, with peak of occurrence in North and South Carolina, Kentucky and Tennessee. Westward to the Mississippi Valley.

Habits: Similar to the typical form, *E. obsoleta obsoleta,* preceding.

Chicken Snake, Banded Chicken Snake, Yellow Chicken Snake, Yellow Rat Snake, Striped House Snake, Magnolia Snake, *Elaphe quadrivittata quadrivittata* (Holbrook)

Size: Up to 6 feet and diameter of approximately 2 inches, but commoner dimensions are 4 – 5 feet.

Form and scalation: Moderately stout; scales of back feebly keeled. Scales quite polished.

Coloration: Bright yellow, pale brown or light olive with four dark brown or black stripes, two on the back and one on each side. The stripes on the sides are usually the width of two rows of scales; those on the back slightly wider than the one row of scales they cover.

The preceding relates to pattern of the average *adult,* this snake undergoing a *slow change* of pattern from youth to maturity. As with the Black Chicken Snake, the young are quite different from adults.

The eggs of this species are creamy white, with soft, leathery shell, about $1\frac{1}{4}$ inch in length and $\frac{7}{8}$ inch in diameter. The freshly hatched snake is about 12 inches long. It is gray, with squarish blotches which tend to send out linelike extensions from their corners, these running longitudinally. It remains a blotched or spotted snake until well towards a yard long, although the extensions from the blotches are now fusing to clearly indicate four longitudinal bands. Above this length the blotches fade and the bands become more evident. Occasional adults, particularly in Georgia and Florida, retain the blotched-banded pattern.

Distribution: Eastward North Carolina to Florida and westward, in the South to the Mississippi. Particularly common in South Carolina, Georgia, Florida and Alabama.

Habits: Typical of the other species of *Elaphe* with exception of partially arboreal habits in climbing into old magnolia and live-oak trees, where it hides in disintegrated knotholes.

Deckert's Rat Snake, *Elaphe quadrivittata deckerti* Brady
   Size, form and scalation similar to preceding.

   Coloration: Orange red, with longitudinal bands and about 40 purplish-brown blotches between the upper bands. Abdomen yellow.

   As noted in description of the typical form (preceding), *E. quadrivittata quadrivittata,* in southern part of its range shows tendency to lose strength of the bands and retain traces of the blotches of immaturity—showing a combination of both. Such specimens show intergradation towards Deckert's Rat Snake, which has assumed particular individuality by isolation among the Keys, with change of environment from mainland specimens.

   Distribution: The upper Florida Keys.
   Habits: Typical of its genus.

Pink Rat Snake, *Elaphe rosacea* (Cope)
   Size: 4 – 5 feet.

   Form and scalation: The form is typical of *Elaphe, but all the body scales are smooth, or nearly so.*

   Coloration: Light brown or pinkish brown with wide transverse blotches of deep pink or pale vermilion. Four rather obscure longitudinal bands—not always present. Abdomen whitish or yellowish, sometimes with small dark spots along each margin.

   In pattern this snake appears to stand midway between Deckert's Rat Snake (the preceding) and the Corn Snake or Red Rat Snake (following), which it most closely resembles from its dorsal coloration. Its pinkish or reddish blotches distinguish it from the former, while from the latter its blotches differ in extending farther down the sides. Also, the abdomen is mostly unspotted. In the Corn Snake the abdomen is boldly marked with black and white.

   Distribution: Appears to be restricted to the lower Florida Keys.
   Habits: Not indicated to differ from other species of its genus.

Corn Snake, Red Rat Snake, Red House Snake, *Elaphe guttata* (Linnaeus)

Size: In the average this is a smaller snake than other species of *Elaphe*. I have seen a few specimens as long as 6 feet, but they are very rare. A specimen of about average size is $51\frac{1}{2}$ inches and $1\frac{1}{4}$ inch in diameter.

Form and scalation: Moderately stout with head fairly distinct. Scales of back very weakly keeled—thus differing from the somewhat similarly colored *E. rosacea* (preceding).

Coloration: One of the most beautiful snakes of North America and the most strikingly colored among large species. The ground color is gray, reddish yellow or pale red. On the back is a series of large crimson or scarlet blotches, narrowly bordered with black. On some examples the blotches are further intensified by narrow white margin outside of the black. On the sides is a smaller series of red blotches, and on some species a lower and smaller series close to margins of the abdominal plates. The abdomen is white with large black squares.

The only eastern species liable to be confused with the Corn Snake are the Pink Rat Snake, Deckert's Rat Snake and the "Milk" Snake. Under the descriptions are points of separation. The "Milk" Snake has *smooth* scales, and the undersurface is quite finely checkered with black and white. The undersurface of the Corn Snake is white, with large black markings, of square or oblong form.

Distribution: The entire southeastern region, but of more frequent occurrence in the coastal states, with preference for pine country.

Habits: See **Corn Snake,** Chapter V.

Gopher Snake, Indigo Snake, *Drymarchon corais couperi* (Holbrook)

Size: Length up to 8 feet. A specimen 6 feet 11 inches long is 2 inches in diameter. Another 7 feet 9 inches long is $2\frac{1}{4}$ inches in diameter.

Form and scalation: Moderately stout; scales smooth, polished.

Coloration: Lustrous black or blue black above and beneath. Chin and throat usually reddish.

Species that might be confused with this are the Black Racer and the Black Chicken Snake or Pilot Blacksnake. The former has satiny scales (without polish) and a white chin. The latter has the scales of the back feebly keeled and the abdomen blotched with slaty black and white.

Distribution: Southern North Carolina to Florida and westward to Texas, but mostly confined to pine or sandy country at lower altitudes, namely, the coastal states. This is a subspecies or northern race of a species extending well into South America.

Habits: The term Gopher Snake comes from the habit of this big reptile of commonly sheltering in burrows of the southern Gopher Tortoise. Frightened in its favorite prowling grounds, the pinelands or "Sandhill" regions of the South, it flashes a glittering length in rush for such retreats. The sight of one of these big serpents trailing its black length over a stretch of pale sand is one to arouse enthusiasm of the naturalist. If retreat is cut off, this snake will flatten the head, strike and vibrate its tail. Despite its long and heavy body, it is not a constrictor. For a large snake its feeding habits are unusual, owing to varied diet. The big Rat Snakes, formerly considered, feed almost exclusively upon warm-blooded prey, rodents and birds, but the Gopher Snake eats rodents, birds, frogs, toads, lizards and other snakes, holding its prey to the ground under a fold of the body and swallowing at the same time.

Few reptiles are so hardy as captives or become so tame or tolerant to handling. Moreover the species is particularly free from parasites, especially mites, which play havoc with many kinds of snakes under captive conditions. This, combined with good-natured demeanor, makes this snake a favorite in study collections.

It is not a rare sight in the South to see one or more of these big snakes in immediate proximity to houses in the outlying districts. They are tolerated by the Negroes as ratters, and specimens have been known to remain for years about a plantation, even being picked up by the children, who regard them as pets.

Pine Snake, White Gopher Snake, *Pituophis melanoleucus melanoleucus* (Daudin)

Size: One of the largest of the eastern snakes, reaching a length of approximately 8 feet, although this is much above the average. A South Carolina specimen, from the pine barrens, is 5 feet long and $1\frac{5}{8}$ inch in diameter.

Form and scalation: Moderately stout and heavy. The head is of curious form, resembling that of a turtle, small in proportion to the snake's size and sharply pointed at the snout, which protrudes over the lower jaw. The scales of the back are keeled and lusterless; those of the sides are polished.

Coloration: Dull white on the back, becoming pure white on the sides. Along the back is a row of large black blotches, quite close together on the forward portion, but posteriorly more separated and in vivid contrast to the whitish body. A row of small blotches on each side, and beneath these a row of black spots in sharp contrast to the marble white of the abdomen.

Distribution: Pine barrens of southern New Jersey to South Carolina and westward to Tennessee.

Habits: See **Pine Snake,** Chapter V.

Southern Pine Snake, *Pituophis melanoleucus mugitus* (Barbour)
Size: Similar to preceding.
Form and scalation: Similar to preceding.
Coloration: This subspecies shows less white and more brown than the typical form. The blotches are not prominent on the anterior portion owing to dark suffusion. They are widely separated and well defined posteriorly.

Distribution: Georgia and Florida to southern Alabama. Checking back to southern extension of the typical form, it may be figured that the Pine Snake within the coastal or Gulf region thus defined represents the subspecies *mugitus.*

Habits: Typical of the **Pine Snake.** See Chapter V.

Ruthven's Pine Snake, *Pituophis melanoleucus ruthveni* (Stuli), represents a Louisiana race in having more crowded blotches than the eastern forms and being largely suffused with rusty brown, although whitish posteriorly with large blotches fairly well defined.

The **Black Pine Snake,** *Pituophis melanoleucus lödingi* (Blanchard), is heavily suffused with black, above and beneath, with little more than white specklings (if any) to denote its relationship to the preceding. Its turtlelike head is a distinguishing character.

Distribution: Listed only from southern Alabama.

Yellow-lipped Snake, *Rhadinaea flavilata* (Cope)
Size: Small; not much over a foot. A 12-inch specimen is $\frac{1}{4}$ inch in diameter.
Form and scalation: Moderately slender; head fairly distinct. Scales smooth and polished. Ventral or anal plate divided.

Coloration: Pale reddish brown, paler on sides, which may be of golden tinge; head darker than body. A dark band from the snout extends to the eye, thence behind the eye to angle of mouth. *The upper lip is bright yellow;* abdomen yellow and unmarked.

Distribution: Coastal states from southern North Carolina to Florida and westward through the Gulf states to Mississippi.

Habits: Secretive and found under loose bark of decaying logs; beyond this, the habits appear to be practically unknown. It remains as a species to be studied and deducted by herpetologists sympathetically observant of the smaller types of snakes.

"MILK" SNAKES, KING SNAKES AND ALLIES

"Milk" Snake, House Snake, Checkered "Adder," *Lampropeltis triangulum triangulum* (Lacépède)

Size: Smaller in the South than through the northern part of its range. A Virginia specimen is 34 inches long and ⅝ inch in diameter.

Form and scalation: Moderately slender; scales smooth.

Coloration: Grayish with a series of large black-bordered blotches along the back. These patches may be chestnut brown, reddish or occasionally ruddy olive. There is a series of smaller blotches on each side in alternation with those on the back. *The dorsal blotches extend down the sides to about the fifth row of scales above the abdominal plates.* This relates to the typical form, *triangulum.* Underside checkered with black and white. With young specimens the dorsal blotches are almost invariably bright red.

Distribution: Southern Canada to Virginia and south through the mountains of the Carolinas and northern Georgia. West to Iowa.

Color Forms: "Intergrades," as defined by science, are intermediates linking one form or subspecies with another. Examples of the "Milk" Snake occurring in Maryland and Virginia and southward come under this head. The tendency is for the blotches to be redder. Also, the blotches extend farther down the sides, are wider along the back and thus constrict the spaces of ground hue to pale, ringlike separations.

Marked intergradation occurs through the southeastern United States in reduction of size, narrowing of head and tendency of red and black to cross the abdomen and produce complete rings, resulting in a form requiring separate description.

Habits: See **"Milk" Snake,** Chapter V.

Cope's "Milk" Snake, "Coral" Snake, *Lampropeltis triangulum amaura* (Cope)

Size: Quite small; seldom in excess of 14 – 18 inches.

Form and scalation: The most unlike the typical form of any of the *triangulum* group. The body is seldom thicker than a pencil, with narrow head and quite pointed snout. Scales smooth and polished.

Coloration: Brilliantly ringed with scarlet, yellow and black. Scarlet bands the widest and usually encircling the body. Yellow rings about half the width of the red and bordered on each side by rings of black, which, on the back, are about the same width as the yellow. Yellow rings widening on the side, thus encroaching upon and reducing the black. Black crossing the abdomen as rings or narrow broken blotches.

Head markings: A yellow ring around the neck behind the head, and in front of it a patch or band of black confined to the top. The snout is red. Head markings and combination (contacts) of ringed colors are of importance in distinguishing this reptile from the poisonous Coral Snake, with which it and the following species, *L. elapsoides,* are often confused.

Distribution: Southeastern United States to the Mississippi Valley.

Habits: Secretive. Feeds upon small lizards, the young of other snakes, and such small species as the Brown Snakes and Ring-necks.

Scarlet King Snake, "Coral" Snake, *Lampropeltis elapsoides elapsoides* (Holbrook)

Size: Smallest of the King Snake genus, seldom exceeding 16 inches.

Form and scalation: Moderately slender, with diameter little in excess of $\frac{1}{4}$ inch. Head narrow with quite sharply pointed snout. Scales smooth and polished.

Coloration: Owing to the rings of scarlet, yellow and black, it is impossible to present a color diagnosis separating this snake from *amaura,* a preceding form of *triangulum.* The scarlet rings are the widest, the yellow about half the width of the red, the yellow rings margined with black which narrows on the sides owing to widening of the yellow. Red, yellow and black encircle the body with the typical form. There is a yellow band behind the head. The head is mostly red with exception of black on the crown.

Comparison with Cope's "Milk" Snake: Checked against the coloration of *L. triangulum amaura,* the description appears identical, and confusingly so when a subspecies, *L. elapsoides virginiana,* occurring in North Carolina and Virginia, has the red areas broken on the abdomen as with some examples of *amaura.* Explanation of the specific rank of *elapsoides* may be quoted from Blanchard, who says:

"This form" (*amaura*) "may be distinguished from *elapsoides* by the greater number of ventral plates (nearly 200), a maximum of 21 instead of 19 rows of scales, the usually greater extent of black on the head, the fact that the snout is usually more or less mottled with black instead of being a uniform red."

Distribution: The typical form is found mostly in the coastal and Gulf states from South Carolina to Florida and westward to Louisiana. The form *virginiana* occurs in Virginia and North Carolina.

Habits: Secretive, feeding upon small lizards and other small snakes. Often to be found hiding under loose bark of fallen trees.

Coral Snakes; Harmless and Poisonous: Owing to similarity of ringed colors, but difference in combination of contacts of the rings, a brief key is of interest in listing four snakes of the Southeast, which may be confused:

A. *Snout red* (nonvenomous)

> Banded above with scarlet, black and yellow, *the yellow bordered with black; abdomen immaculate whitish:*
> **Scarlet Snake,** *Cemophora coccinea.*

> Ringed with scarlet, black and yellow, *the yellow bordered by rings of black:*
> **Cope's "Milk" Snake,** *Lampropeltis triangulum amaura.*

> Pattern similar to preceding:
> **Scarlet King Snake, "Coral Snake,"** *Lampropeltis elapsoides elapsoides.* Also *L. e. virginiana.*

B. *Snout black* (venomous)

> *Red and black rings broad, the black bordered by narrow rings of yellow:*

Coral Snake, Harlequin Snake, *Micrurus fulvius fulvius*. Also *M. f. barbouri.*

Brown King Snake, Mole Snake, *Lampropeltis rhombomaculata* (Holbrook)

Size: Attaining length of about a yard.

Form and scalation: Moderately stout. Head small and not distinct. Scales smooth with moderate luster.

Coloration: Brown, yellowish brown or olive brown, with about 55 obscure, darker blotches on the back, irregular and wavy in outline, narrowly and faintly bordered with black, the blotches 6 – 7 scales wide transversely and 2 – 3 scales along the median region of back. There is a smaller and more obscure, alternating row along each side. Abdomen yellowish white usually with patches of indistinct red arranged in tessellated fashion and sprinkled with gray or black dots.

Unless closely examined, adult specimens may appear uniform pale brown, but with critical examination, in bright light, the blotches are discernible. Young specimens are strongly blotched.

Distribution: Maryland to Tennessee, southward to northern Florida and Alabama. Westward in Mississippi, thence through the valley states of the Mississippi River it overlaps the range of the Yellow-bellied King Snake, *L. calligaster* (following), of which it may ultimately prove to be not more than a subspecies.

Habits: During collecting reconnoiters I have never found this snake to be common, but observed it, during the day, roaming wild meadows where there was chance of its obtaining such food as small rodents, lizards and the young of other snakes. It sometimes hides in the burrows of small mammals, hence its name, Mole Snake. It is a listless captive and not inclined to feed.

Yellow-bellied King Snake, *Lampropeltis calligaster* (Harlan)

Size: Up to 4 feet in length and ¾ inch in diameter.

Form and scalation: Similar to preceding.

Coloration: Grayish brown with series of dark brown blotches transversely wider than long and narrowly bordered with black. A smaller, alternating row on each side and a smaller row at edges of abdominal plates. Abdomen yellowish with square dull blotches, usually of reddish hue. With young specimens the blotches are strongly defined.

Distribution: Extending into Mississippi in the southeastern region, but mostly in the western Mississippi Valley states, northward to Wisconsin and westward to Texas.

King Snake, Chain Snake, Thunder Snake, *Lampropeltis getulus getulus* (Linnaeus)

Size: Attains a length of 6 feet, which is much in excess of the average. A large specimen from Georgia is 60 inches long and 1¼ inch in diameter.

Form and scalation: Cylindrical, moderately stout, with but little taper over greater part of body; head rather small but distinct. The scales are smooth and glossy.

Coloration: Lustrous black with narrow white or yellow cross-bands, which fork on the sides and connect in chainlike fashion. Black beneath with patches of white or yellow.

Northward from central Georgia the pale markings are whitish, but approaching Florida they become yellow. Towards the Mississippi Valley from this latitude a subspecies occurs, with dull markings, designated as the Black King Snake, *L. getulus nigra.*

Distribution: Southern New Jersey to northern Florida; mostly in the Atlantic and Gulf states. *L. getulus nigra* is recorded from West Virginia, Tennessee and adjoining region. There are related forms in Florida.

Habits: See **King Snake,** Chapter V.

Subspecies of *getulus:* Related forms give this species a wide range, even extending westward to the Pacific coast. The typical form, described in the preceding paragraphs, is readily recognized. In its range through latitude from southern New Jersey to northern Florida, about the only variation is in color of the chainlike markings, which, when looked at from above, appear like pale, narrow rings. They are quite white with some specimens, particularly the more northern ones. I have seen such black-and-white examples as far south as central South Carolina. Through Georgia and into northern Florida the tendency is for the dorsal and abdominal markings to become lemon yellow.

The three strictly southern subspecies, *floridana, brooksi* and *hol-brooki,* which are marked variants in coloration, and also their respective ranges are defined in the key of the preceding chapter.

Short-tailed Snake, *Stilosoma extenuatum* (Brown)

Size: Up to 2 feet. An example of this length will have a tail not much longer than 2 inches.

Form and scalation: Owing to extremely slender form and rather diminutive head, not distinct from the slender neck, this species may be regarded by some observers as a "small" snake. There is barely any tapering of the body from central part to anterior or posterior portion (except the short tail length). It appears extremely slender and cylindrical. The scales are smooth.

Coloration: Silvery gray with a large number of rounded but irregular dark dorsal blotches with blackish border, 60 – 70 on the body and about 12 on the tail. The spaces between the blotches on the back are usually speckled with pale red. Sides usually dotted with black, like gunpowder grains. Abdomen blotched with black, which may extend to the sides and upward to form small blotches.

Distribution: This is a rare snake, thus far known only from Marion, Orange and Lake counties, Florida. But few specimens have been collected since its discovery nearly fifty years ago.

Habits: A burrowing species, but otherwise with habits akin to the King Snakes. If disturbed while prowling from its underground lairs, it will strike and vibrate its tail like some of the larger snakes. Two specimens in my collection spent most of their time hiding under slabs of bark, but issued quickly enough when small Brown Snakes were placed in their cage, coiling about the prey, squeezing it to death and engulfing it in actions typical of cannibalistic serpents. They refused small lizards and newborn mice which were quite within range of their swallowing capability.

Scarlet Snake, *Cemophora coccinea* (Blumenbach)

Size: Usually small, but occasionally up to 25 inches (exceptional). Average length 16 inches; diameter ¼ inch.

Form and scalation: Rather slender and cylindrical; not tapering until near head and tail. Snout pointed and projecting; eye small.

Coloration: Wide scarlet blotches (half-ringing the body above), separated by pairs of black half-rings, these enclosing a yellow half-ring about three scales wide. Abdomen immaculate white or yellow with no encroachment of the dorsal pattern. The unmarked abdomen is an important point for separation from *Lampropeltis triangulum amaura, L. elapsoides elapsoides* and *L. e. virginiana.* Also from the poisonous Coral Snake, *Micrurus fulvius fulvius.*

Distribution: Southern New Jersey to Florida, thence westward to

Oklahoma, with principal occurrence in the Atlantic and Gulf states.
Habits: See **Scarlet Snake,** Chapter V.

THE STRIPED WATER SNAKES

This is a small grouping of the Genus *Natrix,* all of which are longitudinally striped and much smaller than the transversely banded Water Snakes. See key of Chapter VII.

Graham's Water Snake, *Natrix grahamii* (Baird and Girard)
   Size: Length about 25 inches, with diameter of about ⅝ inch.
   Form and scalation: Moderately stout; head rather small. Scales roughly keeled.
   Coloration: Back dark brown, often with indistinct pale band along the central area, this narrowly bordered with black. There is a broad band of tan or yellow on each side, in strong contrast to the dark hue above it. This band covers the first three rows of scales and is always bordered with a black stripe beneath and on some specimens by a very narrow black stripe above. The upper labials are yellow; abdomen yellow, usually with a black central stripe.
   Distribution: The lower Missouri River and Mississippi River systems, to Louisiana and Texas.
   Habits: Timid and partially secretive, frequenting borders of streams and lakes or marshy districts. It swims well and feeds upon cold-blooded prey, small frogs, toads, fishes and salamanders, but, unlike the larger water snakes, is less commonly seen, owing to habits of hiding in matted vegetation or derelict objects near the water's edge.

Queen Snake, *Natrix septemvittata* (Say)
   Size: One of the smaller water snakes, from 2 to 2½ feet long. A 2-foot specimen is ⅝ inch in diameter.
   Form and scalation: Relatively more slender than the other Water Snakes. The scales are roughly keeled.
   Coloration: Adults dark brown with three narrow dark stripes on the back which may be indistinct. A yellow stripe on the lower side, covering one half of the 1st and the 2nd rows of scales. Abdomen yellow with two dark stripes in center. The scientific name *septemvittata* indicates seven stripes—there are three on the back, one on

each side and two in the central part of the abdominal area; thus the technical name points to the pattern.

Among individuals the stripes or longitudinal bandings vary in intensity, and it should be noted that some young specimens look like brown garter snakes without a central (dorsal) stripe. The dark stripes on the abdomen, however, readily separate this species from the Striped Snakes (*Thamnophis*). The two close and parallel dark bands in the center of the abdomen may, with occasional specimens, be almost fused. Unless closely examined, or unless the scales are wet, this small Water Snake may appear dull brown, with a pale stripe on each side. Its narrow, lateral stripe immediately distinguishes it from *N. grahamii* with its broad, lateral band, and study of the condensed formulae of the other Striped Water Snakes in the key of Chapter VII should render identification of the members of this small group comparatively simple.

Distribution: Western Pennsylvania to Wisconsin and southward to the Gulf of Mexico.

Habits: See **Queen Snake,** Chapter V.

Clark's Water Snake, *Natrix clarkii* (Baird and Girard)

Size: Attains a length of about 3 feet.

Form and scalation: Moderately stout, scales coarsely keeled.

Coloration: Dark brown or olive brown, with three longitudinal pale bands. The central band is about 3 scales wide; the stripe on each side covers the 3rd and 4th and a portion of the 5th row of scales. beneath yellowish in middle of abdomen and olive to the sides, separating which hues there may be a tinge of reddish brown.

Distribution: Northwestern Florida, southern Alabama, Mississippi, Louisiana and Texas.

Habits: Little known, but appear to be similar to the other Striped Water Snakes, with prevalence along reedy streams and margins of swamps, although this species is partial to brackish water.

Striped Water Snake, *Natrix rigida* (Say)

Size: Seldom exceeding 2 feet in length.

Form and scalation: Moderately stout, the head larger than with the other Striped Water Snakes.

Coloration: Dark brown or olive brown, paler on the sides. Two narrow black stripes along the back (which may not be apparent unless the scales are wet). Abdomen yellow with two rows of dark spots, sometimes fusing to produce dual bands with ragged edges. Upper labials yellow.

Distribution: Has been alleged to occur as far north as southern Pennsylvania, but definitely defined in range from the Carolinas southward to the Gulf of Mexico and northern Florida, westward to Louisiana.

Habits: Little has been noted about this small water snake, which is thus indicated to be rather rare. It has been mentioned as resembling the Queen Snake, *N. septemvittata,* with absence, except obscure tracery, of the lateral bands.

THE LARGER WATER SNAKES

The big species of *Natrix* are marked with wide transverse blotches or bands, which, with old examples, may be obscure on the back and appearing like wide, vertical bars on the sides. Abdominal coloration is important in identification. The young are vividly marked with the same pattern, which usually becomes dull with adults. These are the species commonly seen on branches overhanging streams or about the crevices of old dams. It is their habit to take to the water when alarmed. All of the Water Snakes give birth to living young.

Common Water Snake, *Natrix sipedon sipedon* (Linnaeus)

Size: 3 – 4 feet and from $1\frac{1}{2}$ to $1\frac{3}{4}$ inch in diameter.

Form and scalation: Form quite stout; head distinct from neck and rather flattened. Scales roughly keeled and without luster on dorsal surface.

Coloration: Dull brown, with broad irregular crossbands of reddish brown. These are narrowly separated on the back and much more widely on the sides. In old specimens the back may appear uniform, dull brown or blackish, the markings only apparent on the sides as vertical bars. *Abdomen yellowish, brightly marked with red spots or blotches.*

The typical form, *sipedon,* is distinguished *by the markings breaking into three alternating rows on about the posterior third.* The young are pale gray with blackish crossbands which are very distinct.

Distribution: Southern Canada and New England to Virginia and northern North Carolina in the coastal region. Inland, through the elevated districts to northern Alabama. Westward to Wisconsin and Colorado.

Habits: See **Common Water Snake, Banded Water Snake,** Chapter V.

A form designated as *N. sipedon pleuralis* (Cope) is indicated as having unbroken transverse bars anteriorly and three alternating blotches posteriorly, like the typical form, but areas of ground color between the blotches or bars wider than the darker markings, which is the reverse with *sipedon*. Moreover, the reddish abdominal markings tend to be in two rather irregular (crescentic) but fairly well defined rows, while those of *sipedon* are in spots or red mottlings.

Distribution: "South Carolina westward around the southern extremity of the Appalachian Mountains, Mississippi, Arkansas, and southern Missouri, and northward to southern Illinois and southern Indiana."*

Southern Banded Water Snake, *Natrix sipedon fasciata* (Linnaeus)

Size: 3 – 4 feet long with maximum diameter of about 2 inches.

Form and scalation: Form quite stout; head distinct from neck and somewhat flattened. Scales coarsely keeled, dull and lusterless on back.

Coloration: Pattern and effect of coloration similar to preceding except that the transverse markings are not broken into alternating blotches posteriorly. *The abdomen is spotted or blotched with bright red,* a distinguishing marking for this and the typical form. Adults of this subspecies are more inclined to be a darker brown or even quite blackish than with *N. sipedon sipedon* and the bars on the sides more reddish. The young are strongly marked.

Distribution: Virginia to northern Florida and westward to the Mississippi. Very common along the low waterways and swamps of South Carolina and Georgia.

Habits: Similar to the typical form (preceding).

Cope's Water Snake, *Natrix sipedon pictiventris* Cope

In size, form and scalation this subspecies is similar to the preceding.

Coloration: The transverse bands are similar to *N. sipedon fasciata,*

*Clay. *Copeia,* 1938, No. 4., p. 178.

but the abdominal blotches are more brownish than reddish, fuse across the plates and enclose *yellow spots*—often of lemon hue.

Distribution: Appears to occur only on the Florida Peninsula, where it is very common.

Habits: Typical of the larger water snakes.

Blanchard's Water Snake, *Natrix sipedon confluens* (Blanchard)

In size, form and scalation this form is similar to other subspecies of *sipedon.*

Coloration: This Mississippi race has the effect of having very wide bands, much reduced in number. This results from the bands fusing (in twos), with widely spaced separations of ground color, of pale hue, that appear to form narrow, dorsal rings.

Distribution: "Eastern Louisiana north through southern and eastern Arkansas to southeastern Missouri and west to Texas to about the 98th meridian." (Stejneger and Barbour.)

Habits: Typical of the larger water snakes.

Red-bellied Water Snake, Copper-bellied "Moccasin," *Natrix erythrogaster erythrogaster* (Forster)

Size: 2½ to 3 feet, with diameter to 1½ inch.

Form and scalation: Smaller and relatively less stout than *sipedon;* eyes larger. Scales heavily keeled.

Coloration: Rusty brown, reddish brown or golden brown above, with obscure (but usually without) crossbands. *Abdomen immaculate red, varying from coppery red to crimson.* Young of reddish hue with strong crossbands.

This very striking species, light brown above and uniform red beneath, may be recognized at a glance.

Distribution: Coastal region from southern Virginia to Florida, the Gulf states and the Mississippi Valley states northward into Michigan. The author considers the "headquarters" of this snake to be the river valleys and coastal swamps of South Carolina and Georgia. Here it attains its greatest abundance, largest size and greatest brilliance of color.

Habits: While a typical water snake in habits and association with other semiaquatic serpents, this species is less nervous as a captive, more readily susceptible to handling and feeds particularly well.

Yellow-bellied Water Snake, *Natrix erythrogaster transversa* (Hallowell)

Size: 2½ to 3½ feet long.

Form and scalation: Moderately stout; strongly keeled as with the other water snakes.

Coloration: Dark brown, often olive on sides. The effect is of the patterns in forms of *sipedon,* particularly the posterior portion of *N. sipedon sipedon,* the transverse bands being broken into three series of blotches along the entire length.

There are rounded blotches on the back separated by narrow spaces of ground color about one scale wide. The blotches on the sides may be alternating or only partially so. They are separated by brownish or olive spaces wider than the blotches themselves. The abdomen is almost uniform bright yellow.

Distribution: The lower Mississippi Valley, and to the westward into Kansas, Oklahoma and Texas; southward to Mexico.

Habits: Typical of the Water Snakes.

Brown Water Snake, "Water Rattle," Water-Pilot, *Natrix taxispilota* (Holbrook)

Size: Largest of the North American Water Snakes, attaining a length of 5 feet and diameter in excess of 3 inches.

Form and scalation: Heavily formed, but with long, tapering tail. The head is long and narrow on the plated portion, which is only about half its total length. Behind the plates it widens, producing outline very distinct from the neck. The eyes are small but bulging, situated well towards the snout. Dorsal scales heavily keeled, with dull, lusterless surface.

Coloration: Rusty brown, with series of large, almost square dark brown or blackish blotches along the back. On each side, in alternation, is a similar series about 4 scales wide and 6 scales high. The blotches of the back and sides are seldom in contact. The regularity of pattern and upright character of the lateral markings produce a coarsely banded aspect when viewed from the sides. Yellow to dull lavender beneath, profusely blotched or speckled with dark brown. The young are pale brown with intense, blackish pattern.

Distribution: Maryland to central Florida and westward to Louisiana. Particularly common in swampy waterways of South Carolina, Georgia and Florida.

Habits: The largest specimens I have seen were in river swamps bordering the Savannah, in Hampton County, South Carolina. They were shy when avenue of escape was open, having the habit of sun-basking on heavy boughs overhanging the water and plunging in, with a great splash, when approached. Several specimens, however, were noosed from such situations and put up a fight as savage as a poisonous snake, striking repeatedly and chewing the end of the noosing pole. One big specimen disgorged a river carp 18 inches long. These snakes were even more heavy-bodied than the poisonous Water Moccasins commonly seen in the same swamps and were equally feared by the Negroes.

One reason for respect with which they are held comes from a trait of lying in circular coil, half hidden in matted swamp grass, and strik-ing like a flash if intruder thus suddenly surprises them. This sym-metrically rounded coil is unlike the common positions assumed by other water snakes, and in such places there is always the thought of the dangerous Canebrake Rattler, which coils in similar fashion and in color of dark individuals is not much different; hence a common name, among the Negroes, of this water snake—the "Water Rattle."

The species is a morose captive and can seldom be induced to feed unless provided with a tank and given an opportunity of swimming after living fish.

Green Water Snake, *Natrix cyclopion cyclopion* (Duméril and Bibron)

Size: Closely approaching the size of *taxispilota*. A specimen from Lake Kerr, Marion County, Florida, is 46 inches long and $1\frac{3}{4}$ inch in diameter.

Form and scalation: Heavy-bodied, with long and very distinct head. Eyes placed well forward, as with *taxispilota*. The scales are not so strongly keeled as with other big water snakes, and the body surface has a fair gloss.

This water snake differs from other members of its genus in having a ring of small plates around the eye, separating it from the lip plates or labials.

Coloration: Dark green or olive brown, with numerous narrow black bands crossing the back. These are about the width of one scale, irregular and about 2 scales apart.

On each side is a series of small, vertical bars in alternation with the markings above. Abdomen yellow with darker clouding along edges of the plates. Abruptly beginning at the ventral plate, a marbling effect of light and dark hues extends along the undersurface of the tail.

Distribution: Florida and the Gulf region to Louisiana; northward in the Mississippi Valley to southern Illinois. A Florida form has been designated as *N. c. floridana* Goff. It is abdominally paler than the typical form.

Habits: Similar to *taxispilota.* Captives can seldom be induced to feed unless provided with a tank of living fish.

Diamond-back Water Snake, *Natrix rhombifera rhombifera* (Hallowell)

Size: One of the three largest Water Snakes of North America, attaining a length of close to 5 feet.

Form and scalation: Stout, with very distinct head on which the lip plates are distinct and swollen. Eyes placed well forward. Scales strongly keeled.

Coloration: Olive or brown, with narrow, vertical dark bars on the sides, which fork on the back and thus unite to form a chain of small dorsal rhombs or "diamond-shape" markings. Abdomen yellow, the edges of the plates darkly blotched, this most prominent posteriorly.

Young specimens are yellowish brown, the "diamond" markings and bars on the sides in strong contrast.

Distribution: Common in the lower altitudes of the Mississippi Valley states; northward to southern Illinois and Indiana, eastward to Alabama and southward through Texas into Mexico.

Habits: Typical of the larger Water Snakes. As a captive, however, it is less morose than *taxispilota* and *cyclopion.*

Flat-tailed Water Snake, *Natrix compressicauda* (Kennicott)

Size: A small Water Snake. Measurements of a specimen from the lower Florida Keys is as follows: Length $22\frac{1}{4}$ inches, diameter $\frac{1}{2}$ inch.

Form and scalation: Of moderate thickness; scales strongly keeled.

Tail vertically compressed a short distance from its base for about a third its length. This flattening is not marked and on casual examination may not be apparent. A transverse section of the tail, however, would appear oval—not rounded.

Coloration: Greenish gray or ashy gray, with rather ill-defined and irregular darker transverse bands. With some specimens the markings may appear like clouded blotches on the back, with smaller, alternating spots on the sides. Abdomen dark gray or brown, with central yellow spots.

Distribution: Extreme southwestern Florida, particularly in mangrove swamps and in the mangrove swamps along the Keys, in saline waters.

Habits: Selects rather thick cover, hence not so commonly seen as other water snakes. My captive specimens have been particularly quiet and docile, quite unlike the larger Water Snakes.

SMALLER NATRICINES

Black Swamp Snake, *Seminatrix pygaea* (Cope)
Size: Small, as a member of the Natricine group; length 16 – 18 inches; diameter of a 17-inch specimen, ½ inch.

Form and scalation: Rather stout, head small and not distinct. Body scales smooth and polished; those of the tail faintly keeled.

Coloration: Opalescent blue black. A faint line on the scales, particularly on sides, produces the effect of the scales being keeled. This may indicate *pygaea* as being a degenerate water snake, the lines indicating former keels given way to smooth surface. The sides of the neck are longitudinally, but obscurely, banded with yellow. Abdomen brick red crossed by narrow black bars.

Distribution: South Carolina, Georgia and Florida, with indicated extension into southern Alabama.

Habits: Lurks in aquatic vegetation, a common resting position being with body slanting towards the surface and little more than snout exposed. It also hides under debris along creeks and swamps, hence is not so frequently seen as the larger semiaquatic snakes.

Smooth Brown Snake, *Virginia valeriae valeriae* (Baird and Girard)
Size: Smallest of the so-called Brown Snakes. Length under a foot. An adult from Georgia is 7½ inches long and ¼ inch in diameter.

Form and scalation: Moderately stout, with abruptly tapering tail. Head rather pointed; slightly distinct. *Scales of satiny smoothness.* While there may be faint keels on the posterior portion, these are not apparent unless a specimen is examined with strong glass. On gross examination the indication is of a perfectly smooth-scaled surface, quite different from the strongly keeled Brown Snakes of the two following genera.

There may be confusion in separating this species from the Worm Snake, *Carphophis,* described at the beginning of this chapter, but the head of *Carphophis* is very pointed and of the same width as the neck, while the scales are highly polished, with opalescent glint—quite different from the satiny surface of *Virginia.* Moreover *Carphophis* is pinkish beneath, while the present species is yellowish.

Coloration: Grayish or chestnut brown above, usually with two rows of minute black dots along the back. Abdomen yellowish.

Distribution: Southern New Jersey to Georgia; westward to Tennessee. Very common in the pinelands of North and South Carolina.

A subspecies, *V. valeriae elegans* (Kennicott), extends the range westward to Texas. On gross examination both forms appear alike. If the rows of scales across the body are counted, *V. valeriae valeriae* will be found to have the scales in 15 rows, while with *elegans* they are in 17 rows.

Habits: See **Smooth Brown Snake,** Chapter V.

DeKay's Snake, Brown Snake, Ground Snake, *Storeria dekayi* (Holbrook)

Size: Very small. One of the smallest North American snakes. Average length 10 – 12 inches; diameter slightly exceeding ¼ inch. The largest example the author has measured was 20 inches long.

Form and scalation: Moderately stout; head blunt and fairly distinct. Eyes large; *scales heavily keeled.*

Coloration: Brown or grayish brown; a band of paler tint on the back, bordered with blackish dots. The band on the back is sometimes quite pronounced. Top of head dark. *Abdomen pink.* The hue of the underside is important in identification of the several kinds of small brown snakes of eastern North America.

Distribution: Southern Canada and the entire eastern United States; westward to Kansas and southward into Mexico.

Habits: See **DeKay's Snake,** Chapter V.

Storer's Snake, Red-bellied Brown Snake, *Storeria occipito-maculata* (Storer)

Size: Slightly inferior to preceding—seldom exceeding 12 inches. A 10-inch example is ¼ inch in diameter.

Coloration: Brown or gray above, with or without a pale longitudinal band. *Coral red beneath.* Gray examples have the more brilliant red undersurface.

Distribution: Widely distributed. The eastern United States, mostly inland from the coastal region, in elevated districts, thence westward to the Great Plains and southward to Mexico.

Habits: See **Storer's Snake,** Chapter V.

Florida Brown Snake, *Storeria victa* Hay

Size: Similar to the preceding in form and scalation.

Coloration: Brown above; pale beneath with a row of small black spots along each side of abdomen.

Distribution: "Florida and southeastern Georgia." (Blanchard.) "Near marshes and wet grassy prairies; not common." (Van Hyning.)

Southern Brown Snake, Ground Snake, Small-eyed Brown Snake, *Haldea striatula* (Linnaeus)

Size: Seldom as much as 12 inches long and ¼ inch in diameter; average length about 10 inches.

Form and scalation: Moderately stout; scales coarsely keeled. This smallest of the keeled-scaled little brown snakes may be readily told from the three species of *Storeria* (preceding) by its elongate, markedly pointed head and very small eyes. The species of *Storeria* have a blunt head and comparatively large eyes. The scales of both genera are similarly keeled.

Coloration: Uniform grayish brown or reddish brown above; yellowish white beneath. Often a pale, indistinct band across the top of head.

Distribution: Widely distributed and in some areas very abundant. Virginia to Florida, thence extending west of the Mississippi Valley.

Habits: See **Small-eyed Brown Snake,** Chapter V.

Allen's Snake, Mud Snake, Banded Swamp Snake, *Liodytes alleni* (Garman)

Size: 2 – 2½ feet long. A 24-inch specimen is ¾ inch in diameter.

Form and scalation: Body stout, tapering abruptly toward the head, which is small compared to body bulk and not distinct from the neck. Scales of body smooth, with high polish. A few rows on top of tail are keeled.

Coloration: Banded longitudinally. A broad band of dark brown along the back about 5 scales wide, which also covers a part of the head. On each side of the dark, central area is an olive or dull yellow banding about 2 scales wide and beneath this another band of the darker hue about $2\frac{1}{2}$ scales wide. The abdomen and the 1st, 2nd and half of the 3rd rows of scales, also the upper labial plates, immaculate yellow.

The longitudinal banding, small, flattened head, polished scales and mud-burrowing habits might tend to confuse this species with the Rainbow Snake, *Abastor erythrogrammus* (later described). The *colors* of the two species, however, are quite different.

Distribution: Southeastern Georgia (in the Okefinokee Swamp) and Florida.

Habits: This snake was considered to be rare for many years and but few specimens reached collections in the museums. This came about from secretive habits and disposition to prowl at night. O. C. Van Hyning, of the Florida State Museum, has explained, in *Copeia,* 1932, No. 1:

> "Of sixty-four stomachs examined, seven contained crayfish, making up 73 per cent of the bulk; two contained *Pseudobranchus striatus,*" (an amphibian) "making 14 per cent of the bulk; two contained frogs, making 13 per cent of the bulk, and fifty-five stomachs were empty. Most of these specimens were taken shortly after dark, during the months of July and August 1928, at Payne's Prairie, six miles south of Gainesville, Florida."

In a later publication there is the following note (*Copeia,* 1933, No. 1): "Allen's Mud Snake. In aquatic vegetation and burrowing in muck; locally common."

THE STRIPED OR GARTER SNAKES

These reptiles are close in relationship to the Water Snakes, *Natrix,* both in form and approach among some of them to semiaquatic habits. Their separation in these descriptions from the typical Water Snake genus was for insertion of several rather degenerate species indicated as offshoots of the more aquatic Natricene types. Garter snakes, as with the water snakes and related kinds, give birth to living young.

The genus differs from that of the Water Snakes in having the ventral plate entire, a point of separation from the small Striped Water Snakes.

Ribbon Snake, Slender Garter Snake, *Thamnophis sauritus sauritus* (Linnaeus)

Size: Maximum length about a yard—which is rare. Average length 2 feet, with diameter of ⅜ inch.

Form and scalation: Extremely slender, as will be noted from dimensions preceding. Long and gradually tapering tail a third or more the total length. Scales keeled, dull and velvety on dorsal area.

Coloration: Dark brown or black with vivid yellow stripe along back and a similar stripe on each side *on the 3rd and 4th rows of scales* above the abdominal plates. Dorsal stripe very sharply outlined, producing ribbonlike appearance. Abdomen yellowish white, without markings.

Distribution: Southeastern Canada to northern South Carolina, thence in elevated regions of the Southeast to northern Alabama; westward to Mississippi.

Western Ribbon Snake, *Thamnophis sauritus proximus* (Say)

Size: A much larger form than the preceding and relatively heavier. Common length is to a yard, and lower Mississippi Valley specimens have come into my collection close to 4 feet long.

Coloration: The pattern is similar to *T. sauritus sauritus,* but the central stripe is usually orange or even reddish, while the side stripes are yellow or greenish.

Distribution: Barely enters the southeastern region but must be listed, as it ranges southward from states immediately west of the Mississippi, into Louisiana, possibly into western Mississippi. Its range is through broad latitude, extending into Central America.

Habits: Partially aquatic. Frequents damp meadows, margins of waterways and swamp, often taking to the water when disturbed.

Southern Ribbon Snake, *Thamnophis sauritus sackenii* (Kennicott)

Size: Smaller in size than the other forms of *sauritus.* An adult 18 inches long is ¼ inch in diameter.

Form and scalation: Very slender. Scales strongly keeled with no luster.

Coloration: This common southeastern form of the Ribbon Snake lacks the central stripe, or has at most but a trace of it anteriorly.

There is a bright yellowish stripe on each side on the 3rd and 4th rows of scales. On gross examination this appears to be a very slim, dull brown snake, with a strongly defined pale stripe on each side.

Distribution: Coastal or lowland regions of South Carolina and Georgia; the greater part of Florida, thence the Gulf coast to southern Mississippi.

Habits: The author found this snake very common in Hampton County, South Carolina, along the edges of causeways and ancient rice ditches, always in the immediate proximity to water. It was a miniature, in habits, of the big water snakes, resting on branches over the water and dropping in when frightened.

Common Garter Snake, Striped Snake, *Thamnophis sirtalis sirtalis* (Linnaeus)

Size: Exceptionally a yard long; average length about 24 inches. A large example 31 inches long is ⅝ inch in diameter at thickest part.

Form and scalation: Moderately stout; much heavier in outline than the forms of *sauritus*. Scales strongly keeled, dull and lusterless.

Coloration: Specimens of the coastal portions of the southeastern United States, from Virginia to and including Florida and westward to the Mississippi Valley, are strongly striped, and position of the lateral stripe renders easy identification from the forms of *sauritus*.

The body is brown to olive or blackish with prominent pale stripe along the back and a similar, though less pronounced, stripe on each side on the 2nd and 3rd rows of scales. The abdomen is greenish yellow.

The skin along the sides, between the scales, has numerous white or pale greenish spots, which are often so arranged that a checkerboard or tessellated effect is produced if the body is distended. With specimens of paler hues—light brown or olive—there is often a double row of black spots on the scales themselves, between the stripes, the two rows arranged in alternated or checkerboard pattern. This pattern is particularly evident with examples of South Carolina, Georgia, Florida and the Gulf coast, which are both strongly striped and spotted and more commonly of an olivaceous hue.

In the elevated or mountain regions of the southeastern states the dorsal stripe may be dimmed by suffusion of black, but tessellated skin or scale markings and location of the lateral (side) stripe serve as identifying characters. In one character this snake differs from most other nonvenomous North American serpents. The base of its tongue is red, while the forked portion is black.

Distribution: Southeastern Canada; the entire eastern United States; westward to Wisconsin and Missouri.

Habits: The least inclined of its genus towards semiaquatic habits. See **Common Garter Snake,** Chapter V.

THE LARGER MUD SNAKES

Two large species loom as quite impressive among the reptiles of the southeastern region. Their relationship is puzzling unless conjecture points to origin from tropical sources. In bodily form and colors, these are big and handsome snakes, but their burrowing habits, relatively small heads and dull eyes relegate them among the ranks of "degenerate" types:

Horn Snake, Mud Snake, "Stinging" Snake, "Hoop" Snake, *Farancia abacura abacura* (Holbrook) and related form *reinwardtii* (Schlegel)

Size: Attains a length of 7 feet and diameter in excess of 2 inches. 4 – 5 feet is the average length. A 4-foot example is $1\frac{1}{2}$ inch in diameter.

Form and scalation: Moderately stout, cylindrical in taper along body. Head rather small and not distinct from neck; eyes flat and lusterless. Scales smooth, with high gloss.

Coloration: Lustrous, purplish black above, with large, vermilion, inverted-V-shaped blotches on the sides. Sides of head reddish with row of dark spots along upper labial plates. Abdomen vermilion, blotched with black. The more western form, *reinwardtii,* has blunt bars, with less upward extension.

This lustrous, brilliantly marked snake is among the most striking of the southeastern reptiles.

Distribution: Mostly the coastal region, or close to river systems, in wet and swampy areas, from southeastern Virginia to western Florida—*F. a. abacura.* The form *reinwardtii* extends from western Florida through Louisiana into eastern Texas and up the Mississippi Valley to southern Indiana.

Habits: In South Carolina and Georgia the author collected these big snakes in cypress growth where footing was damp but not too soft for fair going; also along causeways leading through ancient rice ditches, and in growth of gum trees where there were shallow "runs" with inundated margins. After heavy rains and flooding of the low grounds there was much more chance of finding prowling specimens, which appeared to be seeking less watery ground in which to burrow. I have seen them, however, stretched out in shallow pools like water snakes, although they differ in not immediately seeking to escape. Their sight appears to be poor, in keeping with small, dull and flattened eyes. When first handled, they do not attempt to bite, but thrash about with great vigor, twist the tail about one's arm and thrust its terminal part against the skin. The tail is provided with a spine much sharper than with other snakes. The spine of a big specimen is about an eighth of an inch long, like the point of a needle. A pricking by this spine causes one to shrink involuntarily, even drop the snake—and that seems to be the reptile's reason for this unique use of the tail.

Owing to this habit the Negroes hold this snake in great fear. They claim that the tail "sting" is capable of being darted out to considerable length, and that it is very poisonous. I have never noted any indication of this sharp spine having any poisonous properties, but this is the reason for this species being commonly referred to as the "Stinging" Snake.

It is also called the "Hoop" Snake, being alleged to take tail in its mouth and roll like the rim of a wagon wheel. This allegation may come about from a circular posture sometimes assumed by this snake when resting in inundated grass. I have come across specimens in such position and for a moment thought a reptile in this position to be a bicycle tire discarded along the causeway.

Until a few years ago attempts to maintain captive examples were unsuccessful, as they refused to eat. In 1932, however, O. C. Van Hyning, of the Florida State Museum, published a note about examination of stomach contents in a series of specimens of *Farancia*. He found a large percentage to consist of examples of *Siren,* an eellike, burrowing amphibian common in swampy ground. In 1935 George P. Meade, of Gramercy, Louisiana, published an article in *Copeia* showing that the Mud Snake had a keen interest in specimens of *Amphiuma,* another common, eellike amphibian. Mr. Meade's detailed notes were a lead for snake students who had endeavored to keep the big and

handsome burrowing snakes under observation. Since the publication
of this article it has been the general experience that the average
specimen of *Farancia* will feed voraciously upon specimens of *Amphiuma,* even swallow such amphibians a full half the length of the
snake.

Rainbow Snake, Mud Snake, *Abastor erythrogrammus* (Daudin)

Size: Inferior in size to the preceding—seldom exceeding 5 feet.
A 4-foot example is 1¼ inch in diameter. One slightly under 5 feet
long is 2 inches in thickness.

Form and scalation: Proportionately, this is a slightly stouter snake
than the preceding. However, it has the same cylindrical type of body,
highly polished and shining scales, small head, indistinct from the neck,
and dull, flattened eyes with minute pupils. Both this and the preceding
have a very small forked tongue.

Coloration: Very different from the closely allied and similarly
formed Horn Snake. It is purplish black or rich, dark blue with three
narrow, dark red stripes on the dorsal surface. With occasional snakes
the stripes are deep, reddish orange. A band of pale yellow on the
lower side the width of 3 rows of scales. Abdomen red, with two rows
of blue-black spots extending the greater part of its length; often a
row of much smaller spots between the larger ones. Upper labial
plates yellow, each containing a large, dark spot.

The reason for separating the two big and handsome Mud Snakes
into separate genera comes from difference in arrangement of the
head plates.

Distribution: Not so extensive as the Horn Snake. The range is
through the lower, coastal region from southeastern Virginia to
Florida, but indicated to be not farther west than Alabama.

Habits: Apparently similar to the Horn Snake (preceding). As
with *Farancia* it lays eggs, with a soft, tough integument. A 4-foot
specimen laid 43 eggs on July 7. The eggs were one and a half inch
long and one inch in diameter. They hatched on September 15. The
young were 9 inches long and 5/16 inch in diameter.

REAR-FANGED SNAKES

Snakes with short, grooved fangs at the rear of the upper jaw
form a large subfamily of the *Colubridae,* which also contains the even

more extensive subfamily composed of the typical harmless serpents. Rear-fanged snakes inhabit both the New and Old World. Some of the larger ones are capable of producing a dangerous bite, but the smaller ones are comparatively harmless. The very small kinds, as represented by a single species occurring in the southeastern region, may be regarded as entirely innocuous.

The Genus *Tantilla:*

These are very small, slender and secretive snakes, under a foot long on the average and a quarter-inch in diameter. With the exception of one species they inhabit the central and western United States, Mexico, Central and South America. The scales are smooth and opalescent, the head flat and not distinct from the neck. Most of them are characterized by a pale brownish body and black head. Some have a narrow white collar. The width and placing of the collar—or its absence— are points used in identification. Following is outline of the single species occurring in the southeastern region:

Black-headed Snake, Crowned Snake, Miter Snake, *Tantilla coronata coronata* (Baird and Girard)

Coloration: Body uniform pale brown. Head blackish. A narrow whitish collar at base of head which crosses the rear tips of the large posterior shields (parietals). The collar is followed by a blackish band 3 – 4 scales wide.

Distribution: The southeastern region; Virginia to Florida and westward to the Mississippi Valley.

A subspecies, *T. coronata wagneri* (Jan), is described by Blanchard as having: "Head pattern like that of *coronata* but the white band more often nearly obliterated with dark pigment, and the black usually not extending beyond the fourth scale behind the parietals in the mid-line; ventrals fewer, caudals more numerous than in *coronata;* size smaller. The maximum length known is 240 mm.

"*Range:* Peninsula Florida."

Habits: Secretive, but not a true burrower, as indicated by well-developed eyes. Extremely minute grooved fangs are used in paralyzing earthworms and insect larvae, possibly the small ground lizard *Leiolopisma.*

CHAPTER IX

The Southeastern Poisonous Snakes

Two FAMILIES of poisonous snakes are represented in the southeastern region. These are the *Elapidae,* of which there is the Coral or Harlequin Snake, and the *Crotalidae.* The latter is represented by the Copperhead, Water Moccasin and four kinds of rattlesnakes—the Pygmy Rattlesnake, Timber or Banded Rattlesnake, Canebrake Rattlesnake and the Diamond-back Rattlesnake. For descriptions of the families containing these dangerous reptiles, see beginning of Chapter VI.

Among the seven snakes enumerated there are wide differences in form, size and markings. Identification is thus comparatively simple. The most markedly divergent is the Coral Snake, the only species with slender, cylindrical body, narrow head, not distinct from the neck, smooth scales and eyes with round pupils:

Coral Snake, Harlequin Snake, *Micrurus fulvius fulvius* (Linnaeus)

Size: Up to 3½ feet, which is rare. Occasional examples are a yard long. An average-sized adult, from Florida, measures 28½ inches with diameter of ½ inch.

Form and scalation: Slender and cylindrical with but little taper the greater length. Head blunt and slightly distinct from neck. Scales smooth and polished. Pupil round.

Coloration: Broad rings of deep scarlet and blue black, separated by narrow rings of yellow. *Snout black; a wide band of yellow crossing middle of head, and behind this the first black ring of the body pattern.* Each scale within the red rings usually tipped with black. The pattern is continued across the abdomen and may be brighter beneath, owing to less speckling of black.

Red and black rings are from 7 – 12 scales wide; the yellow from 1 – 2 scales wide. There are no red rings on the tail, but alternating black and quite broad rings of yellow.

A subspecies, *M. fulvius barbouri* Schmidt, of southern Florida is distinguished by the red rings being practically clear of black speckling.

Several species of nonvenomous snakes closely "mimic" the colors of the Coral Snake. Mainly, their difference may be quickly determined by *each yellow ring being margined by pairs of black ones.* Compare *Lampropeltis triangulum amaura, L. elapsoides elapsoides, L. elapsoides virginiana* and *Cemophora coccinea* in key of Chapter VII; also detailed descriptions of these similarly colored snakes in Chapter VIII. Head markings are important. The snouts of the harmless snakes are usually red. With the Coral Snake the snout is black.

Distribution: A southern species occurring from central North Carolina to Florida, thence through the Gulf states to Texas and into Mexico. Distribution up the Mississippi is said to be as far north as southern Illinois.

Habits: This is a very dangerous snake from combination of deceptiveness in appearance and actions and the high toxicity of its bite. Its pretty colors and slender form might tempt a misinformed observer to pick it up, taking it for granted that the slender creature is harmless. And again, the actions of the Coral Snake on the ground may seem inoffensive, as it seeks to glide away, with no anterior loops to hint of its trying to strike. Restrained with a stick, it thrusts its head from side to side, but such actions may not appear more than efforts to escape. Misguided persons have handled such specimens and escaped being bitten, but others have not been so fortunate. The action of a Coral Snake is to turn and bite *and chew* in imbedding its short fangs. Of Coral Snake bites that the author has heard of, two out of three were fatal. The poison, a neurotoxin, is drop for drop more lethal than that of a cobra.

The Coral Snake is secretive, although not a typical burrower. It hides in abandoned rodent burrows or under the debris of forest floor. Prowling through such medium, it searches for the young of other snakes. From studies of its food, it seems to feed upon little else but other snakes and ground lizards. It is more frequently to be found prowling on the surface after warm rains. It is oviparous, the eggs being elongate and deposited in decaying bark or damp soil.

The Pit Vipers or Crotalids:

The range of size of these long-fanged snakes is from the Pygmy Rattlesnake, seldom much over 18 inches long, through the Copperhead, average size 2½ feet, the Water Moccasin, 4 – 5 feet, Timber and Canebrake Rattlesnakes, 3½ – 6 feet, to the Diamond-back Rattlesnake, up to 8 feet. All produce living young. These highly dangerous snakes have three outstanding points for identification.

1: The greater number or all the plates under the tail are in a single row—while with nonvenomous snakes all of the undertail plates are in a double row.

2: There is a deep pit, appearing like a hole, on each side of the head, between eye and nostril. (Not present with the nonvenomous snakes.)

3: The pupil of the eye is elliptic or catlike; round with Coral Snake and with all the nonvenomous snakes.

The rattlesnakes, of course, may be recognized by the segmented caudal appendage.

Southern Copperhead Snake, Chunkhead, Highland Moccasin, Pilot Snake, *Agkistrodon mokasen mokasen* (Beauvois)

Size: The largest specimen I have examined was two inches in excess of 4 feet, which was exceptional. The next largest was two inches under 4 feet. This snake was collected in Louisiana. A fairly large example selected for measurement is 33 inches long, 1¼ inch in diameter with head 1 inch in width.

Form and scalation: From comparison of length and diameter, this will be seen to be a stout-bodied snake. The neck tapers, and the head thus appears broad and distinct, nearly as wide as the greatest diameter of body. The scales are distinctly keeled, though not to the extent to impart a rough surface. Most of the plates under the tail are in a single row. The top of the head has symmetrical plates.

Coloration: Pale hazel brown to brownish gray with a series of quite widely spaced large crossbands of rich chestnut brown. These bands are very narrow on the back and quite broad on the sides and when seen from above resemble the outlines of an hourglass. From the sides most of the bands look like Y's with stems directed upward.

On the average specimen several of the bands are broken on the back, forming inverted V- or Y-shaped blotches on the sides. All the bands are darker at their borders and may enclose light patches or centers similar to the ground color. The top of the head is usually of coppery hue. The abdomen is pinkish brown with row of dark spots along the margins. The Copperhead may be said to be a strongly marked snake, with quite vivid pattern carried through the adult stage.

Distribution: The southern form has been emphasized, but it intergrades with the Northern Copperhead in Maryland and Virginia. The range of the species is from central Massachusetts to northern Florida to approximately the latitude of Gainesville, from which there are authentic records; westward to the Mississippi Valley and in the south to Oklahoma and Texas. While a fair number of southeastern snakes have been indicated in range as inhabiting coastal or less elevated regions, swinging, in crescentic distribution through the Atlantic and the Gulf states, the Copperhead occurs throughout the southeastern region. I have observed it both in the low cypress areas of coastal country and high in the mountains of the Carolinas, while records extend it through Tennessee and Kentucky to the great valley bordering the western margin of these states.

Habits: See **Copperhead Snake**, Chapter VI.

Water Moccasin, Cotton-mouth Snake, *Agkistrodon piscivorus* (Lacépède)

Size: Much larger and heavier than the Copperhead. The general size is from 3 – 5 feet and in exceptional cases approaching 6 feet. A 4-foot, South Carolina specimen is $2\frac{3}{8}$ inches in diameter, with width of head $1\frac{3}{4}$ inch.

Form and scalation: Heavy-bodied. Head wide and distinct from neck, with large, symmetrical shields on forward portion. Body scales moderately keeled, less roughly than with the nonpoisonous water snakes. Pupil elliptic. A deep pit between eye and nostril. Most of the plates under tail in a single row.

Coloration: Brightly marked with very immature specimens which are pale, reddish brown, with bands of dark brown, narrowly edged with white. Such examples somewhat resemble the Copperhead Snake, but the bands are not so markedly narrowed on the back.

Half-grown examples are brown to olive with broad and distinct transverse blotches, particularly evident on the sides.

With approach to adult size the ground hue becomes darker, dull brown or olive, and there may be but faint indication of the bands except on the sides. Old specimens may be almost uniformly dark olive or blackish, with no markings. Such may not be very large snakes, as size of adults varies a great deal with the Water Moccasin.

Several points of deduction remain in identifying old and dull-hued examples of the poisonous water snake. They are:

1: The elliptic pupil. 2: The deep pit between eye and nostril. 3: The greater number of plates under tail in a single row. All the nonvenomous water snakes, common in association with haunts of the Moccasin, have *all* the plates under the tail in a double row and the pupil *round*.

Distribution: The Dismal Swamp of Virginia and southward to Florida, thence to the Gulf states and eastern Texas; northward in the Mississippi Valley to southern Illinois.

Habits: Sluggish waterways or swamps with thick marginal vegetation are favorite haunts of this snake. It is sometimes to be seen basking on boughs that overhang the water, whence it plunges in if frightened, diving to the bottom and hiding. It is not so active in effort to escape as the nonvenomous water snakes, and if surprised when coiled on open ground, throws back its head and opens the mouth. This position of threat discloses the white mouth parts; hence the common name of Cotton-mouth Snake. Unlike many snakes which feed either exclusively upon cold-blooded prey or confine their diet to small mammals and birds, the Moccasin feeds upon both cold- and warm-blooded prey and is even cannibalistic in sometimes devouring the harmless water snakes. It produces litters of living young, up to the number of about a dozen. The young from a fair-sized parent are quite large, 8 – 10 inches long and $\frac{3}{4}$ inch in diameter.

While the Water Moccasin will strike in viperine fashion from a lateral loop, it is less excitable than a rattlesnake. This is indicated by disposition of captive specimens, which become tame and lazy and feed without hesitation. This is not said, however, as a suggestion to ease caution in Moccasin country. These snakes are tricky, and temperaments vary. There are far-fetched stories of Moccasins attacking persons in the water. I have never seen indications of these snakes behaving in this way. Water is an avenue of escape, and in wading through southern low grounds, the swimming Moccasins I noted gave me a wide berth.

THE RATTLESNAKES

Pygmy Rattlesnake, *Sistrurus miliarius miliarius* (Linnaeus)

Size: Seldom as long as 24 inches. An average adult is 18 inches long and ⅝ inch in diameter; width of head ½ inch.

Form and scalation: Proportionately quite stout, with wide, distinct head, but unlike the larger rattlers, the tail is relatively long and slenderly tapering, terminating in minute rattle. *Sistrurus* also differs from the main rattlesnake genus—*Crotalus*—in the top of the head having symmetrical shields. The body scales are heavily keeled and lusterless.

Coloration: The typical form is ashy gray with large black blotches on the back, these irregularly rounded and separated on the anterior part by reddish spaces. One or two series of smaller blackish blotches on sides. Abdomen dull white, marbled with black. *S. miliarius barbouri* Gloyd has a darker body hue and three rows of blotches on each side. *S. m. streckeri* Gloyd has the dorsal blotches wider than long, hence not so rounded as the typical form. On gross examination the three forms do not appear dissimilar.

Distribution: The typical form and the two subspecies extend the range of the Pygmy Rattlesnake through the entire southeastern region (except in the higher mountains) from the Carolinas to Florida and westward to Oklahoma and Texas. Specifically *S. m. miliarius* ranges from the Carolinas to northern Georgia, where it intergrades with *barbouri,* which extends throughout Florida and westward to Louisiana. *Streckeri* ranges from Louisiana and southern Mississippi to the westward.

Habits: The confusing, common name of "Ground Rattler" is sometimes used to designate this species. Such a term tends to indicate that other rattlesnakes climb trees. All rattlesnakes are markedly terrestrial and seldom do any climbing except among rocks or into low bushes, where they may lie in wait for birds.

The present species, owing to small size, is the least dangerous of the Crotaline snakes, although its poison is of high toxicity and a bite from it may be a serious matter. Its rattle is so minute that its whirring cannot be heard more than six to eight feet away. It is a fiery little snake, coiling and directing vicious jabs at an intruder. I have most frequently found it in dry, sandy places with bushy growth, sometimes in the pine forests, hiding under slabs of bark. Unlike the larger rattlesnakes which largely confine their feeding to birds and small mammals, the Pygmy Rattlesnake eats small rodents, lizards and frogs. Frogs are quickly subdued by its poison. It produces small litters of young, usually under twelve.

Timber Rattlesnake, Banded Rattlesnake, Mountain Rattle-snake, *Crotalus horridus horridus* (Linnaeus)

Size: Large, from $3\frac{1}{2}$ to 5 feet (exceptionally 6 feet). An adult 4 feet long is $1\frac{3}{4}$ inch in diameter. Width of head $1\frac{1}{2}$ inch.

Form and scalation: Heavy-bodied with wide and very distinct head. Body scales strongly keeled, with velvety surface. Top of head with small scales. Rattle well developed. With very young specimens the future rattle is represented by a black, bulbous knob.

Coloration: Color and pattern in considerable variety. The commoner phase is sulphur yellow or tan, with wide dark brown or black crossbands, usually wavy or pointed at the rear and sometimes broken into three longitudinal rows of blotches, the central or larger ones being rather rhomblike. With darker examples the blotches may be intensified by being margined with yellow. Posterior part of body darker; tail usually black. Occasional specimens are almost velvety black, with little indication of markings. With such snakes the yellowish abdomen appears as if speckled with gunpowder grains.

Distribution: Of general occurrence in elevated parts of the southeastern region. The range is northward to New England and west to the Mississippi Valley.

In coastal regions of the Southeast the typical form is replaced by a subspecies in description that follows.

Habits: See **Timber** or **Banded Rattlesnake,** Chapter VI.

Canebrake Rattlesnake, *Crotalus horridus atricaudatus* (Latreille)

Size: Larger than the typical form (preceding), particularly in the lower Mississippi Valley, where it attains a length of close to 8 feet. More normal size is 4 – 6 feet.

Form and scalation: Similar to the typical form.

Coloration: Gray, pinkish gray or brownish gray, with sooty-black crossbands, pointed at the rear to assume chevron-shaped form. A rusty-red or yellowish band several scales wide on forward part of back. A broad, dark band from eye to angle of mouth.

Distribution: Coastal (swampy) portions of southeastern Virginia, thence the coastal region to extreme northern Florida, southern portions of the Gulf states and the Mississippi Valley into Missouri, Arkansas and southern Illinois.

The first indication of intergrading from the typical form to *atricaudatus,* to the north of the latter's range (in the East), is in wet parts of the pine barrens of southern New Jersey—an unusual situation for rattlers. Here some specimens show a well-marked postorbital band.

Habits: The swampy valleys and attendant lowgrounds of southern rivers form the favorite abode of this snake. I frequently saw them in swamps of heavy cane growth in Hampton County, South Carolina, not far from the Savannah lowgrounds and about 40 miles inland from the coast. The largest and most handsomely marked specimens were received from southern New Orleans. They were pinkish gray, with the black bands in vivid contrast. Mr. M. Marlin Perkins, Curator of Reptiles of the St. Louis Zoological Park, tells me that he has collected big specimens in swampy valleys of the Ozark Mountains in southern Missouri. There are near-by limestone ledges, and in crevices of these the Canebrake Rattler and the Water Moccasin hibernate in company.

This snake appears to be more active and savage than the typical form; more inclined to stand its ground and strike when approached. Certain it is that in the laboratory they are more difficult to handle in extraction and investigations of snake poison.

Diamond-back Rattlesnake, *Crotalus adamanteus* Beauvois

Size: Very large, from 5 to 8 feet. Rattle strongly developed. Dimensions of a specimen from Florida are 6 feet in length and 4 inches diameter of body; width of head 3 inches. The record length appears to be 8 feet 4 inches, and a specimen of this length would have a diameter of about 5 inches, with weight of about 15 pounds.

Form and scalation: Very stout and heavy, attaining greatest diameter of any of the North American snakes. The next heaviest North American snake is the Western Diamond-back Rattlesnake *Crotalus atrox* (*cinereous*), a shorter but proportionately stouter reptile than the eastern one. Body scales are heavily keeled.

Coloration: Brown, greenish gray or olive, with chain of large rhombs or "diamonds" of darker hue, these with yellow borders about the width of a scale. The rhombs usually enclose a patch of the ground color. They become obscure and fuse into crossbands near the tail. There is an oblique yellow band on side of the head anterior to the eye and another behind the eye.

Distribution: The lower or coastal regions from southern North Carolina to Florida and westward to Louisiana; northward up the Mississippi Valley into Arkansas. Particularly common in South Carolina, Georgia and throughout Florida, where it occurs on the Keys.

Habits: King of the rattlesnake clan, largest of its genus, of which there are twenty or more distinct kinds extending the range of *Crotalus* all the way through broad-flung South America to Argentina, the Diamond-back is the world's most powerful known viper. It exceeds the noted Bushmaster in body bulk, breadth of head and poison-gland capacity. While the tropical Bushmaster—the world's longest viper— may exceed 10 feet in length, a coiled 6-foot Diamond-back would make a 10-foot Bushmaster appear inferior. Here is an impressive phase of Nature, brave in defense, but not wantonly attacking. The Diamond-back strikes when the intruder ventures near enough for the snake to sense that its life is in danger. It strikes from a coil with rattle buzzing in warning, and from places where humans should realize that danger is lurking. I have seen men—mostly hunters—go through such places with little pretense of protection, no high boots, no leggings. Such is low brush and ground covered with the broad leaves of dwarf or scrub palmetto. I have seen narrow escapes in which the warning of a rattler was located in time to sidestep it, and I have seen these big reptiles shot and held up for exploitation; but I have always felt a kind of regret on such occasions, which might not be understandable, hence was not mentioned to friends. It concerned the wiping out of an impressive form of life—dangerous as it was.

All dignity, the Diamond-back, if seen in the open, presents a scene not soon forgotten. Its body is thrown into a coil, the neck drawn into lateral loop, the tongue waves slowly, while the rattle is elevated in buzzing warning. From this position the snake can strike a full third of its length. If there is thick brush near by, the deep burrow of a Gopher Tortoise, the gnarled roots of a great pine or the like, a Diamond-back prefers retreat, rattling as it goes, but ready to assume a fighting coil if closely pressed.

Pine swamps and hummock lands are the usual abodes, but these depend upon sufficient food, which, with adult snakes, consists of rabbits and quail—principally the former. Wandering into areas of dwarf or scrub palmetto is mostly in search of rabbits, and these are the places dangerous to human hunters and their dogs, as one large, fanlike leaf may shelter a coiled rattlesnake. Ross Allen, proprietor of the Florida Reptile Institute, at Silver Springs, tells me that in 1937 and 1938 there were extensive fires in Florida and that rabbit hunting has been prosecuted with vigor. In consequence, between fires and hunting, rabbits have been greatly decreased in numbers and on his collecting trips he found Diamond-back Rattlers flat and razor-backed from lack of food.

The author's observations of the Diamond-back Rattler have been mostly confined to South Carolina. Thirteen big specimens were taken in ten days in the bed of a broad "run" or dried stream. The reason for this congregation was obvious. Numerous cottontail rabbits used the hard stream bed as avenue for reconnoiter. While Diamond-backs are alleged to prefer places where water is not far distant, I also saw these big snakes in a section called "the sand hills" which was a miniature desert with scrub oaks and some cactus growth, and insufferably hot at midday. I figured that the snakes sheltered in deserted burrows of the big Gopher Tortoise.

Several barelegged berry pickers were bitten and killed during the course of the year. There were losses among hunting dogs that unwisly forced their way under deserted cabins. The members of my party wore high shoes and leather riding leggings, and no matter where we went, we considered this protection against fang penetration of Diamond-backs.

The big southern rattler is a morose captive, and two out of three refuse to eat. The only way to induce them to feed is to avoid giving them a fright and disturbing them—or to rear the species from young. Here is an interesting experience for the reptile student—noting growth of the snake and development of the rattle. I had one such experience. The snake was well grown in about three years. It added from three four segments to the rattle per year until fully grown and died thirteen years later, after an accident during cage cleaning.

PART FOUR

The Snakes of Western
North America

CHAPTER X

Key to the Snakes of Western North America

THE LOWER MISSISSIPPI water system stands as a high spot of interest in the study of reptiles. It is a meeting place for northern, southern and western snakes. Nowhere else in North America is there such overlapping. Three states in particular illustrate this fusing of reptilian fauna. They are Illinois, on the eastern side of the great river, and Missouri and Arkansas on the west. Illinois, which on a map of the continent is a state of moderate size as compared with others, has typical northern fauna in its upper portion, but in the southern part, in the warm and sheltered river valleys of the Ozarks, one finds kinds of large southern reptiles in abundance. West of the river, in Missouri, the same condition is to be noted, and Arkansas is a sort of focal state with its cypress swamps and background of the Ozarks, which become drier and more sparsely forested than these tumbled elevations to the eastward. Arkansas has most of the southeastern reptiles and some of the typically western ones. The Western Diamond Rattlesnake, *Crotalus atrox* (*cinereous*), a species ranging to the Pacific coast, extends into the mountains of Arkansas. The southeastern fauna also extends into eastern Oklahoma and some of it well into Texas, where, again, there is mixture of forms.

My friend Marlin Perkins, formerly Curator of Reptiles at the Zoological Gardens, at St. Louis, and now Director of the Zoological Gardens at Buffalo, has done extensive collecting in Arkansas. In a letter to me regarding his observations in that state, he says:

"Arkansas presents much interesting mixing of geographical ranges. In central Arkansas we have collected *Crotalus cinereous* and *Anolis carolinensis* under the same rock. For the past four years we have been collecting in southwest Arkansas in the vicinity of Hope, and three different years we have collected specimens of each of four kinds of poisonous snakes in a single day, *Crotalus h. atricaudatus* or *Sistrurus m. streckeri* as the rattlesnake, *A. mokasen, A. piscivorus* and the Coral Snake, *Micrurus fulvius.* I do not think there are many places where this can be done. In this same locality we get the Scarlet Snake, *Cemophora coccinea* and *Lampropeltis triangulum amaura, Elaphe laeta* and *Elaphe o. obsoleta* or the intergrade with *confinis* that could be either.

"If you will look at a map of Arkansas and follow the Missouri Pacific Railroad from where it enters the state in the northeast towards the southwest to where it leaves the state at Texarkana, you will see that this divides the state into two triangles, a southern one in the southeast and a northern one in the northwest. A geological map will show this same division, not by railroad, but by a geological schist, the lower triangle being the area where the Gulf of Mexico at one time extended, and the northern triangle being the elevation of the Ozark and Quachita mountains. The former section, bounded to the east by the Mississippi River and being traversed by the widened St. Francis, Black, White, Arkansas, Quachita and Red rivers, is, as you would expect, a lowland filled with vast swamps. In most of this country as far north as nearly to Pine Bluff, the alligator is found today in numbers. The northern triangle is not the verdant 'Ozarks' you saw in southern Illinois, but a higher, drier and much more rocky old mountainous region, much of which is or was covered with hardwoods as well as pine, and through which flow sparkling, clear-water mountain streams. Over most of this mountainous section ranges the Diamond-back Rattlesnake (Coon-tail of the mountaineers), *C. cinereous.* Found scattered here also, but in the valleys rather than on the mountain tops, is *C. h. atricaudatus* (Velvet-tail). The former snake extends right through from Oklahoma in much the same kind of country. Strangely enough *C. cinereous* extends northeast out of the mountains into southeast Missouri, into Butler County, which is lowland."

If one turns the pages of a series of maps on physical geography, examines a relief map, another relating to summer rainfall, another to average winter temperatures, and a fourth to vegetation, the reason for this fusing of reptile life may be surmised.

Not distant from the Missisippi Valley, the typical West begins rather abruptly as far-flung prairies, the Great Plains, the rise to the Rockies, the deserts, thence mountains of the Pacific region. Over all, from the prairies to the Sierra Nevada, there is marked reduction in average rainfall from the region of the river indicated as defining boundary for herewith listing the western serpents.

On the map area immediately preceding Part Four, there is moderate extension in the Mississippi basin of a number of species defined in Parts Two and Three. All of these are included in the key of the southeastern section, Chapter VII, which is also largely inclusive of snakes ranging through the northeastern section. Thus identification of the snakes of the Mississippi Valley depends largely on the key in Chapter VII and detailed descriptions in Chapters VIII and IX. Such species are partially excluded from the western key. Eastern species, however, northern and southern, which extend into Minnesota or Iowa, or over the western portions of Missouri, Arkansas and Louisiana, are generally included in the western listing.

In the arrangement within the western key, grouping is guided by size, nature of scale covering (whether *smooth* or *keeled*) and coloration. Continuity does not indicate relationship; the latter becomes evident in sequence of the detailed descriptions in Chapters XI–XIII.

A key to the western snakes follows:*

NONVENOMOUS SPECIES†

I. Eyes almost hidden under translucent shields
  A. *Scales smooth*
    (a) *Undersurface with small scales like those of back*
    Size—small (tail very short)

> Reddish brown to lavender above; pinkish beneath:
> **Texas Blind Snake,** *Leptotyphlops dulcis.*
> *Distribution:* Kansas, Oklahoma and Texas to New Mexico.

*Subspecies or varieties, unless markedly different from the typical form, will be listed in supplementary keys in descriptive Chapter XI.

†The rear-fanged snakes are included. They are comparatively harmless.

Pale brown above; white beneath:
Mexican Blind Snake, *Leptotyphlops myopica.*
Distribution: Southern New Mexico; Mexico.

Pale brown above with 6 – 7 rows of dark spots, often fused
into bands:
California Blind Snake, *Leptotyphlops humilis humilis.*
Distribution: Southern California, with subspecies extending
the range throughout Lower California and into Arizona.

Ia. EYES NORMALLY DEVELOPED; PUPIL ROUND
(aa) *Undersurface with transverse shields* (plates under tail in
double row)
Size—small

Dark brown above; pink beneath:
Worm Snake, *Carphophis amoena vermis.*
Distribution: Southeastern Nebraska, thence southward
through Kansas to Texas.

Chestnut to grayish brown above; yellowish white beneath:
Brown Snake, Ground Snake, *Virginia valeriae ele-
gans.*
Distribution: Iowa to Indiana; southward to Texas.

Chestnut brown; a reddish band on each side of back:
Pacific Ground Snake, Brown Snake, *Contia tenuis.*
Distribution: Vancouver Island to central California.

Pale brown; head darker brown:
Slender Dark-headed Snake, *Tantilla gracilis.*
Distribution: Missouri and Kansas through Texas.

Pale brown; head brown with darker hue extending backward
about three scales:
Kirn's Dark-headed Snake, *Tantilla kirnia.*
Distribution: Oklahoma and Texas.

Pale brown, head black, the dark portion extending backward
in pointed shape:
Kennicott's Black-headed Snake, *Tantilla nigriceps.*
Distribution: Kansas to California, southward to Texas, New
Mexico and Arizona.

Pale brown; head black. A white collar at base of large head shields (parietals):
Wilcox's Black-headed Snake, *Tantilla wilcoxi.*
Distribution: Arizona.

Pale brown; head black. A white collar about three scales to rear of large head shields:
Günther's Black-headed Snake, *Tantilla atriceps.*
Distribution: Oklahoma and Texas to Arizona.

Pale brown; head black. Whitish collar not so evident:
Blanchard's Black-headed Snake, *Tantilla utahensis.*
Distribution: Southwestern Utah to eastern California.

Pale brown; head black. A whitish collar 4 – 5 scales to rear of large head plates:
Eisen's Black-headed Snake, *Tantilla eiseni.*
Distribution: Southern California and northern Lower California.

Pale brown; head black. Similar to *eiseni,* but ventral scale count is 134 – 140, as against 165 with the former:
Lower California Black-headed Snake, *Tantilla planiceps.*
Distribution: Southern Lower California.

Dark gray or lustrous black. A bright yellow ring on neck. Abdomen yellow with numerous black spots. Yellow of abdomen not extending above transverse plates:
Prairie Ring-neck Snake, *Diadophis punctatus arnyi.**
Distribution: Illinois and Iowa to Nebraska and Kansas; southward to Texas.

Dark gray or lustrous black. A bright yellow or pinkish ring on neck, which may be broken above. Abdomen yellow or pink; usually spotted. Abdominal hue extending upward into first or first and second rows of scales:
Pacific Ring-neck Snake, *Diadophis amabilis amabilis.**
Distribution: California, with subspecies ranging northward and southward.

*Several subspecies defined in Chapter XI.

Dark gray or lustrous black. A yellowish or pinkish collar, usually indistinct. Yellow or pink of abdomen encroaching to first or second rows of scales. Abdomen more or less spotted:

Southwestern Ring-neck Snake, *Diadophis regalis regalis.**

Distribution: Central Texas to Arizona and Utah; Mexico.

Pale green above; white beneath:

Smooth-scaled Green Snake, *Liopeltis vernalis.*

Distribution: Widely distributed from the Atlantic coast to North Dakota, thence southward through Colorado into New Mexico and Texas.

Very pale brown, each scale darker along the center; abdomen and upper labial plates white:

Taylor's Ground Snake, *Sonora taylori.*†

Distribution: Northern Mexico into southern Texas.

Grayish brown; scales of back with paler margins:

Mosauer's Ground Snake, *Sonora mosaueri.*

Distribution: Lower California.

Pinkish to pinkish gray; scales darker at base:

Pinkish Ground Snake, *Sonora miniata miniata.*

Distribution: Idaho to Arizona.

Pale grayish, with red stripe on back two scales wide:

Striped Ground Snake, *Sonora miniata linearis.*

Distribution: Arizona, Nevada, south-central and eastern California; Lower California.

Yellow, brown, red to blackish. Often with a strongly defined pale stripe along back:

Striped Ground Snake, *Sonora episcopa.*

Distribution: Great Plains region. Central Texas to southeastern Kansas, westward to eastern Colorado and New Mexico.

---

*A subspecies in Arizona.

†These little snakes are difficult to define in a condensed key. Geographical definition should be deducted. Necessarily technical definitions are outlined in Chapter XI.

Deep orange or red above with vivid ringlike markings. Abdomen white with black markings encircling the posterior portion:

Ringed Ground Snake, *Sonora semiannulata semiannulata.* And related forms: *S. s. blanchardi, S. s. gloydi.*

Distribution: Utah, Nevada, Arizona and eastern California; northern Mexico. Eastward to southwestern Kansas and central Texas.

Milk white, pink or yellow, with narrow and vivid ringlike markings above. Abdomen white without encircling markings at rear. Snout spadelike:

Banded Ground Snake, Desert Ground Snake, *Sonora occipitalis.*

Distribution: Deserts of southern Colorado, Utah, Arizona and southeastern California; northern Mexico.

Reddish or orange with about 30 reddish-brown, dark-edged crossbands. *Form stout; snout upturned:*

Hook-nosed Snake, *Ficimia cana.*

Distribution: Western Texas to Arizona; northern Mexico.

Ashy gray with about 46 blackish-gray, transverse bands averaging about one scale wide and extending to about second row of scales:

Strecker's Hook-nosed Snake, *Ficimia streckeri.*

Distribution: Southern Texas; probably northern Mexico.

Red or orange, with 25 or under black transverse bands or half crossrings. *Snout scoop-shaped, but not upturned:*

Banded Burrowing Snake, *Chilomeniscus cinctus.*

Distribution: Deserts of southern Arizona, southeastern California and northern Mexico.

Similar to preceding, but crossbands over 25:

Island Burrowing Snake, *Chilomeniscus punctatissimus.*

Distribution: Islands of Lower California.

Straw color; each scale tipped with black:

Straw-colored Burrowing Snake, *Chilomeniscus stramineus.*

Distribution: Southern Lower California.

Pale brown with black band on back and similar band on each side; abdomen reddish.

Black-banded Snake, *Coniophanes imperialis.*
Distribution: Mexico, but extending into southern Texas.

Wide scarlet blotches or spaces separated by pairs of black half-rings enclosing a yellow half-ring about three scales wide. Abdomen white and unmarked:

Scarlet Snake, "Coral" Snake, *Cemophora coccinea.*
Distribution: The southeastern states to eastern Oklahoma and eastern Texas.*

Ringed with scarlet, yellow and black, the red spaces the widest and in contact with the black. Abdomen closely approaching the dorsal pattern:

Scarlet King Snake, "Coral" Snake, *Lampropeltis triangulum amaura.*†
Distribution: Southeastern United States to Kansas; southward to Texas.

Size—moderate

Scarlet or brownish blotches, black-bordered, extending well down the sides or encroaching upon abdomen. Red areas margined by black, which may be separated by yellow—the pattern ranging to ringed formation. Abdomen always marked with black, either tessellated or more or less ringed from above:

"Milk" Snake, *Lampropeltis triangulum triangulum* (and related forms).
Distribution: The red-marked subspecies of the *triangulum* group range through the greater number of the western states except those of the Pacific region. Supplementary key under "Milk" Snake in Chapter XI.

Red, black and whitish rings of nearly equal width, the red in contact with the black; abdomen carrying the dorsal hues:

---

*See description in Chapter VIII, among southeastern species.

†This is the smallest red-ringed form of *Lampropeltis*. Check with others in succeeding section of key.

Coral King Snake, California "Coral" Snake, *Lampropeltis zonatus.**

Distribution: California and Lower California.

Red, black and whitish rings, the black and pale rings dominating and tending to block out the red areas:

Coral King Snake, Arizona "Coral" Snake, *Lampropeltis pyromelana pyromelana.**

Distribution: Southern Arizona; northern Mexico.

Gray with alternating narrow black rings and wider ones enclosing patches of red. No pale rings. Pale gray beneath invaded by black from above:

Davis Mountain King Snake, *Lampropeltis alterna.*

Distribution: Davis Mountains of western Texas.

A yellow band on back about three scales wide, margined on each side by dark brown or olive band of same width; abdomen yellow. *Snout with a large, flattened shield:*

Banded Flat-nosed Snake, *Salvadora grahamiae grahamiae.*

Distribution: Western Texas, New Mexico and Utah; Mexico.

Similar to preceding, but bands slightly wider:

Arizona Flat-nosed Snake, *Salvadora grahamiae hexalepis.*

Distribution: Arizona, southern California and Lower California.

Black or dark brown with a green or yellow spot in center of each scale:

Green-spotted Racer, *Drymobius margaritiferus.*

Distribution: Southwestern Texas to northern South America.

Pale brown or reddish yellow with central series of small dark blotches, about 55 in number. Abdomen immaculate white or yellow. *Snout depressed,* projecting and sharp:

Slender Gopher Snake, *Arizona elegans elegans.*

*Check with similar colors, but different combination of rings of the poisonous western Coral Snake, *Micruroides euryxanthus,* in succeeding section of key.

Distribution: Central Texas to New Mexico, with related form having higher count of blotches, which extends the range to southern California and Lower California.

Dull reddish brown above; throat and upper lip white. *Excessively slender; head long, narrow and pointed:*
Arizona Vine Snake, *Oxybelis micropthalmus.*
Distribution: Southern Arizona; Mexico.

Size—moderate to large

Alternating black and red blotches along back, the latter quite square. Scales on sides a mixture of orange with red centers and red with black centers. *Unique in this series of the nonvenomous snakes in having the plates under the tail in a single row (undivided):*
Le Conte's Snake, *Rhinocheilus lecontei.*
Distribution: Kansas to Texas; westward to California; Lower California.

Grayish brown with dark brown blotches along back. A series of small alternating blotches on side. Yellow beneath, with dull, square blotches:
Yellow-bellied King Snake, Blotched King Snake, Prairie King Snake, *Lampropeltis calligaster.*
Distribution: Indiana to Wisconsin; southwestward through Kansas to Texas.

Black with a green or yellow spot in center of most of the scales:
Holbrook's King Snake, Salt and Pepper Snake, *Lampropeltis getulus holbrooki.*
Distribution: Mississippi Valley states, including southern Iowa and southern Nebraska, thence through the states southward into Texas.

Black with most of the scales on sides with a yellowish spot. Back without spots except rows to form 40 – 85 dotted crosslines. Abdomen dark, blotched with yellow:
Boundary King Snake, *Lampropeltis getulus splendida.*
Distribution: Boundary regions of Texas, New Mexico and Arizona.

Dark brown or black, with dull ringlike markings, usually not more than the width of one scale:

Arizona King Snake, *Lampropeltis getulus yumensis.*

Distribution: Southwestern Arizona, southeastern California, northern Mexico and Lower California.

Dark brown or black with vividly defined white or yellow ringlike markings two to three scales wide; abdomen dark with the dorsal markings encroaching as blotches. *A pattern variant has a yellow band or row of yellow spots along the back:* *

California King Snake, *Lampropeltis getulus californiae.*

Distribution: Oregon, California and Lower California, to Arizona, Utah and Nevada.

Brown, with a dark purplish dorsal band about five scales wide and extending from head to tail:

Santa Catalina Island King Snake, *Lampropeltis catalinensis.*

Distribution: Santa Catalina Island, Gulf of California.

Size—large

(*Scales smooth, with dull luster—not polished*)

Black above; slaty black beneath. Throat white:

Blacksnake, Black Racer, *Coluber constrictor constrictor.*

Distribution: The Great Plains and eastward to the Atlantic coast.

Bluish green, olive, yellowish green or brown. Pale yellow beneath:

Blue Racer, Yellow-bellied Racer, *Coluber constrictor flaviventris.*

Distribution: Central states to the Dakotas and Wyoming, thence southward to the Mexican boundary.

Olive, brown or yellowish brown, usually with bluish tint on the sides. Yellow beneath:

Western Blue Racer, *Coluber constrictor mormon.*

*Examples with both patterns hatched from the same clutch of eggs.

Distribution: Montana to the Pacific coast. Southward to Idaho, Utah, Nevada and California.

Anteriorly blackish, becoming gray or brown posteriorly:
  Coachwhip Snake, *Masticophis flagellum flagellum.**
Distribution: Eastern states from the latitude of Virginia westward through approximately similar latitude to the Rockies; southward into northern New Mexico. The range includes the more southern prairie states and northern Texas.

Pale brown, gray or greenish, with wide, well-separated transverse bands or blotches anteriorly:
  Blotched Coachwhip Snake, *Masticophis flagellum flavigularis.*
Distribution: Kansas and Colorado, southward through Texas and into Mexico.

Reddish, with numerous transverse markings. Abdomen pink:
  Red Racer, *Masticophis flagellum frenatum.*
Distribution: Utah, Nevada, California, Arizona and southward into Mexico.

Blackish brown to satiny blue black above; abdomen deep pink or reddish:
  Pink-bellied Racer, *Masticophis piceus.*
Distribution: Southern Arizona and Lower California.

Brown or black with a single cream-colored stripe or band on each side:
  Banded Racer, *Masticophis lateralis.*
Distribution: Southern California and Lower California.

Brown or black with a yellow stripe on each side and another close to edge of abdominal plates:
  Schott's Racer, *Masticophis taeniatus schotti.*
Distribution: Northeastern Mexico, extending into southern Texas.

*In considering the forms of *Coluber* and *Masticophis,* it should be noted that the young of those that are unmarked dorsally when two-thirds to fully grown, are usually strongly blotched anteriorly, this pattern beginning to fade when about a year old.

Similar to preceding, but the lateral stripes are quite dimly defined:

Ruthven's Racer, *Masticophis taeniatus ruthveni.*
Distribution: Southeastern Texas; Mexico.

Brown to black, paler on sides with linelike markings through centers of scales, forming fine stripes:

Striped Racer, *Masticophis taeniatus taeniatus.*
Distribution: Extreme western Texas, through New Mexico, Utah, Nevada, Arizona and eastern California; Mexico.

Gray or pale brown posteriorly. Anteriorly marked with pale and dark brown stripes on sides, the pattern fading at about the middle of body:

Half-striped Racer, *Masticophis semilineatus.*
Distribution: Mexico, extending into southern Arizona.

(*Scales polished*)

Blue black; throat reddish; abdomen black:

Indigo Snake, Blue Bull Snake, Blue Gopher Snake, *Drymarchon corais couperi.*
Distribution: Southeastern states to approximately central Texas.

Black, mixed with brown or olive on sides; abdomen dull orange or brown:

Texas Gopher Snake, Blue Bull Snake, *Drymarchon corais melanurus.*
Distribution: Southwestern Texas to northern South America.

Lustrous blue black; blunt vermilion bars on lower sides; abdomen vermilion:

Horn Snake, "Stinging" Snake, "Hoop" Snake, *Farancia abacura reinwardtii.*
Distribution: Western Florida to eastern Oklahoma and into eastern Texas, with extension up the Mississippi Valley.*

*Not included in descriptions of Chapter XI. See descriptions of southeastern snakes.

Iaa. PUPIL ELLIPTIC—SCALES SMOOTH
Size—small

Gray, brown or yellowish, with dark irregular blotches on back and alternating spots on sides:
Rock Snake, Spotted Night Snake, *Hypsiglena torquata ochrorhyncha.*
Distribution: Central Texas northwestward to southern Idaho; central and southern California; Mexico.

Whitish or pale yellow with about 15 brown blotches along back. *Plate on snout (rostral) greatly developed and curled upward. Scales on posterior part faintly keeled:*
Brown's Leaf-nosed Snake, *Phyllorhynchus browni.*
Distribution: Desert portion of Arizona; Mexico.

Whitish or pale yellow, with about 30 dark blotches on back. Snout similar to preceding. *Scales smooth:*
Southwestern Leaf-nosed Snake, *Phyllorhynchus decurtatus decurtatus.**
Distribution: Deserts of Nevada, western Arizona, California and Lower California.

Size—moderate

Pale gray, with about 30 pairs of dark blotches on back; an irregular row of blotches on sides. A lyre-shaped blotch on head. Abdomen white with dark spots on edges of shields. *Head very broad and distinct.* Anal plate usually divided:
Arizona Lyre Snake, *Trimorphodon lyrophanes.†*
Distribution: Utah, Arizona and Lower California.

Similar to preceding. Anal plate usually entire:
Van Denburg's Lyre Snake, *Trimorphodon vandenburghi.†*
Distribution: Southern California.

*A subspecies, P. decurtatus perkinsi, with more widely separated blotches occurs in the deserts of California and Nevada. See Chapter XI.

†Rear-fanged. Not highly toxic, but should be handled with caution.

Gray, with widely separated blotches. Three dark spots on head:
Wilkinson's Snake, *Trimorphodon vilkinsoni.**
Distribution: Western Texas; Mexico.

Gray or yellowish, with large dark and irregular blotches, quite widely separated and extending downward nearly to abdominal plates; yellow beneath:
Bush Snake, *Leptodeira septentrionalis.**
Distribution: Southern Texas and northeastern Mexico.

Size—moderate, but form thick and heavy
 (aaa) *Plates under tail in single row*

Bluish gray or brown above, with traces of three darker brown stripes. Abdomen red or orange, mottled with brown. *Head covered with small scales:*
California Rosy Boa, *Lichanura roseofusca roseofusca.*
Distribution: Southern California and Lower California.

Body hue similar to above, with three clearly and evenly defined reddish stripes from head to tail:
Desert Rosy Boa, *Lichanura roseofusca gracia.*
Distribution: Deserts of southeastern California and western Arizona.

Cream color to deeper yellow, with three vividly defined brown bands from head to tail:
Three-lined Boa, *Lichanura trivirgata.*
Distribution: Southern Lower California.†

Pale gray or grayish brown, with no pattern; yellowish beneath. *Head with anterior shields. Tail almost as blunt as head:*
Rubber Boa, Silver Boa, "Two-headed" Snake, *Charina bottae.*
Distribution: Washington to California; eastward to Idaho, Montana, Wyoming, Nevada and Utah.

---

*Rear-fanged. Not highly toxic, but should be handled with caution.

†This snake may not be more than a form of *roseofusca.* Further collecting in Lower California may produce intergrades to verify this point.

B. *Scales of back feebly keeled*
1a. Pupil round
   (aa) *Plates under tail in double row*
Size—large

Grayish brown with 45 – 55 dark central blotches on body and tail; smaller, alternating blotches on sides. Abdomen yellow. No headbands, or if present, obscure:
    Fox Snake, *Elaphe vulpina.*
Distribution: Extends from the central states into Iowa, Minnesota and eastern Nebraska.

Ashy gray with 50 – 70 rather symmetrical, square dark blotches. Superficial, alternating blotches on sides. Abdomen yellowish, with darker blotches. A dark band from eye to angle of mouth:
    Emory's Rat Snake, *Elaphe laeta.*
Distribution: Kansas, through Oklahoma and Texas into Mexico.

Gray to olive with about 80 narrow transverse blotches:
    Baird's Rat Snake, *Elaphe bairdi.*
Distribution: Texas and probably Mexico.

Yellowish gray, with about 24 dark H-shaped blotches. Differs from other species of *Elaphe* in having small scales separating the labials from eye:
    Davis Mountain Rat Snake, *Elaphe subocularis.*
Distribution: Davis Mountains, Texas.

Lustrous black, numerous scales with white or red edges, these often accentuated into a tracery of dorsal and lateral blotches:
    Pilot Blacksnake, Black Chicken Snake, *Elaphe obsoleta obsoleta.*
Distribution: Eastern states to Iowa, Kansas, Oklahoma and Texas.

Suffused with black, but showing large dorsal blotches of nearly solid black, and blotches on sides. Scales of sides white- or red-edged. Abdomen white blotched with gray:
    Lindheimer's Rat Snake, *Elaphe obsoleta lindheimeri.*
Distribution: Texas and northern Mexico.

Greenish above; white beneath:
> **Green Rat Snake,** *Elaphe chlorosoma.*
> *Distribution:* Mexico, extending into the Santa Rita Mountains, Arizona.

Olive brown above; reddish beneath:
> **Peninsula Rat Snake,** *Elaphe rosaliae.*
> *Distribution:* Southern Lower California.

C. *Scales strongly keeled.*
> *Size—small*

> Brown above; usually a double row of dark spots along back, these often enclosing a pale band. *Pink beneath:*
> > **DeKay's Snake, Brown Snake,** *Storeria dekayi.*
> *Distribution:* Eastern states to Kansas, thence southward to Mexico.

> Brown or dark gray above, often with a paler dorsal band, this sometimes margined with darker dots. *Bright red beneath:*
> > **Storer's Snake, Red-bellied Snake,** *Storeria occipito-maculata.*
> *Distribution:* Eastern states to North Dakota, thence all states southward into Mexico.

> Reddish to grayish brown; yellowish-white beneath. Eyes very small:
> > **Small-eyed Brown Snake,** *Haldea striatula.*
> *Distribution:* Virginia to Florida; westward to Oklahoma and Texas.

> Grayish brown with pale stripe on back margined with black dots. Another stripe, less distinct, on side on 2nd and 3rd rows of scales. *Abdomen white or yellow with two rows of black spots:*
> > **Striped Swamp Snake,** *Tropidoclonion lineatum.**
> *Distribution:* Ohio to southeastern South Dakota, southward in its western range through Iowa, eastern Nebraska, Kansas, Missouri, Arkansas, Oklahoma and eastern Texas.

*Looks like a diminutive member of the Garter Snake genus, but head is relatively smaller, and eyes are small, while the abdomen is marked with double row of black spots.

Size—moderate

Three pale stripes on darker ground hue; dorsal stripe reddish or orange. Lateral stripe greenish or yellow, on 3rd and 4th rows of scales. *Form slender, with tail about a third the total length:*

Western Ribbon Snake, *Thamnophis sauritus proximus.*

Distribution: Southwestern Wisconsin, Iowa, Nebraska, thence the westward Mississippi Valley states through Texas to Central America.

Ashy brown. Three pale stripes, the lateral on 3rd and 4th rows of scales. *Tail about a quarter total length:*

Mexican Garter Snake, *Thamnophis megalops.*

Distribution: Mexico, extending into southern Texas, New Mexico and Arizona.

Brown or black, three prominent yellow stripes, the lateral on 3rd and 4th rows of scales. Often two rows of square black spots (alternating) between dorsal and lateral stripes. *Form moderately stout:*

Plains Garter Snake, *Thamnophis radix.*

Distribution: Abundant in Indiana, thence northwestward into the Canadian Northwest; southward through the Great Plains to Texas.

Three yellow stripes more or less evident on a darker ground hue. *Lateral stripe on 2nd and 3rd rows of scales.* 8 upper labial plates. *Posterior and anterior pairs of chin shields of almost equal length:*

Western Garter Snake, *Thamnophis ordinoides ordinoides** (and related forms).

Distribution: Pacific region from southern British Columbia to California and Lower California. Eastward to Idaho, Utah, Nevada and western Arizona.

Three yellow stripes more or less evident on a darker ground. Lateral stripe on 2nd and 3rd rows of scales. Sometimes red

*Supplementary key to the subspecies in Chapter XI.

between the scales and checkerboard spots between the stripes. 7 upper labials. *Posterior pair of chin shields much longer than anterior.* (Check with *T. ordinoides*):

> **Common Garter Snake,** *Thamnophis sirtalis sirtalis**
> (and related forms).

Distribution: Eastern United States and southern Canada to British Columbia and the entire western United States, mostly north of the latitude of southern Missouri, to California.

Pale brown or straw color; three narrow yellow stripes; laterals on 2nd and 3rd rows of scales. Always strong checkerboard spots between the stripes:

> **Marcy's Garter Snake,** *Thamnophis marcianus.*

Distribution: Oklahoma and Texas to southeastern California; Mexico.

Three yellow stripes on a darker ground. Lateral stripe on 2nd and 3rd rows of scales. Dorsal stripe encroaching to base of head in pointed fashion. Two dark blotches at rear of head:

> **Brown Garter Snake,** *Thamnophis eques.*

Distribution: Western Texas to Arizona; Mexico.

Narrow or indistinct dorsal stripe; lateral stripe obscure. *Head narrow with elongated snout:*

> **Long-headed Garter Snake,** *Thamnophis angustirostris.*

Distribution: Mexico, extending into Arizona and New Mexico.

Brown, with a broad yellow band on each side, bordered with black. Abdomen yellow, usually with a central dark band:

> **Graham's Water Snake,** *Natrix grahamii*

Distribution: The Mississippi Valley states westward to Nebraska, Kansas, Oklahoma and Texas.

Uniform pale green above; yellow beneath; *form very slender:*

> **Keeled Green Snake,** *Opheodrys aestivus.*

Distribution: Southeastern United States and the Mississippi Valley states to Illinois. Westward to Kansas, thence southward and southwest to Texas and New Mexico.

---

*Supplementary key to the subspecies in Chapter XI.

Brown, gray or olive, sometimes reddish anteriorly, with 20 – 30 darker transverse blotches, sometimes broken into three rows. Central part of abdomen yellow or greenish. *Body stout, head wide, snout upturned:*

Hissing "Adder," Spreading "Adder," Hog-nosed Snake, *Heterodon contortrix.*

Distribution: Eastern United States to Minnesota and southward in the West through eastern Nebraska, Kansas, Oklahoma and Texas.

Form similar to preceding. Dull yellow, pale brown or gray with rather small, rounded blotches on back, 25 – 45, and similar blotches on sides. *Central part of abdomen black:*

Hissing "Adder," Western Hog-nosed Snake, *Heterodon nasicus nasicus* (and related forms).

Distribution: Iowa northwestward to Montana, thence all of the states southward to Arizona and Texas; Mexico.

Size—*moderate to large*

Brown above with more or less distinct dark or reddish transverse bands anteriorly, the bands wider than separating areas. Posteriorly the bands are broken into three series of blotches. Yellowish white beneath *spotted with red.* (Young gray and strongly marked):

Common Water Snake, "Moccasin," *Natrix sipedon sipedon.*

Distribution: Eastern United States to Minnesota, thence southwestward to Colorado and all states southward of the range outlined into Oklahoma.

Similar to preceding, but separating spaces of ground color wider than the darker bars:

Mississippi Water Snake, *Natrix sipedon pleuralis.*

Distribution: Ranging from the East into southern Missouri and Arkansas.

Transverse blotches fused in twos, with widely separated, *ring-like* areas of pale ground hue:

Blanchard's Water Snake, *Natrix sipedon confluens.*

Distribution: Lower Mississippi Valley into Arkansas, Kansas, Oklahoma and Texas.

Brownish with obscure blotches along back; alternating blotches on sides. Abdomen *yellow* and unmarked:

Yellow-bellied Water Snake, *Natrix erythrogaster transversa.*

Distribution: Lower Mississippi Valley, westward to Kansas and Oklahoma.

Brown or olive with narrow bars on sides which fork and unite on back to form a chain of small rhombs:

Diamond-back Water Snake, *Natrix rhombifera rhombifera.*

Distribution: Lower Mississippi Valley states westward to Kansas, Oklahoma and eastern Texas; southward into Mexico.

Almost uniform gray to olive with darker hue at bases of scales; some specimens with paler lateral stripe. Abdomen grayish yellow:

Lower California Water Snake, *Natrix valida.*

Distribution: Southern Lower California.

Size—large

Yellow to tan, with central series of large square blotches of reddish brown to black and a smaller series on each side. Abdomen yellow with black blotches on each side. *Snout pointed:*

Bull Snake, Yellow Gopher Snake, *Pituophis sayi sayi.*

Distribution: This and a related form are typically western. The range extends eastward into the prairies of Wisconsin and Illinois, thence all the prairie country southward and southwestward, the greater portion of the Great Plains, and into Mexico. A related form in southern California and Lower California.

Yellowish brown, with rather small, closely set reddish-brown or black blotches along back and row of small dull spots on side. Abdomen yellow with dark blotches at edges of plates:

Pacific Bull Snake, Yellow Gopher Snake, *Pituophis catenifer catenifer.*

Distribution: The typical Pacific Bull Snake and two quite similarly marked related forms extend the range from British Columbia through Washington, Oregon and California into Lower California, thence eastward to Idaho, Utah and Nevada.

Yellow; blotches less crowded than preceding:
San Lucan Gopher Snake, *Pituophis vertebralis.*
Distribution: Lower California, with extension north to San Bernardino County, California.

Yellow, with moderately large dorsal blotches. Difference of head shields. (See descriptive text in Chapter XI):
Mexican Gopher Snake, *Pituophis deppei deppei.*
Distribution: Mexico, but extending over the boundaries of Texas, Arizona and southeastern California.

POISONOUS SNAKES

Ia. *Pupil round*
  A, *Scales smooth*
  (aa) *Plates under tail in double row*
  Size—moderate (form slender)

Crimson and black rings of about equal width, separated by yellow rings of much lesser width. Snout black, a yellow band at rear of head and behind this *the first black ring:*
Eastern Coral Snake, *Micrurus fulvius fulvius** (and related form).
Distribution: Entering the western section (from the East) to Arkansas, southeastern Oklahoma and eastern Texas.

Crimson and black rings of about equal width, separated by yellow rings of near or lesser width. Front part of head black, a yellow band at rear of head and behind this *the first red ring:*
Sonoran Coral Snake, *Micruroides euryxanthus.**
Distribution: Southern Arizona and New Mexico. The only poisonous Coral Snake in the West and entering that region

---

*Check with similarly colored species of *Lampropeltis* and *Cemophora.* With the nonvenomous kinds the combinations of contact of red and black rings are different, although on gross examination poisonous and harmless kinds look alike.

from Mexico by scant margin. The extreme western extension of the eastern Coral Snake is into eastern Oklahoma and Texas.

(a) *Undersurface with small scales like those of back*

Body vertically compressed; tail greatly compressed vertically —paddlelike. Brown above; pale yellow beneath:
Yellow-bellied Sea Snake, *Pelamydrus platurus.*
Distribution: Tropical Pacific and Indian oceans, ranging eastward and northward into the Gulf of California.

Iaa. PUPIL ELLIPTIC. A PIT BETWEEN EYE AND NOSTRIL
  C. *Scales strongly keeled*
    (aaa) *All or most of plates under tail in single row* (undivided)
    Size—moderate to large (form stout)

Pale brown, reddish brown or pinkish gray, with dark brown transverse bands narrow on the back and wide on the sides. Abdomen usually pinkish brown. Pattern remaining strongly defined with adult examples:
Copperhead Snake, Chunkhead, Highland Moccasin, *Agkistrodon mokasen mokasen.*
Distribution: Eastern United States and the more southern Mississippi Valley states with extension westward into Kansas, Oklahoma and Texas.

Pale or reddish brown. Broad dark reddish-brown bands, not narrowed on the back as with the preceding:
Broad-banded Copperhead, *Agkistrodon mokasen laticinctus.*
Distribution: Oklahoma to about the central part of Texas.

Dull brown, olive or suffused with black. Broad transverse bands obscure with adults except on sides. (Young reddish with strong crossbands):
Water Moccasin, Cotton-mouth Snake, *Agkistrodon piscivorus.*
Distribution: Southeastern states and southern Mississippi Valley, not farther west than Missouri, Arkansas, eastern Oklahoma and eastern Texas to the lower Rio Grande.

RATTLESNAKES*

Size—small (symmetrical plates on head; rattle minute)

Grayish, with black dorsal blotches. Abdomen gray, suffused with black:
Pygmy Rattlesnake, *Sistrurus miliarius streckeri.*
Distribution: West of the Mississippi this subspecies of an eastern type extends into southeastern Missouri, thence southwestward through Arkansas, central Oklahoma, to central and eastern Texas.

Size—moderate (rattle moderately developed)

Brown or gray with dark brown or blackish blotches, wider than long. A row of smaller, alternating blotches on sides:
Massasauga, *Sistrurus catenatus catenatus.*
Distribution: Central states westward through Iowa to Nebraska and southward through Kansas.

Brown or gray with dark brown or blackish blotches not wider than long. Lateral markings reduced to spots.
Edwards' Massasauga, *Sistrurus catenatus edwardsii.*
Distribution: Southern Kansas through Oklahoma, southwestward to southeastern New Mexico, western and central Texas and northeastern Mexico.

(Greater part of head with small scales; rattle strongly developed)

Grayish, with dark dorsal blotches separated by narrow crossbands paler than the body hue. Head dark, with two pale stripes from snout extending *beneath* the eye:
Willard's Rattlesnake, *Crotalus willardi.*
Distribution: Appears rare and to range into the Santa Rita Mountains of Arizona from northern Mexico.

*The sizes indicated for the genera *Sistrurus* and *Crotalus* relate to run of sizes among the rattlesnakes—small under two feet, moderate to approximately a yard, and large if over that length.

Greenish gray with narrow and regular ringlike markings of black, widely spaced apart:

Green Rattlesnake, *Crotalus lepidus.*
Distribution: Boundary region of Texas, New Mexico and Arizona; northern Mexico.

Brown or gray with three rows of dark round spots anteriorly, tending to fuse into transverse bars posteriorly:

Spotted Rattlesnake, *Crotalus triseriatus pricei.*
Distribution: Northern Mexico, extending into southern Arizona.

Pale gray, yellow or light buff with alternate darker blotches and whitish interspaces. *A blunt horn over each eye:*

Horned Rattlesnake, Sidewinder, *Crotalus cerastes.*
Distribution: Deserts of southern Nevada, Utah, Arizona, southeastern California and Lower California.

Size—moderate to large

Grayish, crossed by rather symmetrical, close-set ringlike bands, sometimes not well defined:

Tiger Rattlesnake, *Crotalus tigris.*
Distribution: Southern Nevada, western Arizona and southern California.

Greenish gray, tan or brown, with a series of dark rounded saddles along back, these yellow-edged:

Prairie Rattlesnake, *Crotalus viridis viridis.*
Distribution: The Great Plains from about the 96th Meridian to the Rockies and southern Canada to Texas, the range including all the states within the boundaries outlined.

Sage green to buff, with well-separated, dark and rounded dorsal saddles margined with black and assuming ringlike formation on posterior fourth and tail:

Great Basin Rattlesnake, *Crotalus viridis lutosus.*
Distribution: The Rockies to the Sierras, including eastern Oregon, Idaho, Nevada and western Utah.

Gray, tan or brown, with dark blotches in close contact, these often rhomboid in outline and pale-bordered. Sometimes black,

the pale margins of blotches remaining to form a rhomboid chain:
Pacific Rattlesnake, *Crotalus viridis oreganus.*
Distribution: British Columbia to southern California, western Idaho and Nevada; northern Lower California. The only rattlesnake of the greater portion of the Pacific region in the United States.

Sandy hue, pinkish or red. Faint and well-separated, rounded blotches:
Grand Canyon Rattlesnake, *Crotalus viridis abyssus.*
Distribution: Grand Canyon of the Colorado River, Arizona.

Straw or cream color with no markings, or faint, well-separated blotches. Smallest of the *viridis* group:
Midget Faded Rattlesnake, *Crotalus viridis concolor.*
Distribution: Mountains of eastern Utah.

Dull white or pinkish, with obscure, separated blotches tending to be angular on sides:
Mitchell's Rattlesnake, Bleached Rattlesnake, White Rattlesnake, *Crotalus mitchellii mitchellii* (and related form).
Distribution: Arizona, Colorado Desert to southern California; Lower California.

Yellowish or drab, a chain of rhomboid or diamond markings, the points usually not quite in contact:
Mohave Diamond Rattlesnake, *Crotalus scutellatus.*
Distribution: New Mexico, Arizona, southern California and northern Lower California.

Rusty red with chain of dull white "diamonds" in contact:
Red Diamond Rattlesnake, *Crotalus ruber.*
Distribution: Southwestern California; Lower California.

Gray, sandy yellow or pinkish, a chain of dark, pale-bordered diamond markings, the points in contact. *As with the two preceding species the tail is almost white, with several black rings:*
Western Diamond Rattlesnake, "Texas" Rattlesnake, *Crotalus atrox atrox.*
Distribution: Most of northern Mexico, northward through Texas into Oklahoma, western Arkansas and southern

Missouri; westward through southern Colorado, southern Utah, New Mexico and Arizona to southeastern California. Subspecies extend the range into Lower California. (See Chapter XIII.)

Reddish; rhombs rather obscure:
Cedros Island Diamond Rattlesnake, *Crotalus exsul.*
Distribution: Cedros Island, west coast of Lower California.

Gray, a chain of rather small rhomboid markings in strong contrast, these tending to form bars on sides:
Cope's Rattlesnake, *Crotalus enyo.*
Distribution: Extreme southern Lower California.

Olive or rich yellowish brown; dark diamond markings brightly outlined, usually not in contact, their lateral edges tending to extend downward on the sides as bands. *Tail black:*
Black-tailed Rattlesnake, *Crotalus molossus molossus.*
Distribution: Southern Texas to southern Arizona; Mexico.

Yellow, brown, sometimes blackish, with dark crossbands, often angulate at rear and with some examples broken into three rows of blotches:
Banded Rattlesnake, Timber Rattlesnake, *Crotalus horridus horridus.*
Distribution: An eastern form which extends to the West into Iowa, Missouri, Arkansas, eastern Oklahoma and eastern Texas—elevated districts. In regions of low altitude the subspecies *atricaudatus,* with reddish band on the back, takes the place of the typical form. (See southeastern key.)

Each part of this field book is close in arrangement to a book in itself. There may be occasional cross reference to *habits* already mentioned in preceding sections, but for identification purposes each part is distinctive. However, the reader will undoubtedly have been interested to check one section or part against the others, and in so doing a summary of northeastern species will be seen to have been comparatively simple, as but about three dozen were considered. With the southeastern species and related forms, a much greater number came under consideration. With the far-flung West the listing grew to more formidable proportions. Hence summarization of the preceding key, of the West, in order not to be interminable and confusing, is reduced to consideration of genera or grouping of species.

Three additional Families entered into the listing of the typically western reptiles. These were the Blind Snakes (*Leptotyphlopidae*), the Dwarf Boas (true members of the *Boidae*) and a Sea Snake (representing the *Hydrophidae*). Also, there was a fair number of rear-fanged snakes, of which, in the eastern listings, there was but one small species.

Summarization of the genera, indicating size of members, their coloration and pattern, follows, which, with check back to the key, may suggest leads toward identification. The listing, at most, is but rough indication of sizes and markings. (Detailed descriptions, in formal continuity of relationship, are taken up in Chapters XI, XII and XIII.)

Genus	Representative	Size	
Leptotyphlops	Blind Snakes	Small	
Carphophis	Worm Snakes	"	
Storeria	Brown Snakes*	"	
Virginia	" " *	"	
Sonora	Western Ground Snakes**	"	
Tantilla	Black-headed Snakes†	"	
Diadophis	Ring-necked Snakes‡	"	
Liopeltis	Smooth Green Snake	Small	No body
Opheodrys	Keeled Green Snake	Moderate	pattern
Oxybelis	Vine Snake	"	
Charina	Rubber Boa	"	
Coluber	Racers	Large	
Masticophis	Whip Snakes, Racers[1]	"	
Drymarchon	Indigo or Blue Bull Snakes	"	
Elaphe	Rat Snakes[1]	"	
Pelamydrus	Sea Snake (poisonous)	"	

*Sometimes dots along back.

**Some species under ringed definition.

†Head darker than body.

‡Yellow ring on neck.

[1]See other pattern groupings, seven genera being thus split according to coloration.

Hypsiglena	Rock Snake	Small	
Phyllorhynchus	Leaf-nosed Snakes	"	
Lampropeltis	"Milk" Snake, Prairie King Snake	Moderate	
Arizona	Smooth-scaled Gopher Snakes	"	
Rhinocheilus	LeConte's Snake	"	
Heterodon	Hissing "Adders"	"	
Trimorphodon	Lyre Snakes	"	
Leptodeira	Bush Snakes	"	Blotched pattern*
Sistrurus	Pygmy Rattlesnakes (poisonous)	"	
Crotalus	Smaller Rattlesnakes (poisonous)	"	
Natrix	Water Snakes	Moderate to Large	
Elaphe	Rat Snakes	Large	
Pituophis	Bull Snakes	"	
Masticophis	Racers	"	

Ficimia	Hook-nosed Snakes	Small	
Heterodon	Hissing "Adders"	Moderate	
Natrix	Water Snakes	Moderate to Large	
Masticophis	Racers	"	Transversely banded
Agkistrodon	Copperhead and Water Moccasin (both poisonous)	"	
Crotalus	Rattlesnakes (poisonous)	"	

Cemophora	Scarlet Snake	Small	Ringed pat-
Sonora	Ground Snakes	"	tern above,
Chilomeniscus	" "	"	and with
Lampropeltis	King Snakes	Moderate	some ex-
Micrurus	Coral Snakes (poisonous)	"	tended across
Mircuroides	" " "	"	abdominal
Crotalus	Green Rattlesnake "	"	portion

*If blotches are extended across the back to be laterally wider than dor-
sally long (longitudinally) they may be confused as transverse bands, but the
latter have been herewith grouped as markings that extend well down the
sides toward margins of the abdominal plates.

Genus	Representative	Size	
Drymobius	Mexican Racer	Moderate to Large	Body dark. Many scales containing a yellow or green spot
Lampropeltis	King Snakes	"	
Natrix	Diamond-back Water Snake	Large	Chain of "diamond" markings along back
Crotalus	Diamond-back Rattlesnakes (poisonous)	"	
Contia	Pacific Ground Snake	Small	
Coniophanes	Black-banded Snake	"	
Tropidoclonion	Striped Swamp Snake	"	
Thamnophis	Garter Snakes, Striped Snakes	Moderate	Banded or striped lengthwise
Natrix	Water Snakes	"	
Salvadora	Flat-nosed Snakes	"	
Lichanura	Three-lined Boas	Moderate	
Masticophis	Striped Racers	Moderate to Large	

Among these genera, the egg-laying (oviparous) species are in the majority, as evidenced by such habits with *Salvadora, Masticophis, Coluber, Drymobius, Drymarchon, Elaphe, Pituophis, Cemophora, Lampropeltis, Heterodon, Rhinocheilus, Carphophis, Diadophis, Liopeltis, Opheodrys, Trimorphodon* and *Leptodeira*.

Species producing living young (viviparous) make up the genera *Storeria, Virginia, Natrix, Thamnophis, Tropidoclonion* and a few others.

Of the poisonous species the Coral Snakes, *Micrurus* and *Micruroides,* lay eggs, while all of the Pit Vipers—the Copperhead and Water Moccasin, *Agkistrodon,* the Pygmy Rattlesnakes, *Sistrurus* and all the larger rattlers, *Crotalus,* produce living young.*

There is food selection in much variety, including insects, earthworms, salamanders, frogs, toads, fish, lizards, rodents and birds. A fair number of species feed upon snakes of other kinds. As an indication of variance of food habits in comparing genera, it may be noted that the large Racers take both cold- and warm-blooded prey and are

*The Yellow-bellied Sea Snake is likewise viviparous.

not constrictors. The King Snakes, *Lampropeltis,* feed upon snakes, lizards and rodents and are strong constrictors. Members of the Genus *Elaphe* (Rat Snakes), feed mostly upon warm-blooded prey, rodents and birds and are powerful constrictors. With *Thamnophis* and *Natrix,* the Garter and Water Snakes, the food consists almost entirely of cold-blooded prey, including earthworms, tadpoles, frogs, toads and fish, and such snakes have no power of constriction. The Hog-nosed Snakes, *Heterodon,* feed largely on toads and occasionally upon frogs, but much prefer the former. They have no power of constriction.

Among the poisonous serpents, the Coral Snakes feed upon lizards and other snakes, the Copperhead upon frogs, rodents and birds, the Water Moccasin upon frogs, fishes, birds and sometimes other snakes, while the larger rattlesnakes largely confine their feeding to mammals and birds. The young of some of the desert Rattlesnakes eat lizards, while with the small rattlers of the Genus *Sistrurus* there is variance in selection of food as with the Copperhead Snake. With such powerful rattlesnakes as the adult Diamond-backs, of several kinds, I have not seen inclination to accept any food other than warm-blooded prey.

CHAPTER XI

The Nonpoisonous Western Snakes

CONTINUITY OF THE following descriptions indicates relationship of genera and follows the usual trend of formal, or scientific, listing. It will be noted that this sequence is quite different from that of the key of Chapter X. There, for purposes of gross identification, groupings were guided by selection of *smooth-scaled* forms, and *keeled-scaled* forms and these again were split into minor groups arranged as to size of the members with supplementary annotation relating to *coloration* or outstanding characters. Condensed *distribution* figured as an important point for deduction, which is often a main factor in "running down" identification among snakes.

THE BLIND SNAKES
Family *Leptotyphlopidae*

These are the most degenerate serpents of North America, about as thick as an orange stick and as a rule less than 12 inches long. The head is blunt and of the same width as the neck, the tail extremely short and blunt or about a twentieth the reptile's total length. The scales are smooth, with a high luster and the same above and beneath, there being no transverse abdominal plates. The eyes are imbedded under translucent shields and appear as mere dots, hence nearly useless except to distinguish light from darkness. These tiny snakes dig long tunnels underground and feed upon worms and small insects. They represent a family with numerous species in the New and Old World tropics, many of their kinds living in anthills.

Texas Blind Snake, *Leptotyphlops dulcis* (Baird and Girard)
  Size: 8 to 12 inches, with diameter a scant ¼ inch.

Form and scalation: Cylindrical and wormlike, with highly polished scales. Body encircled with overlapping scales, the scales of back and abdomen being similar.

Coloration: Lavender to reddish brown above; pinkish beneath. In a bright light the polished scales reflect an iridescent or silvery luster.

Distribution: The most eastern species of the Blind Snakes. From northern Mexico it extends into Texas, Oklahoma and Kansas and westward to New Mexico. It is rare in Oklahoma and Kansas.

Habits: Little is known. As a captive it burrows and hides. Specimens have been found during excavation work or occasionally aboveground after rains.

Mexican Blind Snake, *Leptotyphlops myopica* (Garman)

Size: Similar to preceding.

Form and Scalation: Similar to preceding. There is a slight difference in head plates, which, technically applied to *myopica,* are defined as "two upper labials in front of ocular plate." To trace such definition with a miniature among serpents requires a magnifying glass and keen knowledge of head-shield combinations. With the Blind Snakes, the ocular is the large shield through which the eye may be dimly seen. With *dulcis,* there is a simple plate, bordering the upper lip in advance of each ocular.

Coloration: Paler above than *dulcis;* whitish beneath.

Distribution: Mexico, but ranging over the border into southern New Mexico.

Habits: As with *dulcis,* little is known. The species is a secretive burrower.

California Blind Snake, *Leptotyphlops humilis humilis* (Baird and Girard)

Size: Similar to preceding.

Form and scalation: Similar to preceding, with exception of the top head plates. With *dulcis* and *myopica,* there is a pair of small plates separating the oculars from the row of scales that extend along the center of the back and terminate at the shield (rostral) that extends over the snout. With *humilis* these small shields (supraoculars) are absent, and the oculars, beneath which the eyes are imbedded, are in contact with the central row of dorsal scales.

Coloration: Pale lustrous brown, longitudinally banded or spotted with chocolate hue, the markings usually in seven rows.

Distribution: Southern California from the coast to and including the mountains.

Desert Blind Snake, *Leptotyphlops humilis cahuilae* Klauber
Size: Typical of the Blind Snakes.
Form and scalation: Similar to the typical form but having a higher dorsal scale count.
Coloration: Pale, lustrous brown, with five moderately indicated bands or rows of spots.
Distribution: Colorado and Yuma deserts of California and Arizona.
Habits: Laurence M. Klauber, who has added much to the knowledge of the western reptiles, writes about the habits of western Blind Snakes:*

"*L. humilis* seems to prefer stony ground rather than sandy areas. It must be largely subterraneous, although the fact that two specimens have been found crushed by automobile traffic on the highway would indicate that it occasionally travels abroad. Most of the specimens brought to the San Diego Zoological Society during the past eight years were found under stones or during the course of excavations. . . .

"This snake when aboveground seems to progress with less lateral undulations than do other snakes. On smooth surfaces it attempts to employ the tail spine to aid in its motion. When placed in loose or sandy soil, it burrows immediately. It is never peaceful or quiet when aboveground, but continually searches for something in which to burrow; it is therefore difficult to photograph."

Another subspecies, *L. humilis slevini* Klauber, inhabits the Cape Region of Lower California.

THE DWARF BOAS
Family *Boidae*

These miniatures, of a family containing the largest snakes of the American tropics, occur in North America to the number of three species. Two are confined to the Pacific region; the third (*Charina*)

Transactions of the San Diego Natural History Society, Vol. 6, No. 23, July 1931.

ranges eastward to Wyoming. The scalation is small and fine, the scales relatively much smaller and more numerous than with the Colubrids, or typical harmless snakes. Also, the plates of the abdomen are reduced in transverse width, while the plates under the tail are undivided. *The pupil is elliptic,* the body stout, with blunt tail.

Rosy Boa, *Lichanura roseofusca roseofusca* (Cope)
Size: Attains length of a yard, which is above the average. An example of that size would be about an inch in diameter, with tail about 4 inches long.
Form and scalation: Stout and heavy-bodied with quite stubby tail. Scalation of body very fine, almost granular. Head with irregular scales.
Coloration: Bluish gray or brownish gray above, with traces of three lengthwise, but irregular, stripes. Abdomen red or yellowish, mottled with brown.
Distribution: Southern California, west of the mountains; northern Lower California.
Habits: A very quiet and timid snake, seldom attempting to bite, but rolling into compact loops in which it hides its head when handled. The writer has induced them to take young rodents.

Desert Rosy Boa, *Lichanura roseofusca gracia* Klauber
Size: Dimensions similar to preceding, as is form and scalation.
Coloration: Body hue similar to preceding, but there are three evenly defined reddish stripes from nose to tail.
Distribution: Desert regions of southeastern California and western Arizona.

Three-lined Boa, *Lichanura trivirgata* Cope
Size, form and scalation, similar to *roseofusca.*
Coloration: Pale yellow or light brown, with three vividly defined dark brown or reddish stripes from snout to tail. The dorsal band is about 4 scales wide and those on each side about 5 scales wide, the bands separated by spaces $3\frac{1}{2}$ scales in width.
Distribution: Southern Lower California. It is possible that this is no more than a subspecies of *roseofusca* of more northern distribution.

Rubber Boa, "Two-headed" Snake, Silver Snake, *Charina bottae* (Blainville)

Size: A good-sized adult is 20 inches long, with diameter of ¾ inch; tail 2½ inches long.

Form and scalation: Very stout, with tail almost as blunt as head. Body scales smooth, polished and small. Forward portion of head with fair-sized shields.

Coloration: Bluish gray or brownish gray, with no markings. Abdomen yellowish and immaculate.

Distribution: The Pacific region from Washington through California and eastward into Montana, Idaho and Wyoming; Nevada and Utah. This includes the most northward range of any New or Old World member of the *Boidae.*

Habits: As a captive this is a very quiet snake, but not particularly timid. It submits to handling without nervous actions. If much disturbed, it may roll the body into compact loops like a ball, hiding the head in the center of its folds. It is more contented if provided with means to hide and will burrow into sand. It prefers small rodents and constricts them in the same manner as large members of the *Boidae.*

THE COLUBRINE SNAKES
Family *Colubridae*

Under this grouping is the great majority of the nonvenomous serpents of North America. Sizes range from less than a foot in length to an excess of eight feet. Scales may be smooth or heavily keeled, and coloration and pattern show great variety. A number of the species are of high economic value in rodent control.

Worm Snake, *Carphophis amoena vermis* (Kennicott)

Size: Very small. A 10-inch adult is ¼ inch in diameter.

Form and scalation: Moderately stout, scales smooth and lustrous; opalescent. Head not distinct, with pointed snout. The eyes are very small.

Coloration: Purplish black or dark brown above; pink beneath.

Distribution: Missouri to eastern Nebraska, southward through Arkansas, Kansas and eastern Oklahoma to Texas.

Habits: See **Worm Snake,** Chapter V.

THE RING-NECKED SNAKES
Genus *Diadophis*

Several Mississippi Valley forms of these small snakes extend west-ward into Missouri, Kansas, Arkansas, Oklahoma and Texas. Also, there are typically western species. To clarify the races encroaching from the East, a supplementary key of these forms is helpful:

I. Bluish black, dark gray or olive; a bright yellowish ring at base of head. Abdomen with or without a row or rows of black spots.

a. Abdomen with or without a single row of black spots:
Eastern Ring-necked Snake, *Diadophis punctatus edwardsii* (Merrem).
Distribution: Eastern United States to Wisconsin, thence southward through Missouri and into Arkansas.

b. Abdominal spots numerous, often in two jagged rows:
Prairie Ring-necked Snake, *Diadophis punctatus arnyi* (Kennicott).
Distribution: Western Illinois, Iowa, Missouri, Kansas, Arkansas and Oklahoma to Texas.

c. Abdominal spots thickly massed and irregular:
Mississippi Ring-necked Snake, *Diadophis punctatus stictogenys* Cope.
Distribution: Mississippi Valley into Missouri and Arkansas and southward to Texas.

The typically Western Ring-necked Snakes follow in outline or supplementary key to denote the several forms. All are characterized by body of monotone hue above, smooth scales with fair luster and yellow or reddish ring at base of head, which may be slightly broken above and vary from 1 to 4 scales wide. The abdomen is yellow, pink or of coral hue. The maximum length of Pacific forms is about 20 inches, which is well above the average. The southwestern forms of *regalis* occasionally attain a length of 24 inches.

PACIFIC FORMS

I. *Neck ring prominent*

Neck ring often broken above. Abdominal hue extending upward up ½ to 1½ scale row. Abdomen with black spots:
> **Pacific Ring-necked Snake,** *Diadophis amabilis amabilis* (Baird and Girard).

Distribution: California, in the regions about San Francisco and the San Joaquin and Sacramento valleys.

Neck ring usually complete. Abdominal hue covering 1½ to 2 of the lower rows of scales. Abdomen lightly spotted:
> **Van Denburgh's Ring-necked Snake,** *Diadophis amabilis vandenburghi* Blanchard.

Distribution: Ventura to Santa Cruz County, California.

Neck ring wide, usually 1½ to 3 scales, and unbroken. Abdominal hue covering 1½ to 2½ rows of scales. Abdomen but lightly spotted:
> **Northwestern Ring-necked Snake,** *Diadophis amabilis occidentalis* Blanchard.

Distribution: Sonoma County, California, northward to the Columbia River.

Neck ring broad, usually reddish. Abdomen lightly spotted or immaculate:
> **Coral-bellied Ring-necked Snake,** *Diadophis amabilis pulchellus* (Baird and Girard).

Distribution: Western slopes of the mountains from southern Oregon to central California.

Neck ring usually complete. Abdominal hue only encroaching upward into the lower row of scales. Abdomen strongly spotted:
> **San Bernardino Ring-necked Snake,** *Diadophis amabilis modestus* (Duméril and Bocourt).

Distribution: San Bernardino Mountains, Los Angeles County and Santa Catalina Island, California.

Neck ring usually complete. Abdominal hue barely encroaching into the lower row of scales:

Southern California Ring-necked Snake, *Diadophis amabilis similis* Blanchard.

Distribution: Southwestern San Bernardino County, California and northern Lower California.

SOUTHWESTERN FORMS

II. *Neck ring fairly prominent or obscure*

Neck ring present, 2 – 4 scales wide. Bluish gray above, yellow or reddish beneath with numerous black spots:

Arizona Ring-necked Snake, *Diadophis regalis arizonae* Blanchard.

Distribution: Arizona and northern Mexico.

Neck ring obscure; sometimes absent:

Southwestern Ring-necked Snake, *Diadophis regalis regalis* (Baird and Girard).

Distribution: Central Texas, New Mexico, Arizona, southern Utah; northern Mexico.

Habits: All of the Ring-necked Snakes are quite similar in habits. As a rule they prefer rather damp, shaded places and during the day hide under flat stones or loose bark. Their food consists largely of earthworms and salamanders. All are egg-laying (oviparous). Their eggs contain well-developed young and hatch more quickly than with other oviparous species, often in less than a month's time. See **Ring-necked Snake,** Chapter V.

THE HOG-NOSED SNAKES, HISSING "ADDERS"
Genus *Heterodon*

These thick-bodied snakes, of fair size, wide head, sharply upturned snout and strong markings are quite unmistakable. Their unusual make-up is intensified by habits of greatly extending the neck and head and hissing when frightened, a combination unique among North American serpents. One species extends from the Atlantic seaboard through the states of the Mississippi basin to Minnesota. Another is typically western, ranging from the prairie states through the Great Plains and southward to Arizona and Mexico.

Eastern Hog-nosed Snake, Spreading "Adder," Flat-headed "Adder," Hissing "Adder," Puff "Adder," *Heterodon contortrix* (Linnaeus)

Size: Heavy-bodied, commonly $2\frac{1}{2}$ feet long and over an inch in diameter. Examples a yard long are not rare. A 3-foot specimen is $1\frac{1}{2}$ inch in thickness.

Form and scalation: In proportion to length this is an exceptionally thick-bodied snake. The head is wide and distinct, the snout sharp and upturned. When the snake is angry, the head and neck are excessively flattened, producing sinister aspect. The scales are keeled.

Coloration: Colors and markings are variable, but the commoner hues are yellowish or brown with dark brown or black irregular blotches, which may form crossbands or be broken into three series of markings. Some specimens have bright shades of yellow or brick red, these particularly evident on the anterior portion. Occasional specimens are slaty gray or entirely black. *With the average specimen the abdomen is mostly yellowish.*

Distribution: The eastern United States to Minnesota, thence southward through the states on the western side of the Mississippi River to Texas.

Habits: See **Hog-nosed Snake,** Chapter V.

Western Hog-nosed Snake, *Heterodon nasicus nasicus* Baird and Girard

Size: Similar to preceding.

Form and scalation: Snout more sharply upturned than preceding.

Coloration: Pale brown or straw color, with a series of closely set darker blotches along the back, and two rows of smaller, alternating spots on sides, the effect being a spotted pattern. *Abdominal coloration is important, as there is a wide area of black covering the central portion.*

Distribution: The prairie states and Great Plains to Montana, thence through all states southward to Texas and Arizona, northern Mexico. In western Texas, southern New Mexico, southern Arizona and northwestern Mexico there is a form designated as *H. nasicus kennerlyi* (Kennicott).

Habits: Similar to preceding. The principal food is toads, although immature specimens appear to feed upon small lizards.

THE GREEN SNAKES
Liopeltis and *Opheodrys*

These are characteristic snakes, hence unmistakable in identification, as both are uniform, bright leaf green above, a coloration not matched by other North American snakes. They are of small to moderate size. The two species are likewise readily determinable, one having smooth and the other strongly keeled scales. Both have wide distribution in the eastern United States and extend well into the West.

Smooth Green Snake, *Liopeltis vernalis* (Harlan)

The author cannot become reconciled to the recent placing of this species in the same genus as the Keeled-scaled Green Snake. Not alone is the scalation very different, but relative body thickness and tail length are at great variance.

Size: Greatest length about 20 inches, but average size is not much over a foot with diameter of ¼ inch.

Form and scalation: Of relative, moderate thickness; the scales smooth, with satiny luster.

Coloration: Uniform pale grass green above and whitish beneath. Just before shedding the skin, the body hue may appear grayish green or bluish. Very young examples are olive or bluish green.

Distribution: Ranges from a wide eastern habitat westward to North Dakota, thence southwestward through Colorado to New Mexico and Texas, with occurrence in all states to the eastward.

Habits: Insectivorous snakes, which are not persistent burrowers, are in the minority, but the Smooth Green Snake appears to feed mostly upon insects, preferring soft-bodied larvae, crickets, grasshoppers and spiders. It is most frequently found in wild meadows, but occurrence is "spotty." It is common in some areas, but not to be found in others that appear equally favorable. It is oviparous, depositing rather a small number of much elongated eggs.

Keeled Green Snake, *Opheodrys aestivus* (Linnaeus)

Size: Larger than the Smooth Green Snake. The length is from

2 – 3 feet, but one of the latter dimensions would be less than ½ inch in diameter.

Form and scalation: Extremely slender, with excessively long tail which may exceed a third of the total length. Scales roughly keeled.

Coloration: Uniform pale, bright green above and bright yellow beneath.

Distribution: A much more southern reptile than the Smooth Green Snake. From its eastern range it crosses the Mississippi Valley at the approximate latitude of southern Illinois, thence extends to Kansas and southwestward to New Mexico, with occurrence in the entire area eastward of the boundaries outlined.

Habits: See **Keeled Green Snake,** Chapter V.

THE RACERS AND WHIP SNAKES

Two genera are under consideration, *Coluber* and *Masticophis,* the latter particularly elongate, slender and extremely active.

Blacksnake, Black Racer, *Coluber constrictor constrictor* (Linnaeus)

Size: A large specimen is about 6 feet long and slightly over 1 inch in diameter. 4 – 5 feet is the average length.

Form and scalation: Relatively slender, with head but slightly distinct. Scales smooth, with luster like a gun barrel—satiny.

Coloration: Satiny black above, black or dark slaty gray beneath. A more or less evident patch of white on the chin, sometimes extending to the throat.

Young specimens are gray, with brownish blotches, these more prominent anteriorly. They become quite black when about 2 feet long.

Distribution: Eastern United States and crossing the Mississippi Valley, but not far beyond the longitude of Iowa, thence southward. Westward of this range it intergrades with the Blue Racer, a subspecies of dull olive or bluish-green hue, with yellowish abdominal hue.

Habits: See **Blacksnake, Black Racer,** Chapter V.

Blue Racer, Green Racer, Yellow-bellied Racer, *Coluber constrictor flaviventris* (Say)

Size: Usually smaller than the typical form (preceding). Average $3\frac{1}{2} - 4\frac{1}{2}$ feet long, but occasionally to 6 feet.

Form and scalation: Form similar to the Blacksnake. Scales smooth, with satiny luster.

Coloration: Bluish green, pale or dark olive above. Abdomen yellow, with chin and throat of paler yellow; upper labial plates yellow.

Very young specimens have strong dorsal blotches.

Distribution: The Mississippi Valley states and ranging through Iowa to the Great Plains, thence southward to New Mexico and Texas.

Habits: Similar to the typical form—the Blacksnake. Its diet includes lizards, and young specimens eat grasshoppers.

Western Blue Racer, *Coluber constrictor mormon* (Baird and Girard)

Size: Smaller than the Blue Racer of central and southwestern parts.

Coloration: Similar to the preceding. Its standing as a subspecies is not strong, and it appears to overlap *flaviventris* in the Southwest. However, it extends the range of its species from coast to coast.

Distribution: Southern British Columbia to California and eastward to Montana, Idaho, Nevada and Utah.

Habits: The food includes lizards, other snakes and grasshoppers, also small rodents.

Coachwhip Snake, *Masticophis flagellum flagellum* (Shaw)

Size: A large specimen will be about 7 feet long, with greatest diameter of about $1\frac{1}{4}$ inch. $4-5$ feet is the usual run of western examples.

Form and scalation: Although a long and hence impressively large snake, the form is very slender, a 5-foot specimen being barely an inch in diameter. The scales are smooth and almost lusterless.

Coloration: Body coloration varies according to areas. In the lower Mississippi Valley states the common coloration is blackish anteriorly and pale brown or gray on the posterior half. Some specimens are thus very striking, being sooty black anteriorly and very pale posteriorly. Some are mostly satiny black with exception of the tail. Westward there is more tendency to brown, gray or dull olive. Young specimens are of rather pale hue and strongly blotched.

Distribution: Eastern states from about the latitude of Virginia westward along similar latitude to the Rockies. Southward to northern New Mexico, with occurrence in all states to the eastward, with intergradation with the not greatly dissimilar *flavigularis,* which extends the range of the species through Texas and into Mexico.

Habits: See Coachwhip Snake, Chapter VIII.

Blotched Coachwhip Snake, Prairie Whipsnake, *Masticophis flagellum flavigularis* (Hallowell)

Size: Up to 6 feet in Texas, but more commonly about 4 – 5 feet in other parts of its range.

Form and scalation: Similar to the typical form.

Coloration: Greenish gray to pale brown from head to tail, with more or less evident large and quite widely separated darker blotches, these stronger anteriorly.

Distribution: Kansas and Colorado, southward through Oklahoma and eastern New Mexico through Texas to Mexico. Texas examples are the more strongly marked.

Habits: Similar to the typical form—extremely active and feeding upon small rodents, birds, lizards, other snakes and amphibians. Immature specimens eat grasshoppers.

Red Racer, Red Whipsnake, *Masticophis flagellum frenatum* (Stejneger)

Size: Smaller than the preceding forms, usually 3 – 5 feet long.

Form and scalation: Body very slender; tail very long. Scales smooth, with dull luster.

Coloration: Pale reddish brown. Many of the scales have darker tips, and some are narrowly margined with pink. The anterior part is crossed by narrowly separated dark bands, these not very distinct. They represent partial retention of juvenile pattern. Abdomen mostly pink, which may be mixed with yellow or clouded with gray. The pink abdomen is quite different from the dull whitish undersurface of the related (preceding) forms.

Distribution: The southwestern region, often in desert areas. Nevada, Utah, Arizona and southern parts of California; ranging into northern Mexico.

Habits: Extremely active and fast in movement. The food includes lizards.

Pink-bellied Racer, Pink-bellied Whipsnake, *Masticophis piceus* (Cope)

Size: 3½ – 4 feet long.

Form and scalation: Very slender, with long tail. Scales smooth and satiny.

Coloration: Uniform dark reddish brown to satiny blue black above. Pink or pinkish red beneath.

Differs from the Red Racer (preceding) by much darker body hue and, in adults, absence of anterior dorsal blotches.

Distribution: Southern Arizona and Lower California.

Habits: A very active, desert reptile.

Banded Racer, Banded Whipsnake, *Masticophis lateralis* (Hallowell)

Size: 3 – 4 feet long.

Form and scalation: Moderately slender. Scales smooth, with satiny luster.

Coloration: Dark brown or black, with a single yellow stripe on each side extending from neck to tail. On brown examples the pale stripes are narrowly margined with black. Abdomen yellow with dark blotches under chin and throat. Upper lip plates (labials) yellow.

Distribution: Southern California and Lower California.

Habits: Inhabits dry, sterile areas, and is extremely active.

Half-striped Racer, Arizona Whipsnake, *Masticophis semilineatus* (Cope)

Size: 3 – 5 feet.

Form and scalation: Very slender, with long, tapering tail. Eyes relatively large. Scales smooth and without luster.

Coloration: Reddish brown to dark brown with three to four dark to blackish stripes on the sides. The body hue between these stripes is paler than on the back, hence it may be difficult with some examples to determine whether the pattern consists of pale or dark stripes. The striped or banded pattern continues only half the length of the body, when it fades out.

Distribution: Arizona; northern Mexico.

Habits: A desert species and extremely active.

Striped Racer, Striped Whipsnake, *Masticophis taeniatus taeniatus* (Hallowell)

Size: 3 – 5 feet.

Form and scalation: Very slender; tail long; eyes large. Scales smooth and satiny.

Coloration: Dark brown to blackish on back, paler on sides, which may be yellowish, with a black line extending through the center of each scale, this interruption of ground hue and yellow edges of scales imparting the appearance of narrow black and yellow lines. The black-yellow-striped aspect of the sides is most pronounced anteriorly. Posteriorly there is usual reduction to a single streak of pale hue towards the tail. The head is dark, usually with a white spot in front and behind the eyes.

Distribution: Quite broadly distributed in the Southwest, including southeastern California, Utah, western Colorado, Nevada, Arizona, New Mexico and western Texas.

Habits: I have seen these snakes in the deserts of southeastern California, roaming during the day in excessively high temperature. They rapidly glide from one clump of sagebrush to another and when pursued over the sand outdistance a man in running. The collector, under such conditions, is hampered by yielding footing, but I am convinced that these snakes can glide about as fast as a man can run.

Girard's Whipsnake, *Masticophis taeniatus girardi* (Stejneger and Barbour)

Size, form and scalation: Similar to the typical form (preceding).

Coloration: Dark bluish brown or pitch black along the back. A bright yellow line follows the lower half of the first row of scales above the abdominal plates and the edge of the abdominal plates. Above this is another covering the fourth row of scales and the edges of the row above and beneath it. The effect is of satiny black with two vividly defined stripes of pale yellow or yellowish white. With brownish examples the anterior portion may have dark transverse blotches, imparting combination of transverse and longitudinal markings.

Distribution: Western Texas; northern Mexico.

Ruthven's Racer, *Masticophis taeniatus ruthveni* Ortenburger

Size: Similar to preceding.

Form and scalation: Typical of the Whipsnakes.

Coloration: Described as:

"Olive gray anteriorly, changing to reddish brown on the posterior portion. These hues may be darker. A constant character consists of yellow anterior edges of the dorsal scales, which is very evident when the skin is distended. The abdomen is yellowish anteriorly, changing to bluish gray on the middle third and pinkish or light reddish on the posterior portion. With the adult there may be faint traces of stripes on the neck, but these become obscure along the body. The chin and upper labials are yellowish white." (Ortenburger.)

Distribution: Extreme southeastern Texas and Mexico.

Schott's Racer, Banded Whipsnake, *Masticophis taeniatus schotti* (Baird and Girard)

Size: 3 – 4 feet long.

Form and scalation: Body slender; head long and narrow. Scales smooth and satiny.

Coloration: Dark gray or olive to blackish, with two yellowish-white stripes on lower sides, the first along the lower row of scales, the upper covering junction or edges of 3rd and 4th rows. The lower stripe is margined above with black, the upper margined with black on each side, producing the effect of two dark bands enclosing a pale stripe. The pale stripes fade toward the posterior portion.

Scales along the back often narrowly margined with yellow, which is evident when the body is distended. Abdomen yellow or pinkish, with some examples showing tinge of red along sides.

Distribution: Southern Texas; northeastern Mexico.

Lower California Whipsnakes: Four species are restricted to Lower California and islands adjacent to the coast. Their characters are outlined:

No stripes. Dark brown anteriorly, paler posteriorly. Scattered dark scales on sides:

Clarion Island Whipsnake, *Masticophis anthonyi* (Stejneger).*

Distribution: Clarion Island, off the west coast of Mexico.

Body striped. Blackish brown becoming cream color on sides, with two dark stripes in the pale area:

Cape San Lucan Whipsnake, *Masticophis aurigulus* (Cope).

Distribution: Southern Lower California.

*Herewith listed, but barely entering the scope of this field book.

Body striped. Brownish or black with a single white stripe or band on each side:

Barbour's Whipsnake, *Masticophis barbouri* (Van Denburgh and Slevin).

Distribution: Espiritu Santo Island, off eastern coast of southern Lower California.

The following species is mostly tropical, but is said to extend into southwestern Texas:

Green Spotted Racer, *Drymobius margaritiferus* (Schlegel)

Size: 2½ to 3 feet.

Form and scalation: Moderately slender. Scales smooth and polished.

Coloration: An attractive species that may be recognized at a glance. It is black or dark brown, with a bright green or yellow spot in the center of each scale. While the spotting is similar to that of the king snakes to be found along the boundary, the effect is more vivid, while this is a much more slender and active snake.

Distribution: Extending northward from South America, Central America and Mexico into extreme southwestern Texas. It represents a tropical genus of about a dozen species. Its occurrence in Texas appears to be rare and collectors in the boundary region have sought to establish additional records. It is one of the collector's prizes in clarifying extension of distribution of tropical kinds.

Habits: The writer has often seen this snake in Panama, but its excessive activity and rush through tick-infested vegetation has resulted in escape of most specimens. Captives have thrived and elicited interesting remarks because of the unique and attractive markings. They preferred frogs to other food.

THE GENERA *DRYMARCHON, SALVADORA* AND *PHYLLORHYNCHUS*

Blue Bull Snake, Mexican Rat Snake, *Drymarchon corais melanurus* (Deméril and Bibron)

Size: One of the longest of the North American snakes. Maximum length about 8 feet. A 7-foot specimen is approximately 2 inches in diameter.

Form and scalation: A powerfully built snake with smooth and polished scales, the head fairly distinct.

Coloration: The western form, occurring in southern and southwestern Texas, has considerable olive or dull brown on the upper portion. There is no body pattern, but the posterior portion is usually quite black. Usually a considerable portion of the undersurface is dull orange or yellow.

The wide distribution and color variation of this big snake is particularly interesting. The typical form inhabits tropical South America, over a wide area, including the Amazon Valley. Here it grows to be close to 10 feet in length, is lustrous blue black anteriorly and golden yellow posteriorly, a quite startling combination as it swiftly glides through the jungle. In its range northward through the Central American countries there are color variants, some clay color, with black-edged scales. The particularly handsome and uniform lustrous blue-black form of the Southeast has already been described under the head of **Indigo** or **Gopher Snake,** in Chapter VIII. It ranges into eastern Texas.

Distribution: The Blue Bull Snake, herewith designated as a form of the *corais* group, intergrades with the eastern Indigo Snake, *Drymarchon corais couperi,* in the area of the lower Rio Grande, is well defined in southern Texas, thence extends through Mexico into Central America.

Habits: As I have observed both the North American and tropical forms of *corais* and can see no marked difference in habits, the reader is referred to notes on the **Indigo Snake** in Chapter VIII.

Banded Flat-nosed Snake, Patch-nosed Snake, *Salvadora grahamiae grahamiae* Baird and Girard

Size: Size moderate, possibly attaining a length of close to a yard. An example, however, that is clearly adult measures 2 feet 4 inches in length, with greatest diameter of $\frac{1}{2}$ inch.

Form and scalation: Moderately stout; head but slightly distinct from neck. Snout blunt and square owing to enlarged development of rostral shield, which is in the form of a patch, straight across the anterior part and extending backward in triangular outline. Body scales smooth.

Coloration: A wide yellowish band on central part of back from head to tail. This is about 3 scales wide and bordered by a dark brown or olive band of about the same width. Beneath the brown band to edges of the abdominal plates the scales are pale brown to olive. Yellow beneath.

There is variation in the pattern. The brown bands may be more or less distinct, or broken into rows of dark blotches. The dorsal band, however, remains distinct and of quite constant width. The upper labial or lip plates are yellow.

Distribution: Texas, New Mexico and Utah, ranging well into Mexico. It is common along the boundary of the United States.

Habits: Quite active, part of its food consisting of lizards.

Arizona Flat-nosed Snake, Arizona Patch-nosed Snake, *Salvadora grahamiae hexalepis* (Cope)

Size, form and scalation: Similar to the preceding.

Coloration: This form has bands slightly wider than *grahamiae* and is defined as having "a second inferior ocular plate formed from the summit of the fourth superior labial plate, so that the fifth only enters the orbit." It extends its species into the desert regions of Arizona and eastern California, and like most desert reptiles its hues are rather pallid and faded.

The **Chaparral Patch-nosed Snake,** *Salvadora grahamiae virgultea* Bogert, carries the range of *grahamiae* from the desert to the Pacific coast and to Lower California. Its body hue is much darker, often blackish, making the dorsal band appear very distinct, somewhat like that of a west coast garter snake, but the blunt rostral or nose shield is a distinguishing character.

Brown's Flat-nosed Snake, Leaf-nosed Snake, *Phyllorhynchus browni* Stejneger

Size: Small—not much over 12 inches.

Form and scalation: Moderately stout; head but little distinct, scales on the anterior portion faintly keeled, but appearing smooth unless examined with a glass. On the posterior portion the carination is fairly distinct. Tail short; about one eighth the total length.

The head is quite unique, short, thick and chunky, the eyes very large *with elliptic pupils.* The rostral or plate on the snout is greatly developed—far more so than with *Salvadora.* It appears as if it were patched on and curls over the snout in size and character to produce an abnormal appearance. Another rare character among North American colubrine snakes is a row of small scales between the upper labials and the orbit—best seen with a glass with this small species.

So far as I can recall, this genus and *Hypsiglena* contain the only North American colubrine snakes without rear fangs, which have elliptic pupils.

Coloration: Dull white or pale yellow, with about 15 brown blotches on the back, which are paler in the middle. White beneath.

Distribution: Southern Arizona.

Habits: Nothing appears to be known, except that it is a desert reptile.

Southwestern Leaf-nosed Snake, *Phyllorhynchus decurtatus decurtatus* (Cope)

Size: Small, slightly exceeding 15 inches. Tail short—less than $\frac{1}{10}$ the total length.

Form and scalation: Moderately stout. Differs from the preceding *in having smooth scales.*

Coloration: Whitish or pale yellow, with about 30 dark blotches on back and one or two rows of spots on the sides.

The greater number of dorsal blotches serve as a character distinguishing *P. decurtatus* from the related *P. browni,* to which in addition it has one or two rows of spots on the sides.

Distribution: Southern Nevada, southwestern Arizona, southern California and Lower California.

To within a few years ago these Leaf-nosed Snakes were thought to be very rare. But few specimens were in collections of museums. It is now known that they are common in a number of areas, but being nocturnal are not often observed or collected. The automobile and its headlights have changed the technique of reptile observation, particularly of the nocturnal snakes of the deserts. Laurence M. Klauber, in a Bulletin of the Zoological Society of San Diego, Number 12, September 1935, states that but few specimens of *browni* or *decurtatus* had in past years been in the collections of scientific institutions. Recently, over 165 specimens, mostly of *decurtatus,* are at hand, and previously known ranges have been greatly extended.

In his article about the Leaf-nosed Snakes, Klauber describes a new subspecies, *P. decurtatus perkinsi,* characterized by high ventral scale count and small, widely separated body blotches. Its range is described as widespread through the deserts of California and Nevada.

THE RAT SNAKES
Genus *Elaphe*

An important grouping of ten large North American species and related forms. All have more or less feebly keeled scales. They are strong constrictors, and egg-laying, or oviparous. Snakes of this genus are of economic value owing to rodent-eating habits.

Fox Snake, *Elaphe vulpina* (Baird and Girard)
Size: 4 – 5 feet; exceptionally 6 feet.

Form and scalation: Stoutest of the Rat Snakes. The tail is particularly stout and tapers abruptly to a sharp point. The scales are distinctly keeled.

Coloration: Pale brown or yellowish with large, rich brown blotches along the back and row of smaller, alternating blotches on each side. Beneath the lateral row, close to margin of abdominal plates, is a yet smaller series of blotches, or dark spots. Abdomen yellow, with dusky spots or blotches. *There are usually no headbands;* if present they are obscure. Sides of the head usually tinged with orange yellow or red.

Distribution: This species crosses into the western section of the continental map by entering the states of South Dakota (southeastern portion), Minnesota, Iowa and Nebraska. Burt defines it as "a typical inhabitant of the rolling prairie habitat that is so characteristic of the upper Mississippi River Basin (above the Missouri river system)."

Habits: Compared with other species of *Elaphe* this is a ground snake, seldom ascending trees or bushes. Its food consists of rodents and birds, but largely the former. It is hardy as a captive. When first captured it emits a strong-smelling secretion from glands at base of the tail. The odor is like that of a fox, hence the common name. As a factor in rodent control and with habits that lead it into burrows in search of such prey, it is of high economic value and should everywhere be protected.

Emory's Rat Snake, Prairie Rat Snake, *Elaphe laeta* (Baird and Girard)
Size: Among average run of specimens, this is the smallest of the north American Rat Snakes, also it is the most proportionately slender. 3 – 4 feet long is a fair length. A very exceptional individual from

Kansas was 7 feet long. It was found along the margin of a railroad cut, in open, prairie country.

Form and scalation: Moderately stout. Scales so feebly keeled that only a few rows along the back show the faintest carinations on gross examination.

Coloration: Ashy gray, with brown or olive-brown blotches along the back, longer than wide, rather symmetrically oblong in outline, narrowly margined with black and separated by intervals of two to three scales. There are smaller, alternating blotches on the sides.

Head markings form a strong character for identification. A dark band extends from behind the eye past the angle of the mouth to the neck. There is a dark bar across the head in front of the eyes. These head markings readily separate this species from the Fox Snake, with which head markings are obscure or absent. The abdomen in *E. laeta* is yellowish with gray blotches.

Distribution: Western Missouri and Kansas, western Arkansas and Oklahoma, through Texas to central Mexico.

Habits: This prairie species, with habits of prowling into the burrows and nests of small rodents that are destructive in grain-cultivating areas, deserves recognition as of economic value and should be protected. It is a strong constrictor and hardy captive with gentle habits.

Pilot Blacksnake, Black Chicken Snake, *Elaphe obsoleta obsoleta* (Say)

Size: Attaining length up to 8 feet and diameter of 2 inches, although this is in excess of the average, which is 4 – 5 feet.

Form and scalation: Relatively stout, with indication of strength and weight, the head quite wide and distinct from neck. Scales polished, those of the dorsal surface feebly keeled.

Coloration: Shining black, but with tendency of scales to show white or red edges, which, when body is distended, indicate tracery of large dorsal and smaller lateral blotches. Abdomen gray, blotched with white.

May be confused with the Blacksnake or Black Racer, but the faintly keeled scales of the back, the *polished* scalation and white edges of the scales indicating body blotches, together with blotched underside, are characters for separation. Young specimens are gray and strongly blotched, and two subspecies, following this description of the typical form, substantiate these markings.

Distribution: Ranging widely through eastern North America and westward to Iowa, Missouri, Kansas, Oklahoma and Texas.

Habits: See **Pilot Blacksnake,** Chapter V.

Lindheimer's Rat Snake, Texas Rat Snake, *Elaphe obsoleta lindheimeri* (Baird and Girard)

Size: Similar to the typical form.

Form and scalation: A heavy-bodied and powerful constricting snake, with dorsal scales feebly keeled.

Coloration: With this Texas form the uniform blackish appearance gives way to a strongly blotched snake, owing to encroachment of yellow, orange or reddish hue around the borders of many scales, the black remaining as large dorsal saddles, with smaller dark rows along each side. The skin between the scales is brick red or yellow, farther accentuating a blotched pattern. I regard this form as subspecifically distinct from *E. obsoleta obsoleta.*

Distribution: Texas.

Habits: Similar to the typical form. A strong constrictor, feeding upon rodents and birds, but so specifically upon the former as to be of economic value and hence to be protected.

Gray Rat Snake, Gray Chicken Snake, *Elaphe obsoleta confinis* (Baird and Girard)

Size: Rather smaller than the two preceding forms. An adult slightly under 5 feet long is $1\frac{1}{4}$ inch in diameter.

Form and scalation: Relatively heavy-bodied. Scales of back feebly keeled.

Coloration: With this form the markings of the young are retained to maturity. The body hue is gray, with large, dark brown saddles along the back, these sending out longitudinal extensions from their corners to indicate H-shaped formation. There is a row of smaller blotches on the sides and, beneath, a smaller row near margin of the abdominal plates. Numerous scales show white edges, as with the typical form. Abdomen white, blotched and spotted with gray.

Distribution: South Atlantic to southern Mississippi Valley states, but recorded westward into the prairie country as far as Kansas, thence southward to eastern Texas.

Baird's Rat Snake, *Elaphe bairdi* (Yarrow)

Size: Similar to *E. laeta* (previously described).

Form and scalation: Moderately stout. Scales of the median dorsal rows so faintly keeled that carination is barely discernible. A technical point to be noted relates to the rear pair of chin shields, which are so small that they differ little in size from the general chin scalation.

Coloration: Has the largest number of dorsal blotches of any of the North American members of *Elaphe*. The body is brownish to gray, with row of narrow, transverse dark brown blotches to the number of about 80, becoming faint near the tail. There are smaller and fainter blotches on the sides. A dark bar extends across the head. While the pattern resembles that of *E. laeta* (preceding), the latter has not much in excess of 50 dorsal saddles—including tail markings.

Distribution: The range, as known, is restricted. The original specimens were collected near Fort Davis, fifty miles northwest of Presidio, Texas. Otherwise it is known only from Matagorda County, Texas. It remains as a prize for collectors to further investigate the extent of its range.

Habits: No definite observations appear to have been made.

Davis Mountain Rat Snake, *Elaphe subocularis* (Brown)

Size: Appears to attain large size—5 – 6 feet.

Form and scalation: Body quite stout; dorsal scales feebly keeled. Among North American Rat Snakes this species is unique in having small scales separating the orbit and upper lip plates—labials.

Coloration: Orange yellow on the forward portion, paler posteriorly. Occasional examples are yellowish gray. There is a row of rather square black blotches along the back, about 24 in number, which send forward and backward from their corners a narrow black band or line, each like a thick-stemmed H. There are obscure blotches on each side. Head yellow, with eyes quite large.

Distribution: Known from the Davis Mountains, southwest of Pecos, Texas. The area it inhabits appears to have been but little investigated by collectors. The species may range well into Mexico.

Habits: Dr. Arthur Erwin Brown, who named the species, sent me several immature specimens. Their ground color was pinkish and the blotches sooty black. They were fed mice and young birds, and as they grew their color changed to orange yellow, the blotches becoming less vivid. They spent most of their time in branches of a small tree.

Green Rat Snake, *Elaphe chlorosoma* (Günther)

Size: 4 – 5 feet.

Form and scalation: Form typical of *Elaphe.* There are but faint keeled scales on the central portion of back.

Coloration: There is no pattern. The general hue is olive or dull greenish. Numerous scales are black at the base, with upper and lower whitish edge when the body is distended. White beneath, without markings.

Distribution: Mexico, extending into the Santa Rita Mountains of Arizona.

Habits: Unrecorded.

Peninsula Rat Snake, *Elaphe rosaliae* (Mocquard)

Identification may be deducted by range. This appears to be the only species of *Elaphe* occurring in Lower California. It has been defined as "olive brown above, without markings, reddish beneath." The dorsal scales are very faintly keeled.

Distribution: Central and southern Lower California.

THE GENUS *ARIZONA*

Slender Gopher Snake, Sharp-nosed Gopher Snake, *Arizona elegans elegans* (Kennicott)

Size: Up to 3½ feet, and ¾ inch diameter. Tail moderately long; about 6 inches in a 3-foot specimen.

Form and scalation: A rather slender snake, with narrow head and depressed snout, producing a sharp and wedge- or scoop-shaped outline. Scales smooth and rather polished.

Coloration: Reddish yellow or pale gray, with rather faded central series of transverse darker blotches, about twice as transversely wide as long, usually edged with darker brown or black. One or two series of smaller blotches on side.

Distribution: Central Texas to New Mexico; northern Mexico.

Southwestern Slender Gopher Snake, Faded Snake, *Arizona elegans occidentalis* Blanchard

Size, form and scalation: Similar to the typical form.

Coloration: Less markedly defined than with the typical form. With typical *elegans* the dorsal blotches are seldom over 55 in number. With *A. e. occidentalis* they range from over 55 to 77. Technically defined, *A. e. elegans* has a scale count (obliquely around the body) of 29 to 31

rows. The subspecies *occidentalis* has a lesser number of scale rows—
27 or, occasionally, 29.

Distribution: The range defines identification of this form. It
occurs from southeastern Arizona to southern California and into
Lower California.

THE BULL SNAKES, WESTERN GOPHER SNAKES
Genus *Pituophis*

These are stout, strong-bodied constricting snakes of large size. All
of the western forms are yellowish in body hue, with darker dorsal
blotches. The head is of moderate width, the snout bluntly pointed.
These snakes have a habit of hissing when frightened, being provided
with an erectile filament in front of the breathing passage against
which air from the lungs is forcibly expelled. The farmer or rancher
who kills these snakes is exterminating beneficial types figuring in control or balance of rodents that are destructive to agriculture, particularly ground squirrels or spermophiles, sometimes called gophers, and
pouched rats, which are also called "gophers." Protection of economic
reptiles has been discussed, but little has been done. If protection
accorded to the smaller birds were extended to useful reptiles, more
practical considerations might be checked. Prejudice against "snakes"
has produced a picture poorly consistent with endeavors of agriculturists to carry on economically. It also includes destruction of hawks and
owls, many of which are of high economic value. There are workers of
the soil who understand and respect the wild denizens which prowl
their lands, but there are as many whose scant knowledge of the fauna
is dominated by legendary prejudice.

Bull Snake, Gopher Snake, Yellow Gopher Snake, *Pituophis*
sayi sayi (Schlegel)

Size: Up to 8 feet. Average length $4\frac{1}{2}$ to 5 feet. A 5-foot example is
$1\frac{1}{2}$ inch in diameter.

Form and scalation: A strong-bodied snake of moderately stout form.
Head fairly distinct. Snout bluntly pointed and projecting over lower
jaw. Scales of the back moderately keeled; those of the sides smooth
and polished.

Coloration: Straw color to orange or ruddy yellow, with series of large, rather square blotches of dark reddish brown or black along the back and smaller blotches of lighter shade along each side. When the skin is distended it will be seen to match the hue of the scales of the lighter areas, but may be reddish within the areas of the blotches. Head yellow, usually with dark band in front of eyes and a dark bar extending obliquely from behind the eye. The lip plates are bordered with black. Abdomen yellow with row of black blotches on each side.

There is considerable variation, some specimens having narrow red margins about the scales, with adjoining skin of the same bright hue.

Distribution: The prairie region and Great Plains. Eastward it extends into the prairies of western Wisconsin and Illinois. Northward it is recorded from Minnesota, thence in southward line it enters the drier portions of Missouri, Arkansas (western portion), Oklahoma, thence to Texas. From this eastern boundary it ranges northwestward through South Dakota to the Rockies, even extending into southern Canada. It occurs in all of the states to the southward, being particularly common and reaching its largest size in central and western Texas.

A subspecies, *affinis,* more heavily and darkly spotted on the sides, extends the range to Arizona, southern California and Lower California.

Habits: In an article listed as Contribution No. 79 from the Department of Zoology, Agricultural Experiment Station, Kansas State Agricultural College, Frederick L. Hisaw and Howard K. Gloyd enumerate habits of the present species under the title, "The Bull Snake as a Natural Enemy of Injurious Rodents." Among a number of points brought out, it is explained that the writers, while making a study of the pocket gopher (a burrowing rodent destructive to grain), noticed that several large bull snakes under observation had wounds or scars along the sides of their bodies which appeared to have been made by the teeth of rodents they had captured. This led to intensive observation of the feeding habits of this species. Extracts from the article read:

"As the gopher or rat passes, the reptile strikes it a savage blow, seizes it in its mouth and rapidly coils about it. The blow usually throws the victim off its feet and, as it turns on its side or back, the first coil of the snake's body is looped about it. Other coils are added in proportion to the size of the animal captured. . . . When satisfied that the victim is dead, the snake releases its hold, seeks the anterior end and begins swallowing.

"The bull snake is also an active and efficient burrower and apparently is able to capture burrowing rodents in their subterranean tunnels. In several instances burrows of the pocket gopher were found which had been opened from the outside. The excavated earth had been piled in concentric ridges. The animal responsible for this unusual circumstance was unknown until a bull snake was seen in the actual performance."

Speaking of indicated actions of Bull Snakes in underground burrows, as evidenced from observations of captive specimens, Hisaw and Gloyd continue:

"A snake is very sensitive to contact stimuli and in the dark recognizes prey very quickly by this means. If, when in the act of killing a victim by use of the coils, another animal comes in contact with the snake's body, it is at once pressed against the side of the cage or constricted by another series of loops. A single snake has been known to kill as many as three half-grown rats in this way at one time."

The authors of this article made various tests in feeding captive Bull Snakes and figuring the weight in nourishment required by each snake during its period of activity between hibernation intervals and quiescent lapses preparatory to skin-casting—the weight of rodent food consumed applied against the weight of feeding reptile. The Bull Snakes were thus tabulated, and in a summary of the article it is explained:

"The average number of pocket gophers per acre of alfalfa of moderate infestation is about eight. A Bull Snake . . . about five feet long has the potentiality of destroying annually all of these animals on one and one-half acres. Pocket gophers are relatively large rodents, so it would be possible for the Bull Snake to eat many more individuals of a smaller species of mammal, and there is little doubt but that this snake is important as a natural check on the entire rodent population."

The article contains data from Mr. Percy L. De Puy, from work in connection with the United States Department of Agriculture, Bureau of Biological Survey, which estimates damage from the type of rodent that forms a large part of the food supply of adult Bull Snakes. Mr. De Puy's estimate of damage was based on several hundred answers to inquiries sent to farmers. The deduction was that two dollars and fifty cents per acre is a fair estimate of annual loss due to ravages of pocket gophers.

Pacific Bull Snake, Yellow Gopher Snake, *Pituophis catenifer catenifer* (Blainville)

Size: Smaller and lighter in form than the preceding. I have not seen a specimen in excess of 5 feet long. A $4\frac{1}{2}$-foot example is approximately $1\frac{1}{4}$ inch in diameter.

Form and scalation: Moderately stout, head proportionately rather small; snout pointed. Scales moderately keeled.

Coloration: Compared with the forms of *sayi* (preceding), this species has a much greater number of—hence more closely set—dorsal blotches. With the forms of *sayi* there are from 35 to 65 dorsal blotches. With *catenifer,* they average about 90, the blotches being rather square and symmetrical.

Body hue ranges from straw color to dull yellowish brown, reddish brown or blackish. There are obscure and smaller blotches on the sides. Abdomen yellow, with small dark blotches at the margins of the plates. The head is almost without marking.

Distribution: The typical form inhabits the Pacific region west of the Sierra Nevada, ranging from British Columbia to California.

P. catenifer annectens (Baird and Girard), with average lesser number of dorsal blotches (75) extends the range from the coastal region of southern California to northern Lower California.

P. catenifer deserticola Stejneger, of richer yellow, strongly defined and often reddish, black-bordered blotches and bright red skin between the scales, inhabits the deserts of Nevada, Utah and southeastern California, ranging northward to eastern Washington.

The intergrades between these forms of *catenifer* are often difficult to define, one way or the other. At the most, the subspecies are not strong, *deserticola* being the more evident, as an inhabitant of desert areas and having red skin between the scales.

Habits: Habits are typical of the genus and indicated in description of *P. sayi.* When angry, this snake, as with all species of *Pituophis,* will exhale air in a long and sharp hiss, made possible by voluntary raising of a cartilaginous filament in front of the breathing passage. It also vibrates the tail and, if in dry vegetation, produces a buzzing sound. It lays yellowish-white eggs, with tough, leathery integument. It is a powerful constrictor.

While its food includes birds and eggs of ground-nesting species, the prey consists largely of rodents, and this species, being of high economic value, should be protected. In the hay and grain belts where such snakes are to be found, ground squirrels, as well as other destructive rodents, are a serious factor in figuration of losses to agriculturists. This author, in many miles of motoring through California, has gone through planted sections where ground squirrels were so numerous that many were killed as they crossed the roads. With background like this it would seem that state- or county-issued booklets to farmers might serve as practical deterrent to the common practice of killing every snake to be found.

Lower California Gopher Snake, *Pituophis vertebralis* (Blainville)

Size, form and scalation: Similar to *P. catenifer;* the scales of the back, however, are faintly keeled, while those of the sides are smooth.

Coloration: Blotches less numerous than with *catenifer,* well separated and from 40 – 50 in number. From this pattern the species more resembles the southwestern form of *P. sayi,* but the head is unmarked, lacking the dark oblique band behind the eye of *P. sayi affinis,* which may overlap the range of *P. vertebralis* in northern Lower California.

Distribution: All of Lower California and extending northward into San Bernardino County, California.

Mexican Gopher Snake, *Pituophis deppei deppei* (Duméril and Bibron)

Size: Large—to 6 feet.

Form and scalation: Distinguished from other species of *Pituophis* by arrangement of the head plates, which are the average normal for North American nonvenomous snakes. With species of *Pituophis* other than *deppei* there are four prefrontals.

In simple terms this arrangement of head shields may be defined: In the center of the head is a large subtriangular shield called the frontal, and in front of this (with the usual run of head shields) is a pair termed the prefrontals. In front of these is a pair contacting the nostrils—the internasals. This is the head-shield arrangement of

P. deppei. With the other species of *Pituophis* there is a row of *four* prefrontals in advance of the large central shield (frontal). This is a positive character distinguishing *P. deppei* from *P. sayi* and *P. catenifer,* all of whose ranges overlap.

Coloration: The usual Bull or Western Gopher Snake pattern— yellow or yellowish brown with dorsal series of rather square dark blotches and a row of smaller blotches on sides.

Distribution: Mexican, but extending over the boundaries of western Texas, New Mexico, Arizona and southeastern California.

THE KING SNAKES
Genus *Lampropeltis*

This quite characteristic genus is of interest from points of distribution, radial differences between subspecies and typical forms, vivid and handsome markings, and habits. All have smooth scales, are constrictors and egg-layers. The western kinds range from small to moderate and quite large size.

The "Milk" Snake Group:

This is one of a grouping of related forms which scientists designate as "difficult" in defining or separating subspecies, owing to divergence of patterns and colors from the typical form, which is fair-sized, with large dorsal blotches of brown, reddish brown or olive. There are smaller blotches on the sides. The abdomen is white, boldly marked with black spots, which may indicate checkerboard pattern. This is *Lampropeltis triangulum triangulum,* commonly called the "Milk" Snake, Spotted "Adder" and House Snake. It ranges over eastern North America, with extension to the Carolinas and westward to Iowa. Throughout these boundaries its pattern is fairly constant, the only tendency being downward extension of the dorsal blotches. This form attains a length of slightly more than a yard.

Westward and southward great differences occur in pattern and size of this snake. Southward and westward of the range area approximately outlined, the related forms are smaller, with pattern of dorsal portion appearing ringed with red, yellow and black; with some the markings crossing the abdomen and encircling the body. Such western forms are commonly called Scarlet King Snakes and "Coral" Snakes.

A condensed list, to deduct comparison among these forms, appears to be the best approach to identification, plus checking of distribution, which may be a main point in plucking a troublesome specimen from doubt surrounding its identity.

A deductive list of the "Milk" Snakes follows:

Blotched pattern

Gray with strong, rounded brown, reddish or olive blotches, which are black-bordered. A series of smaller, alternating blotches on each side. The blotches extend down the sides to about the 5th, sometimes as low as the 4th or even 3rd row of scales above abdominal plates. With young specimens the blotches are usually very red and accentuated by the spaces between them being whitish or yellowish. Abdomen white, with square black spots. Moderately slender; head not distinct. Length to a yard or slightly more:

"Milk" Snake, House Snake, Checkered "Adder,"
Lampropeltis triangulum triangulum (Lacépède).

Distribution: Eastern North America, with western extension to Minnesota and Iowa in the north, but in the southern Mississippi states intergrading with red or ringed forms.

Gray or grayish yellow, with large reddish, sometimes reddish-brown, black-bordered blotches, which vary in extension to the 3rd, 2nd or 1st row of scales above abdominal plates. The wider the extension of blotches the more ringed appearance of the snake dorsally. From above this form may appear red or reddish brown with narrow, pale rings, bordered with narrower rings of black. There is usually a row of black spots on the sides. If the lateral spots contain red or brown, it is safe to assume that such specimens are intergrades between *triangulum* and *syspila*. Smaller than *L. triangulum triangulum*—rarely as much as 2 feet long:

Red "Milk" Snake, *Lampropeltis triangulum syspila* (Cope).

Distribution: Ohio to Iowa. Southward in the east to Tennessee and in the states immediately west of the Mississippi to Arkansas. The western extension includes Kansas and Oklahoma.

Ringed forms

With these forms, the red areas are bright, usually scarlet and extend to the edges or within the margins of the abdominal plates.

The anterior and posterior margins of black appear as black rings, not much narrower than the red areas, and separated by yellow or whitish rings—which are remaining traces of ground hue of the typical form and *syspila*. Some of the black, dorsal ringlike markings may cross the abdomen. The effect above is of a snake brightly ringed with scarlet, yellow and black. This results in a frequent name of "Coral" Snake, which may confuse these forms with the poisonous Coral Snakes of the extreme southward portion of this chapter's section. With exception of eastern Texas, Oklahoma, and southern Arizona and New Mexico, no poisonous Coral Snake occurs in any part of the western region. Size moderate, seldom as much as 24 inches:

Western "Milk" Snake, Ringed King Snake, "Coral" Snake, *Lampropeltis triangulum gentilis* (Baird and Girard).

Distribution: The western range extends obliquely from South Dakota to Utah and eastern Arizona, and general distribution may be gauged by records from Colorado, Nebraska, Kansas, Oklahoma, western Texas and northern Mexico.

Black rings predominating and reducing the red to narrow patches. 25 to 40 whitish rings. The black markings cross the abdomen as broad bands. Size rather small; average under 24 inches:

Mexican Ringed "Milk" Snake, "Coral" Snake, *Lampropeltis triangulum annulata* (Kennicott).

Distribution: Southeastern Texas and adjacent Mexico.

Vividly ringed with broad areas of scarlet, margined with black and separated by yellow, the pattern, including the red, usually encircling body. Differs from *gentilis* in more completely ringed pattern above and beneath, in sharply pointed head and smaller size—seldom exceeding 18 inches:

Cope's "Milk" Snake, Scarlet King Snake, "Coral" Snake, *Lampropeltis triangulum amaura* (Cope).

Distribution: Southeastern United States, with extension to Kansas, Oklahoma and Texas.

It might seem, after glancing through the preceding list of the "Milk" Snakes, or *triangulum* group, that the procession of forms indicates a phase of evolution taking place among snakes. The differences between the large and blotched *L. triangulum triangulum* of northern parts and the diminutive and brilliantly ringed *L. triangulum amaura* of southern habitat are great. Placed side by side, without smoothing intergrades to show relationship, they appear like entirely different species.

As the Western "Milk" Snake (*gentilis*), Cope's "Milk" Snake (*amaura*) and the Mexican Ringed "Milk" Snake (*annulata*) closely contact the ranges of the poisonous Coral Snakes (*Micrurus* and *Micruroides*) in the South and Southwest, and are commonly called "Coral" Snakes, a word about differentiation is important.

The ringed appearance and colors of both nonvenomous and poisonous kinds are strikingly similar, but with the species under consideration, there is unvariable difference in arrangement or combination of the rings. This may be outlined:

1. *With the harmless species, the red is margined or in contact with the black rings. 2. With the poisonous kinds the red is margined or in contact with the yellow rings.* Also, the harmless kinds usually have a reddish snout, while the poisonous kinds have a uniformly black snout.

Habits of the "Milk" Snakes: It will be noted that I have used quotes when the term of "Milk" Snake enters the text. The term has long been applied but is a gross misnomer. These snakes do not seek milk, and the presence of the larger forms around barns is prompted by search for small rodents. They are useful reptiles, but branded by silly legend. The habits of the larger, or typical, form are described in Chapter V—under **"Milk" Snake.** The smaller forms feed upon small snakes and lizards.

California Coral King Snake, *Lampropeltis zonatus* (Blainville)

Size: Moderate, average about 24 inches; occasionally approaching a yard in length.

Form and scalation: Moderately stout, head fairly distinct. Scales smooth and quite polished.

Coloration: This is another of the handsomely ringed members of its genus, but differs from the vividly marked forms of the *triangulum* group in being much larger, hence very striking. Moreover, it inhabits the Pacific region.

The pattern is quite symmetrical, consisting of 35 – 45 white or pale yellow rings, narrowly bordered with black, which separate brilliant red areas nearly equal to the width of combination of black and yellow. The red may be of lesser width with some specimens, but dominates the pattern. Abdomen similar to the upper hues, though the rings may be broken.

Distribution: Forested areas of California and Lower California. The similarly colored southwestern poisonous Coral Snake does not appear to contact the range of this species.

The author collected several of these snakes in the mountains of California. They were hiding under the loose bark of large fallen pines. They appeared to be quite rare, and each specimen was figured as quite a prize, startling as it was disclosed, like a handsome necklace, in the forest debris. I carried one specimen for a mile or more, not wanting to place it in a bag with some other snakes. It coiled about my hand and made no attempt to bite. My captive examples took young mice and other small snakes, but were diffident feeders.

Arizona Coral King Snake, *Lampropeltis pyromelana pyromelana* (Cope)

Size: An average-sized example is 30 inches long and ½ inch in diameter.

Form and scalation: Moderately stout; head fairly distinct. Scales quite polished.

Coloration: Body encircled with brick-red, white and black rings, the black rings bordering the red, or forming pairs to enclose the pale rings—the usual ringed king snake pattern.

Anteriorly, the red areas are about as wide as their marginal black rings, but in the central portion the black encroaches on the red, breaking it up or almost blotting it out in places and producing irregularity of pattern except for fairly symmetrical continuance of the white rings. The snout is usually white. The abdomen carries fair continuance of the dorsal markings.

This is a less symmetrically marked snake than the closely related Pacific ringed species (*zonatus*), although the effect of coloration is handsome and striking. It ranges into the habitat of the southwestern poisonous Coral Snake, which it resembles in coloration, but there is difference in combination of rings, which is defined in the summary of the *triangulum* group and ringed forms preceding.

Distribution: Utah, Arizona and northern Mexico.

Habits: Several captive specimens were gentle when handled. They took very young mice but were shy feeders.

Davis Mountain King Snake, *Lampropeltis alterna* (Brown)

Size: Moderate. Slightly in excess of 2 feet.

Form and scalation: Moderately stout; scales smooth and fairly polished.

Coloration: One of the ringed King Snakes, but with pattern differing from other species in its genus.

The ground color is slaty gray, crossed at intervals of 3 – 5 scales by ringlike bands of black, which are alternately wider and narrower, the wide ones covering from 2 – 3 scales on the middle of the back and more or less split on the top dorsal portion with scarlet. The narrower black bands (or rings) are about 1 scale wide. There are 19 red and black bands and an equal number of the alternating, narrow ones. The abdomen is grayish white, blotched with black and partially invaded by the black, ringlike bands from above.

Distribution: Known only from the Davis Mountains, Jeff. Davis County, Texas.

Habits: As yet unknown. This snake remains as a prize for further investigation of collectors.

Prairie King Snake, Blotched King Snake, Yellow-bellied King Snake, *Lampropeltis calligaster* (Harlan)

Size: Moderately large, up to 4 feet; more commonly $2\frac{1}{2}$ to 3 feet.

Form and scalation: Moderately stout; body quite cylindrical; head quite small and not distinct. Scales smooth with fair luster.

Coloration: Grayish, dull yellowish or olive brown with a dorsal series of (usually) quite prominent and rather symmetrical blotches about 8 scales wide (transversely) and about 3 scales long. These blotches are narrowly bordered with black and indented at front and rear. Beneath the dorsal blotches is a smaller, alternating row and beneath these a smaller row in touch with edges of the abdominal plates. The abdomen is yellow, with blotches of deeper yellow. With some specimens the abdominal hues are pinkish or pale red. There is a dark band across the forward part of the head and another from eye to the angle of the mouth, also an arrowheaded blotch covering the central and rear part of the head.

Strongly marked specimens might be confused with Emory's Rat Snake, *Elaphe laeta,* previously described. A positive correction, however, will be found in examination of the scales along the central part of the back. With *E. laeta* these top rows are keeled, quite faintly, but readily seen in a bright light. In the Prairie King Snake all the scales are smooth.

Variations: L. *calligaster* is subject to considerable variation. There is difference in intensity of the blotches which may come from suffusion of ground color with smoky hue. This suffusion is, in some examples, concentrated on the sides along the lateral blotches, producing a banded effect. Bandlike suffusion of black may be evident on the back, on each side of the dorsal blotches, and such specimens thus appear striped with black. Despite such suffusion with dark pigment, however, the pattern may be detected if the snake is examined in a good light. Young specimens are pale and strongly marked.

Distribution: Indiana to Minnesota, southward to include Iowa, Nebraska, Missouri, Arkansas, Kansas, Oklahoma and the greater part of Texas.

Habits: Burt, in an article about Kansas reptiles, notes about the Prairie King Snake: "Often found in pastures and along roadways, as well as about rock ledges, but they are not as abundant as the bull snakes."

From the author's experiences, this snake is delicate as a captive, as it is a poor feeder. This does not seem to come from nervous disposition, as most specimens are quiet and gentle. The food of wild specimens consists of small rodents, occasional birds, lizards and other snakes. The poor feeding of captive specimens may result from lack of duplication of the species of prey this species obtains in its home environment. That has been checked with some other kinds of snakes where sources of obtaining environmental food species were possible.

This snake is a strong constrictor and oviparous. Its eggs hatch in about 6 weeks.

The larger **King Snakes**; *Getulus* Group:

Designation of this subheading may appear incongruously specific, when, from the first listing of the Genus *Lampropeltis,* we have been considering serpents more or less spoken of as King Snakes. The kinds herewith entering the listing, however, dominate in size among members of the genus and have by far the widest range. One species is concerned, its forms distributed from the Atlantic to the Pacific coasts, and a remarkable change of pattern takes place in this far-flung range. In the Atlantic region the King Snake, *Lampropeltis getulus getulus,* is black, with pale, ringlike markings above. There are subspecies with weaker bands, or lacking these, in Florida. Approaching the Mississippi Valley, the rings give way to speckled pattern or yellowish spot within each scale—the Salt and Pepper King Snake. Farther west, in Texas, the sides are speckled, but rows of pale dots cross the back, again indicating the pale bands or narrow half-rings of the eastern form. Continuing west are forms where the dots are fused into linelike rings which intergradation builds to stronger markings in approaching the Pacific region, where *L. getulus californiae* is again strongly half-ringed, even more vividly than its far-removed eastern ally. As identification of the members of this group is not difficult, and geographic consideration is a helpful factor, the forms will be considered in the usual type of descriptive listing of this book, beginning with the one which occurs in the eastern part of the present chapter's section, thence following forms ranging westward.

Holbrook's King Snake, Salt and Pepper Snake, *Lampropeltis getulus holbrooki* Stejneger

Size: 3½ to 4 feet, with average of about a yard in the southern parts of its range.

Form and scalation: Fairly stout; head but little distinct. Scales smooth and polished.

Coloration: Black or very dark brown with a pale green, yellow or white spot in the center of each scale. The abdomen is yellow, with large dark blotches.

In some specimens there may be a tendency of crowding of spots across the back to indicate dotted crossrings, but the areas between these dotted lines have spotted scales.

Distribution: The Mississippi Valley from southern Illinois to Louisiana. In the west to southern Iowa and eastern Nebraska. Particularly common in Missouri and Arkansas, but extending into the prairies of Kansas and Oklahoma; Texas.

Habits: The food consists of rodents, small birds and snakes and, as with all the forms of *getulus,* this snake is markedly cannibalistic, attacks and kills poisonous serpents and has immunity to their venom. It is hardy as a captive, though often irritable, striking with a sharp, short hiss. Aside from irritability to be often noted, it is typical of the *getulus* group. For habits, see **King Snake,** Chapters V and VIII.

Boundary King Snake, *Lampropeltis getulus splendida* (Baird and Girard)

Size: Rather smaller than the preceding form; seldom over a yard.

Form and scalation: Similar to *L. getulus holbrooki.*

Coloration: Sides spotted as with *holbrooki* (preceding), but the back is black, with few or no spots except regularly spaced, transverse rows to form 40 – 85 dotted crosslines. The abdomen is mostly black, with yellow blotches.

Distribution: Northern Mexico, but extending into the boundary regions of Texas, New Mexico and Arizona.

Arizona King Snake, *Lampropeltis getulus yumensis* Blanchard

Size: Similar to *splendida* (preceding).

Form and scalation: This far-western form shows a decrease of body bulk in the *getulus* group. A 32-inch example is ¾ inch in diameter.

Coloration: Dark brown or black; little or no lateral spotting. Ringlike markings across back, usually not more than the width of one scale.

Distribution: Southwestern Arizona; southeastern California, Sonora and Lower California.

California King Snake, *Lampropeltis getulus californiae* (Blainville)

Size: Rarely over a yard. A specimen measured at the time of writing is 30 inches long and ¾ inch in diameter.

Form and scalation: But moderately stout. Head fairly distinct. Scales smooth, with rather dull surface. This is the smallest and most slender subspecies of the *getulus* group.

Coloration: There are two patterns, one quite the reverse of the other, thus:

1. *Black or dark brown, dorsally ringed with white or bright yellow.*

2. *Black or dark brown, a white or bright yellow band the length of the back.*

The more commonly patterned California King Snake is that which appears ringed above. The body may be jet black or brown with well-separated milk-white or yellow ringlike crossbands, which are narrow on the back and widened on the sides, crossing the abdomen as broad blotches. Top of the head is dark; the plates of the snout and upper labials are white or yellow.

The pattern variant, which is banded lengthwise, and not recognized as a subspecies, is lustrous black or dark brown, with a white or pale yellow stripe or band about two scales wide along the center of the back from behind the head to and including the tail. No other large smooth-scaled snake of the West has such marking, hence this unique variant is unmistakable. In southern Lower California the longitudinally marked specimens have the band broken into close-set spots.

Klauber has demonstrated that clutches of eggs of the California King Snake may contain both pattern phases. (*Herpetologica.* Vol. 1, No. 1, July 1936, pp. 18 – 27.)

Distribution: The name, California King Snake, is partially a misnomer, as this snake, in ringed pattern, ranges from southern Oregon throughout California to northern Lower California and eastward to southern Nevada, southwestern Utah and most of Arizona.

The striped examples appear to be found only in southern California and Lower California.

Habits: Similar to habits described under **King Snake,** Chapters V and VIII. In the average this is a very gentle snake and readily submits to handling. Also it is hardy and attractive as a captive, taking small rodents, lizards and occasionally other snakes. From noting a considerable number of specimens I am inclined to regard it as less induced to attack and eat snakes than other subspecies of the *getulus* grouping.

Santa Catalina Island King Snake, *Lampropeltis catalinensis* Van Denburgh and Slevin

In size and body outlines this species is similar to the preceding, but its pattern is unique among the King Snakes.

Coloration: Brown, with purplish-brown band about 5 scales wide, from head to tail. Within the band, at fairly regular intervals of three to four scales, are single scales containing a yellow spot. The abdomen is blackish, marked with yellow along the margins of the shields.

Distribution: Appears to occur only on Santa Catalina Island, in the Gulf of California.

Habits: The habits of species of snakes on the islands in the Gulf of California remain to be satisfactorily recorded. Their isolation, in separation from the mainland and restriction in variety of food, offers fascinating subjects for study.

MISCELLANEOUS GENERA

Pacific Ground Snake, Brown Snake, *Contia tenuis* (Baird and Girard)

Size: Small, maximum length not much over 12 inches.

Form and scalation: Moderately stout; tail very short and sharp. Head flat and blunt at snout, not distinct from neck. Scales smooth.

Coloration: Brown above, with a reddish-brown band on each side— these bands more or less obscure. They traverse the 4th row of scales and may be margined beneath by black dots. A black band from eye to angle of the mouth. Abdomen yellow, margined with black.

Distribution: Vancouver Island and the Pacific states, excluding extreme southern California.

Le Conte's Snake, *Rhinocheilus lecontei* Baird and Girard

Size: Moderate—2 – 2½ feet. A 2-foot specimen is ½ inch in diameter.

Form and scalation: Moderately stout; head small and but slightly distinct. Snout sharp and much flattened on its undersurface—scoop-shaped. Scales smooth.

By a unique character this species differs from all other North American Colubrine snakes, the plates under the tail being undivided, or in a single row.

Coloration: Alternate black and bright red blotches on the back, the former the larger and extending farther down the sides, the red symmetrically square or transversely oblong in outline. If the red areas are of oblong outline, they may appear like quite broad, well-separated rings if the snake is examined from directly above. On the lower sides there is commonly a mixture of orange scales with red centers and others red with black centers.

With occasional specimens the paler areas on the back are orange, each scale having a bright red dot. Unless closely examined the effect of these areas is deep, ruddy yellow. Abdomen dull white, with dark blotches at the margins of numerous plates.

Distribution: Kansas, thence westward from that approximate latitude to California. Southward to Texas and northern Mexico; Lower California.

Habits: This is a constricting snake, feeding upon small rodents, lizards and other snakes. My specimens have shown preference for lizards. They were quiet and gentle, but I would list the species as difficult to maintain in captivity.

The Genus *Sonora:*

These are very small snakes, their average length slightly under 12 inches. Six species appear to be separable. Two are prettily marked in ringlike fashion, and two are commonly striped along the back. With the brightly patterned kinds there is variation in markings. Without scale counts identification may be unsatisfactory from technical point of view. Scientifically this little grouping is rated as "difficult" to diagnose satisfactorily. All of the species are confined to the western region. Their scales are smooth, with satiny luster. They have been called "ground snakes" owing to secretive habits. A scholarly résumé of the genus was recently presented by William H. Stickel, in *Copeia,* 1938, No. 4.

Descriptions of the separable species follow:

Taylor's Snake, Ground Snake, *Sonora taylori* (Boulenger)

Size: Measurements of an adult are $10\frac{1}{2}$ inches in total length; tail $2\frac{1}{8}$ inches.

Form and scalation: Moderately stout; scales smooth with dull surface. Defined as having rounded abdomen and normal snout with 13 scale rows—obliquely counted across the body.

Coloration: There is no pattern. The body hue is pale brown, each scale darker along the center. The abdomen and upper-lip plates are white.

Distribution: Appears to be the most restricted of its genus, and to be rare. Recorded from counties of southeastern Texas, thence as far northward as San Antonio. Recorded from adjacent Mexico.

Habits: Secretive. Hides under flat stones and in crevices.

Striped Ground Snake, *Sonora episcopa* (Kennicott)

Size: Measurements of an adult are 10 inches in total length; tail $2\frac{1}{2}$ inches.

Form and scalation: Moderately stout; scales smooth, with dull luster. Abdomen rounded; snout normal. Scales in 15 rows—obliquely counted across body.

Coloration: Yellow to reddish, occasionally greenish or very dark, sometimes with paler dorsal area three scales wide extending along the back. With average specimens most of the scales are tipped with a darker hue. There are pattern variants that may appear barred with darker hues. The underside is greenish white or yellow.

Distribution: Great Plains region. Central Texas to southeast Kansas; westward to eastern Colorado and New Mexico. While many specimens are longitudinally marked, this is the only striped *Sonora* of the Great Plains region, where it is common.

Habits: Secretive.

The **Pinkish Ground Snake,** *Sonora miniata miniata* Stickel, is referred to, as to range, in Stickel's recent article, as follows:

"Specimens assigned to this form have been seen from the following places. Arizona: Maricopa (Mesa and vicinity, Phoenix, near Aquila, near Wickenberg), Mohave (Kingman), Yavapai (Prescott, near Congress Junction), Pima (region of Santa Catalina Mts.) counties. Idaho: Ada County (Snake River Canyon)."

The **Striped Ground Snake,** *Sonora miniata linearis* Stickel, is structurally similar to the typical form, but distinguished by having a distinct vermilion dorsal stripe "usually quite sharp-edged, contrasting in color with the sides. . . . The sides are bluish gray to brownish gray, instead of reddish to brown."

Length of an adult is about 12 inches. There are 14 – 15 scale rows and approximately 180 abdominal plates and 47 caudals.

Distribution: The range is fairly wide, including Arizona (Yuma County), California (Imperial, Riverside, San Bernardino and San Diego counties), southern Nevada and Lower California.

Mosauer's Ground Snake, *Sonora mosaueri* Stickel, is recorded only from Comondu, Lower California. It is of uniform coloration, of grayish brown, with tendency of the dorsal scales to have paler margins. Length is about 12 inches; scale rows 14 – 15.

Banded Ground Snake, *Sonora semiannulata semiannulata* Baird and Girard

Size: Similar to the preceding.

Form and scalation: Abdomen rounded. Scale rows 15 – 16.

Coloration: Very brightly marked, in ringlike form. Deep orange to red, with jet-black crossbands extending nearly to the abdominal plates. Abdomen white. Some of the black markings of the upper surface may cross the extreme posterior part of the abdomen (or tail) and thus form rings.

Distribution: Southern Kansas to central Texas and all states westward to Idaho and southeastern California; northwestern Mexico.

Habits: Burt, in presenting some records about the reptiles of Kansas, speaks about the habits of *semiannulata* (*Transactions Kansas Academy of Science,* Vol. 36, 1933): "This snake is found under flat prairie rocks in much drier situations than those selected by *Diadophis punctatus arnyi.*"

Blanchard's Ground Snake, *Sonora semiannulata blanchardi* Stickel, with range defined as from El Paso, Texas, to New Mexico and adjacent northern Mexico, may have the bands only partially present and scale rows reduced to 14.

Gloyd's Ground Snake, *Sonora semiannulata gloydi* Stickel, with restricted range indicated as the Grand Canyon National Park in Arizona, as so far recorded, has wider black bands than the paler interspaces of the typical form, with scale rows 14 – 15. The black bands may cross the abdomen.

Sharp-snouted Ground Snake, Ringed Ground Snake, *Sonora occipitalis* (Hallowell)

Size: Up to 12 inches.

Form and scalation: Similar to others of its genus, but snout is much more protruding—spadelike.

Coloration: Milk white, pale pink or yellow, with narrow black ringlike markings above, separated by intervals of about five scales, these markings seldom more than encroaching beneath the edges of abdominal plates. Abdomen immaculate white. A black crescent at rear of head, the points directed anteriorly.

Distribution: Desert regions from southern Colorado to western New Mexico, Arizona and southeastern California.

Habits: Secretive; in desert sand and issuing at nightfall. This snake literally "swims" in the desert sands, its progress facilitated by its scoop-shaped snout. It is thus the most specialized of its genus.

The Genus *Ficimia:*

Small snakes with smooth scales and a wedge-shaped snout which turns sharply upward. The contour of the head is similar to that of

the Hog-nosed Snakes, but the reptiles of the present genus are miniatures and have smooth scales.

Hook-nosed Snake, *Ficimia cana* (Cope)

Size: 8 – 10 inches in total length; tail sharp.

Form and scalation: Moderately stout. Head not distinct, triangular,
the pointed snout upturned. Scales smooth.

Coloration: Orange yellow to reddish, with about thirty reddish-
brown, dark-edged crossbands, which may break on the sides into small
blotches. A broad band across head in front of eyes extending to the
labial plates; another band across the rear part of head. Abdomen immaculate white or pale yellow.

Distribution: Western Texas to Arizona and possibly northern
Mexico. This species is a rarity in collections and further notes from
collectors may extend its range.

Habits: In an article on this snake, by Edward H. Taylor, are the
following descriptions, based on two specimens collected in New
Mexico (*Copeia,* 1931, No. 1, pp. 4 – 7):

> "This specimen . . . is a female and not improbably the mate of
> the male" (collected at the same time and place), "as it was taken
> about fifty feet from the other specimen only a few minutes later.
> . . . The male snake when first found remained motionless, perhaps
> blinded by the light which I carried; but immediately on being
> touched, it began to writhe and throw its body into strange contor-
> tions, as if in agony, sometimes almost throwing itself off the
> ground. It would continue these actions for several seconds. . . .
> Wright tested the female and found that she reacted in practically
> the same manner as the male. These tactics were repeated time and
> again by the two specimens, and even when in the collecting sack
> they continued these same gyrations and jumping movements. . . .
>
> "The terrain where they were found was a large flat, covered
> with short, very sparse grass, the soil largely free from sand or
> gravel. A large number of mounds thrown up by rodents (probably
> a species of *Dipodomys*) were scattered about the terrain. A rain
> had fallen, probably sometime in the morning, and the surface of the
> ground was still moist."

Strecker's Hook-nosed Snake, *Ficimia streckeri* Taylor

Size: The type specimen is 12 inches in total length, with tail $1\frac{5}{8}$
inch and approximate diameter of $\frac{3}{8}$ inch.

Form and scalation: Approximately similar to *F. cana* (preceding).
Coloration: Taylor's original description is quoted:

"Above dull ash gray, each scale edged with slightly darker gray,
the body color extending as far as the outer scale row but growing
somewhat less dense laterally; a few minute grayish flecks on the
outer scale row; body traversed by 46 transverse, dark, blackish
gray bands which reach laterally to the second scale row, the bands
averaging one scale length in width, a few of them broken. . . ."

Distribution: The type specimen was collected "three miles east of
Rio Grande City" (southern Texas) "along a highway, about mid-
night of July 13, 1930. . . ."

This species is either of considerable rarity or extremely secretive.
As far as I am aware, no specimen, since the type described by Taylor,
has been found. Here is another source of investigation for the reptile
collector.

Spotted Night Snake, Rock Snake, *Hypsiglena torquata ochrorhyncha* (Cope)*

Size: Small. An average-sized adult is 15 inches long with diameter
of ⅜ inch.

Form and scalation: Moderately stout; head fairly distinct. Scales
smooth.

Differs from other North American Colubrine snakes (except Phyllorhynchus *and the few rear-fanged species) in having the eye with
vertical (elliptic) pupil.*

Coloration: Gray to grayish brown, with irregular, dark blotches
along the back, narrowly margined with black; two small alternating
series of blotches or dark spots on each side.

A dark band through each eye extends to the neck; a central band
from rear of head, the three usually uniting to form a large blotch.
Abdomen white.

Distribution: Western Texas to southern Kansas, New Mexico,
Arizona, Utah, southern Idaho, Nevada, southern California, Lower
California and northwestern Mexico.

Habits: The few captive specimens I have had refused food. I found
a small lizard (*Sceloporus*) in the stomach of a dead specimen and

*Recently suggested as belonging among the rear-fanged snakes. While it
has posterior enlarged teeth, these show no traces of grooves for conduction
of poison.

the eggs of a small lizard or snake in another. The elliptic pupils indicate nocturnal habits.

The Genus *Chilomeniscus*:

Three species of these very small, burrowing sand snakes inhabit the deserts of southwestern North America. The body is cylindrical, with smooth scales, the head narrow and not distinct, with elongated, wedge- or scoop-shaped snout, which protrudes considerably beyond the lower jaw. From geographical consideration alone, their separation as species is rendered clear. Only one occurs in the United States.

Banded Sand Snake, *Chilomeniscus cinctus* Cope

Size: Very small. An adult from Arizona is 9 inches in total length; tail 1¼ inch.

Form and scalation: Moderately stout; head not distinct. Snout elongated, much flattened and protruding to form a burrowing scoop or wedge.

Coloration: Deep orange to reddish, with black crossbands which nearly reach the abdominal plates, invade the undersurface, or with some specimens encircle the body as black rings. The separating spaces of ground color are about as wide as the bands or rings. In examples having encircling bands, these may be broken along the central part of the abdomen, but are intact under the tail. There are from 17 – 23 bands or rings on the body and 3 – 5 on the tail. The top of the head is black, the snout reddish.

Distribution: Deserts of southern Arizona, southeastern California and northwestern Mexico.

Habits: A desert reptile adapted for life in yielding sands. It spends as much time beneath the surface as above it, its scooplike snout enabling it to thrust its way quickly beneath soft medium and to travel horizontally while thus concealed. While progressing a few inches beneath the surface, its presence is indicated by slight undulations of the sand, similar to the undulations produced by a body going through water. When frightened it really "swims" into the sand, its actions similar to those of some of the highly specialized reptiles of the Sahara of Africa, where certain snakes and scooped-nosed lizards are called "sand-fish," owing to gliding beneath the surface, thence traveling quite rapidly.

Island Sand Snake, *Chilomeniscus punctatissimus* Van Denburgh and Slevin

Form and size are similar to the preceding, but the body crossbands are about 32 in number, with about 7 on the tail.

Distribution: Isla Partida, Espiritu Santo Island, Lower California.

Straw-colored Sand Snake, *Chilomeniscus stramineus* Cope

Size and form similar to preceding.

Coloration: Pale straw color, each scale tipped with black or containing a small black spot.

Distribution: Desert areas of southern Lower California.

THE WATER SNAKES
Genus *Natrix*

These snakes are never found away from the immediate vicinity of water; in fact most of them spend as much time in the water as out of it. They are agile swimmers, and to plunge into pond or stream is their usual method of evading the intruder. They seldom take any but cold-blooded prey, which includes frogs, toads, fishes and even crayfish. They cannot be rated as of any economic value, but again, despite fish-eating habits, they should not be regarded as distinctly harmful to game fish. The shooting of Water Snakes along game streams is prompted by combination of hatred for snakes and magnified thought of depredation among sportsmen's trophies.

The headquarters of the Water Snake genus is southeastern North America, with most abundant occurrence in the low coastal regions. The range of genus, however, extends northward to southern Canada. The Mississippi and its tributaries provide extension of habitat well into the West, although this terminates at about the central part of the western region. The Striped or Garter Snakes, *Thamnophis,* which are closely allied, and in distribution extend from the Atlantic to the Pacific coasts, are largely aquatic in the western United States. Thus, while the Genus *Natrix* (the typical Water Snakes) drops out to the far westward, the semiaquatic species of *Thamnophis* exhibit similar habits right through to the Pacific region.

For the user of this field book who is studying the snakes of the states with eastern boundaries bordering the Mississippi River, reference to the key in Chapter VII and descriptions in Chapter VIII will be useful. While the several parts of the book are practically com-

plete within themselves as to sectional inclusion of species, a re-
description of the southeastern snakes extending into the Mississippi
Valley would produce a rather interminable continuity and interfere in
following the numerous suggestions I have received about "sectioning"
the map of North America.

Detailed descriptions follow to include those Water Snakes which
extend westward of the Mississippi Valley:

Graham's Water Snake, *Natrix grahamii* (Baird and Girard)

Size: A rather small species, with maximum length of about a
yard—which is exceptional. Dimensions of an average-sized specimen
are given: Total length 25 inches; diameter ⅝ inch.

Form and scalation: Relatively more slender than the larger Water
Snakes. Head small and not distinct. Scales strongly keeled.

Coloration: Differs from other Water Snakes, in following descriptions, in having lengthwise striping or banding—there being no transverse markings. Back dark brown, with indistinct pale stripe narrowly
margined with black. On each side is a broad band of yellow in strong
contrast to the dark hue above. This band covers the first three rows
of scales and is bordered at its lower portion by a black stripe, which
extends along the edges of the abdominal plates. The lateral yellow
area extends forward to cover the upper labial plates. The abdomen is
yellow, usually with a black stripe in the center.

Distribution: The valleys of the Mississippi and Missouri rivers.
In the western part of its range it is recorded from Iowa, Kansas and
Oklahoma. It ranges southward into eastern Texas.

Habits: Most frequently seen on low branches overhanging water,
into which it drops when frightened. Unlike the larger water snakes it
is quite quiet and gentle as a captive. It is fond of frogs and small fish.

Common Water Snake, Water "Moccasin," *Natrix sipedon sipe-don* (Linnaeus)

Size: Average length is about 2½ feet, but exceptional examples reach
a length of 4 feet. Following are measurements of a quite large specimen: Total length 3 feet 6 inches; diameter 1⅜ inch.

Form and scalation: Stout; head distinct. Scales strongly keeled.

Coloration: Dull brown or dark gray when adult, with more or less
distinct darker transverse bands anteriorly, which break into three
series of blotches posteriorly, the larger being on the back. Yellow
beneath, brightly spotted or blotched with red.

In old specimens the dorsal bands may be very obscure, there being no defined markings except bars of paler ground color on the sides. In such specimens the red-spotted abdomen is an aid to identification. Others may show little indication of the ground color, when seen from above, except dull pale, narrow ringlike bands indicating separation of the blotches. With these, again, the red-spotted abdomen is a guiding point for deduction. Occasonal specimens are very dark brown and called "black" water snakes. I have not examined specimens that were actually black, but this occurs with the southern forms. If the bodies of very dark adults with obscure markings are held under water, the pattern becomes somewhat apparent. Young specimens are gray with strongly contrasted blotches.

Distribution: The range is wide, extending from southern Canada and the eastern United States to Minnesota, Colorado and Oklahoma. Burt, in a list of Kansas reptiles, says: "This is the common water snake or (false) water moccasin of Kansas. . . ." Curtis, in *The Snakes of Iowa,** says: "This is the common banded snake found in streams practically everywhere in the state. . . ."

Habits: See **Water Snake,** Chapter V.

A related form, crossing the Mississippi into southern Missouri and Arkansas, is listed as *N. sipedon pleuralis* (Cope). It is marked similarly to the typical form, but the ground hue between the darker bands is wider than the bands themselves, which is the reverse with *N. s. sipedon.* Also, the reddish abdominal markings are restricted to two irregular rows of crescentic blotches rather than numerous red spots.

Blanchard's Water Snake, *Natrix sipedon confluens* (Blanchard)

Size: Similar to the preceding, or typical, form.

Form and scalation: Typical of the larger Water Snakes; stout, with distinct head. Scales strongly keeled.

Coloration: This form is quite distinct. Adults are dark brown; almost blackish. The tendency is for the bands to fuse in twos, and thus become confluent, blocking out indications of ground hue except as widely separated, pale ringlike areas between the fused blotches. The abdomen is not so brightly spotted with red as with the typical form.

Distribution: The southern Mississippi Valley, but mostly on its

*Iowa State College of Agriculture, Bulletin 239, 1926.

western side. Recorded from Missouri, Oklahoma, Arkansas, Louisiana and Texas.

Yellow-bellied Water Snake, *Natrix erythrogaster transversa* (Hallowell)

Size: Moderately large—2½ to 3 feet long when adult.

Form and scalation: Stout, head distinct. Scales strongly keeled.

Coloration: A row of dark blotches along back, separated by narrow lines of paler ground color, about one scale wide. Alternating blotches on the sides separated by brown or olive spaces wider than the blotches themselves. Abdomen bright yellow and unmarked.

The pattern along its entire length is similar to that on the posterior part of *sipedon*. The yellow and unmarked underparts are characteristic. With the more eastern, typical form, *N. erythrogaster erythrogaster,* the abdomen is bright red and unmarked (Red-bellied Water Snake).

Distribution: Louisiana to Arkansas, Oklahoma and Kansas. Westward through Texas to New Mexico. Extends the farthest westward of the typical Water Snakes.*

Habits: Typical of the larger Water Snakes.

Diamond-backed Water Snake, *Natrix rhombifera* (Hallowell)

Size: Large, not uncommonly to 4 feet, and occasionally to 5 feet. A 4-foot specimen is about 2 inches in diameter.

Form and scalation: Very stout and heavy, with wide and distinct head; upper-lip plates swollen and protruding. Scales strongly keeled.

Coloration: Dull olive or brown, with chain of rather narrow black markings enclosing diamond-shaped areas of body hue. From the lower angle of each rhomb is a vertical black band about two scales in width extending down the side. Abdomen dull yellow, with many of the plates heavily blotched with brown or black.

As with all the larger Water Snakes, the young have a strongly defined pattern.

Distribution: The lower Mississippi Valley, extending into Kansas and Oklahoma, thence southward through Texas, into Mexico.

Habits: A particularly savage Water Snake, which fights furiously when restrained or, if cornered, strikes repeatedly. If frightened and

*With exception of *N. valida* (Kennicott), a rather small species with black spots on the sides and unmarked abdomen, widely separated in inhabiting western Mexico and Lower California.

there is an avenue of escape, however, it plunges into the water and hides. Its favorite basking place is on boughs overhanging the water, from which it drops when alarmed. One of my specimens swallowed a carp twelve inches long.

As with all members of the Water Snake genus, the young are produced alive, and there may be as many as fifty in a litter, although the number of young varies greatly.

The **Lower California Water Snake,** *Natrix valida* (Kennicott), is grayish to olive with little or no markings except black speckling at bases of scales. The abdomen is uniform grayish yellow. Some specimens have an obscure lateral band. The range appears to be restricted to southern Lower California and western Mexico.

THE GARTER SNAKES
Genus *Thamnophis*

Eight species of these rather characteristic snakes respectively inhabit parts of western North America. One or more occur in all parts of this region. These species, with their related forms (subspecies), have wide ranges—one extending from the Atlantic to the Pacific coast; a few are restricted in habitat. All are striped or banded lengthwise, the common pattern being a central dorsal stripe and a stripe along each side. Some have checkerboard spots between the stripes. With a few forms the stripes may be indistinct, the dorsal or the laterals lacking. About 4 feet is the maximum length of any, and this is above the average. Form ranges from slender to quite stout outlines. There is tendency to semiaquatic habits, and some kinds are as persistent in lurking near water as the species of *Natrix*—the typical Water Snakes. All feed upon cold-blooded prey, frogs, toads, small fishes and earthworms.

Situation of the lateral stripe, as to scale rows, is an important point in identification, as also is deduction of geographical range. All have strongly keeled scales.

Western Ribbon Snake, *Thamnophis sauritus proximus* (Say)
Size: Moderate—2 – 4 feet. A 30-inch specimen has a diameter of ⅝ inch. This form grows particularly large in Texas.

Form and scalation: Slender, with proportionately long tail, which is about a third the total length. Scales strongly keeled.

Coloration: Dark brown, olive or blackish, with three pale vivid stripes, the stripe on each side covering the 3rd and 4th rows of scales and accentuated by a band of dark brown or black beneath it covering the 1st and 2nd rows of scales above the abdominal plates. The abdomen is immaculate greenish white.

The dorsal stripe is usually of quite a different hue from those on the sides. It may be bright orange, with the lateral stripes greenish yellow, or the dorsal stripe may be red and the lateral ones yellow, this common with Texas specimens.

Distribution: The Mississippi Valley states, westward to Iowa, Nebraska, Kansas and Oklahoma, southward through Texas to Central America.

Habits: Frequents swampy places or small streams and often takes to the water. It is very active and feeds upon frogs, toads and small fishes. Among captive specimens I have noted that it differs from the larger garter snakes in not feeding upon earthworms. It is agile in climbing and ascends into small bushes. The litters of young are smaller than with the more heavy-bodied species of *Thamnophis*. I have not noted more than fifteen young in a litter.

Mexican Garter Snake, *Thamnophis megalops* (Kennicott)

Size: 2 – 3 feet. A 24-inch specimen is ½ inch in diameter.

Form and scalation: Stouter than T. *sauritus proximus* (preceding), about midway in relative thickness between that form and the really stout-bodied garter snakes. The tail is about a quarter the total length. Head quite distinct, with proportionately large eyes.

Coloration: Pale tan to grayish brown, with three narrow yellow stripes, the dorsal and lateral stripes of the same color, the latter covering portions of the 3rd and 4th rows of scales. Many of the scales have narrow black edges or carry black spots, but these do not produce the checkerboard pattern between the stripes as with most of the species that follow.

Distribution: Ranging northward from Mexico into southern Texas, New Mexico and Arizona.

Habits: Frequents the borders of streams and takes to the water when frightened.

Plains Garter Snake, *Thamnophis radix* (Baird and Girard)

Size: One of the largest of the Garter Snakes, attaining length of

4 feet. The following measurements are of an adult: Total length 32 inches; diameter ¾ inch.

Form and scalation: Quite stout, as will be noted from proportions in preceding measurements. Head distinct; scales strongly keeled.

Coloration: Variable in body hue, which may be light to dark brown, olive or blackish. Three strongly defined pale stripes, the dorsal wider than the lateral ones and usually of darker hue. The average color of the dorsal stripe is orange, while the stripes on the sides are paler. The lateral stripes are on the 3rd and 4th rows of scales. This is the only large and stout-bodied western Garter Snake with lateral stripes on the scale rows indicated. In the other large species the side stripes are on the 2nd and 3rd rows of scales.

With paler specimens there is a strong double series of alternating black spots between the stripes, imparting a checkerboard pattern. Abdomen pale, with a row of black spots extending along margins of the plates.

Distribution: Abundant in the northern portion of the Great Plains. The range is from western Ohio, Illinois, Missouri and Kansas to the eastern slopes of the Rockies, thence into the Canadian Northwest. Curtis, in *The Snakes of Iowa,** says: "This is the commonest species of striped snake or garter snake in most parts of Iowa." Burt, outlining records of distribution of reptiles of the Middle West, explains: "This snake is a typical prairie-inhabiting species, which often lives in fence rows, sparse woods, gardens, and pastures."

Habits: Ranges through variety of terrain, forest, plains and prairie, rocky ground and quite sterile regions. It may be noted as terrestrial or along streams, where it takes to the water when alarmed and dives to the bottom to hide. It seldom takes other than cold-blooded food, such as frogs, toads and fishes. Like most of the larger Garter Snakes it is able to thrive upon earthworms, when larger prey is unobtainable. I have kept captives for several years upon such diet. Living young are produced up to and possibly more than three dozen in a litter.

The **Common Garter Snake,** *Thamnophis sirtalis sirtalis* (Linnaeus), and subspecies or related forms are best treated under concise listing for comparison. This listing should be checked with the key in Chapter X for comparison with other species of *Thamnophis.* The term "Common Garter Snake" is rather grossly applied for con-

*Iowa State College of Agriculture, Bulletin 239, 1926.

venience, as in some areas of the West where *sirtalis* occurs other species may be more abundant.

Following is diagnosis of the *sirtalis* group, the preliminary paragraph relating to all forms:

Size: 2 – 4 feet; average about 2½ feet. *Form* rather stout; head distinct; scales strongly keeled. *Of the two central pairs of chin shields, the rear ones are much the longer.* Side stripes, if present, on the 2nd and 3rd rows of scales.

Brown, green, olive or blackish, with three tan, yellow or greenish stripes. If the body is not blackish, there is usually a double row of dark spots between the stripes in checkerboard pattern. *No red on sides.* Abdomen pale yellow or greenish:

Common Garter Snake, *T. sirtalis sirtalis* (Linnaeus).
Distribution: Southern Canada and the entire eastern United States, westward to Arkansas and Missouri and in the north to Minnesota and Iowa.

Brown, green, olive to blackish, with three narrow yellowish or greenish stripes. Two rows of dark spots between the dorsal and lateral stripes, the upper row commonly almost fused into a continuous blackish band, the lower row of spots distinct and *the spaces between these spots bright red:*

Red-barred Garter Snake, *T. sirtalis parietalis* (Say).
Distribution: Overlaps the range of the typical form in Minnesota, Iowa and Missouri. Thence broadly occurs westward to Nevada, Utah and Idaho and northward to Manitoba.

Three yellow stripes. Upper row of spots between the stripes fused to a blackish band. Lower spots nearly obliterated by bright red blotches on each side, which may fuse into a red (or salmon-colored) band:

Red-spotted Garter Snake, *T. sirtalis concinnus* (Hallowell).
Distribution: Pacific region, west of the Sierra Nevada, including northern California, Oregon and Washington; northward to British Columbia and Vancouver Island.

Olive to blackish, a strong central rich yellow or orange stripe; usually no lateral stripes:

One-striped Garter Snake, *T. sirtalis infernalis* (Blainville).

Distribution: Oregon and California, with extension eastward into Nevada. Occurs in forested and grass areas without extension into sterile parts.

Habits: Among the preceding forms the habits are quite similar. See **Garter Snake,** Chapter V.

The **Western Garter Snake,** *Thamnophis ordinoides ordinoides* (Baird and Girard), and subspecies or related forms present even more complication than the widely ranging *sirtalis* group. Here there are seven subspecies for consideration—all of the Pacific or near-by regions. Form and striping may be similar to members of the *sirtalis* group, but there is one point of identification that immediately separates all the forms of *ordinoides* from confusion with the former: *Both pairs of central chin shields are of about equal size.* With *sirtalis* the posterior pair is much the longer. Under this consideration the group may be defined in condensed paragraphs for comparison.

Habits: Among the related forms of *ordinoides,* habits vary in selection of environment from forest to sterile areas and semiaquatic habits. *Vagrans* in selection of environment is often practically a water snake:

A. *Stripes strongly evident*

A yellow dorsal stripe and a yellowish stripe on each side on 2nd and 3rd rows of scales. Two rows of dark spots between stripes, the separating spaces reddish brown to bright red, particularly when the scales are distended, as the skin between them carries much of the color:

Pacific Garter Snake, *T. ordinoides ordinoides* (Baird and Girard).

Distribution: Washington, Oregon and coastal California.

Dorsal stripe very distinct and of richer yellow (even reddish) than lateral stripes. Body hue generally brownish, but with stripes intensified by darker borders, with little or no indication of spots between the stripes:

California Garter Snake, *T. ordinoides elegans* (Baird and Girard).

Distribution: The mountain slopes of California and Nevada.

Sage green to gray; dorsal and lateral stripes narrow. Two rows of rounded black spots between the stripes, the upper row breaking into the central stripe: .

> **Gray Garter Snake,** *T. ordinoides vagrans* (Baird and Girard).

Distribution: Eastern Washington, Oregon and eastern California to Idaho and Arizona; Lower California. The author has found this snake common along narrow streams in gorges along the eastern slopes of the San Bernardino Mountains in California.

B. *Stripes faint or absent*

Body clouded with black; stripes faint; spots between the stripes barely evident:

> **Black Garter Snake,** *T. ordinoides atratus* (Kennicott).

Distribution: Coastal region of California.

Body brown or blackish, stripes faint or absent. Spots between the stripes faint or absent. Has a higher scale count than *atratus,* which is ordinarily up to 21, while the present subspecies ranges to 22 and 23:

> **Northwestern Garter Snake,** *T. ordinoides biscutatus* (Cope).

Distribution: Southern British Columbia, Vancouver Island and northern California.

Body dull gray; no central stripe. Lateral stripe barely evident, but over its location one row of clearly defined spots:

> **Couch's Garter Snake,** *T. ordinoides couchii* (Kennicott).

Distribution: Central and northern California with range northeastward to Nevada and Idaho.

Dark olive, brownish to blackish. Dorsal stripe obscure or absent. Lateral stripe faint greenish yellow. Spots usually absent:

> **Hammond's Garter Snake,** *T. ordinoides hammondii* (Kennicott).

Distribution: Southwestern California and northern Lower California.

Marcy's Garter Snake, *Thamnophis marcianus* (Baird and Girard)
Size: Average size of adult 21 inches; diameter ¾ inch.

Form and scalation: Rather stout, as indicated by preceding dimensions. Head distinct; scales strongly keeled. A heavier species than *sirtalis* or *ordinoides.*

Coloration: Yellowish to light brown (straw color) above, with a very narrow, pale yellow stripe on the back and less distinct yellowish stripe on side. The dominating feature of the markings is two rows of square black spots between the stripes, in alternation or checkerboard pattern. It is thus the most strongly spotted of any of the garter snakes.

Top of the head is olive, with a yellow crescent on each temple and a blackish collar posteriorly. The abdomen is immaculate white.

Distribution: An abundant species from Oklahoma and Texas to southeastern California; northern Mexico.

Habits: An attractive snake that is particularly hardy as a captive, feeding upon frogs, toads, fishes and earthworms. With exception of the dorsally red-striped and laterally red-marked members of *Thamnophis,* this has been my favorite species of the genus. It has a long life under observation, is uniformly gentle, and its young may be easily reared upon earthworm diet.

Brown Garter Snake, *Thamnophis eques* (Reuss)

Size: 2 – 3 feet, with maximum diameter of about ¾ inch.

Form and scalation: Rather stout; head distinct; scales strongly keeled.

Coloration: Pale to reddish brown, with whitish or pale yellow dorsal stripe and a broader stripe on each side covering the 2nd and 3rd rows of scales. The dorsal stripe widens behind the head, then comes to a point into the rear of the posterior head plates. Anteriorly there are two well-indicated rows of dark spots between the stripes. The lower row may encroach upon the lateral stripe to give it a serrated outline. There is a pair of large, dark blotches at the rear of the head. The abdomen is immaculate white or yellow.

Distribution: Abundant in Texas and extending westward to Arizona and northward into Utah. It ranges through Mexico into northern Central America.

Habits: Another large and attractive member of the Garter Snake genus, hardy and gentle as a captive.

Long-headed Garter Snake, *Thamnophis angustirostris* (Kennicott)

Size: 2 – 3 feet.

Form and scalation: Moderately stout; scales strongly keeled. Head more elongated and narrow than with any other species of *Thamnophis.*

Coloration: All the stripes are faint. The dorsal stripe is narrow and may be very indistinct. The laterals are also rather obscure and situated on the 2nd and 3rd rows of scales. Body hue is brown and presents a finely spotted appearance, owing to many of the scales having darker edges. The two rows of dark lateral spots present in several other large species of Garter Snakes are obscure or lacking.

Distribution: Ranges quite widely through Mexico and northward into southern Arizona and southwestern New Mexico.

Striped Swamp Snake, *Tropidoclonion lineatum* (Hallowell). Optional: *Thamnophis lineatum*

Size: Rather small, up to 18 inches, but commonly not much over 12 inches. A 14-inch example is ⅜ inch in diameter.

Form and scalation: Moderately stout; tail short. Head small and pointed, of the same width as neck with small eyes. Scales strongly keeled.

Coloration: Gray or brown with three whitish or yellowish stripes, one on the back, bordered with black dots, and a less strong one on each side on the 2nd and 3rd rows of scales. Abdomen whitish, with *double row of black spots along the center.* This character distinguishes it from species of *Thamnophis,* which it resembles in its stripings.

Distribution: Southeastern South Dakota to Texas and all the states east of the indicated longitude to the Mississippi Valley.

Habits: Secretive, hiding under flat stones, logs or debris. As a rule it frequents rather open places, often lowlands, near rivers, although it does not appear to be semiaquatic. It gives birth to living young, the litters small, not over twelve and more commonly seven to eight. As a captive it will take earthworms.

THE SMALL BROWN SNAKES
Storeria, Haldea and *Virginia*

These little snakes are seldom over a foot long and usually of lesser length. From wide eastern range, they extend but moderately into the West. They are characteristically dull brown. With *Storeria* there may be a paler band along the back. With *Storeria* and *Haldea* the scales are strongly keeled. With *Virginia* the scales are smooth, or so faintly keeled on the posterior portion that such character is not discernible except upon minute examination with a glass. All of these little snakes are secretive, hiding under flat stones or debris.

DeKay's Snake, Brown Snake, *Storeria dekayi* (Holbrook)

Size: Seldom much exceeding 12 inches. The following measurements are of a fair-sized adult: Total length 12 inches, diameter slightly exceeding ¼ inch.

Form and scalation: Moderately stout; head fairly distinct. Eyes large. Scales strongly keeled.

Coloration: Rather dark brown, sometimes grayish brown, often with a streak or band of paler tint along the back, this bordered on each side with black dots. Abdomen pinkish.

Very young specimens are dark gray or blackish, with grayish-white ring around the neck. They might be confused with the young of Ring-necked Snakes (*Diadophis*), but are readily separated by their keeled scales.

Distribution: The range is wide, extending from the Atlantic coast to Minnesota, thence southward through Texas into Mexico.

Habits: See **DeKay's Snake**, Chapter V.

Storer's Snake, Red-bellied Snake, Brown Snake, *Storeria occipitomaculata* (Storer)

Size: Smaller than the preceding—seldom as much as 12 inches. An average length is 10 inches, with diameter of ¼ inch.

Form and scalation: Similar to *S. dekayi.*

Coloration: There is frequent variation of body hue from brown to gray. A common coloration is rather pale brown, with or without a paler band along the back. *The abdomen is bright red.* Gray specimens vary from slaty gray to darker, with or without a paler band, the latter sometimes yellowish. Some gray examples have a double row of black dots (others, white dots) along the back. With grayish examples the abdominal red is particularly brilliant. There are no abdominal markings beyond encroachment, from the sides, of a powdery margin of bluish gray.

Head markings are characteristic. The head is darker than the body, and at its rear is a yellow spot, and at each side of this, on the neck, is a pair of similar, though smaller, spots. Young specimens are blackish, with whitish collar like immature examples of *S. dekayi.*

Distribution: The range westward is broader than with DeKay's Snake, extending from the Atlantic coast to South Dakota, thence southward through Texas into Mexico. As with *dekayi,* however, occurrence appears to be favorable to wooded areas, where there is some moisture.

Habits: Secretive, hiding under flat stones or logs and feeding upon earthworms, slugs and insect larvae. Among ten specimens giving birth to living young, the litters varied in number of young from 6 to 13 and dates of birth from August 18 to September 4. The young are extremely small, of lesser diameter than a wooden match. I have had no difficulty in inducing them to take "pinworms" (young earthworms) driven from the ground by electric current. Adult specimens thrive upon earthworms. See habits of **Storer's Snake,** Chapter V.

Small-eyed Brown Snake, Ground Snake, Worm Snake, *Haldea striatula* (Linnaeus)

Size: Following are the dimensions of an adult: Total length 11 inches; diameter ¼ inch.

Form and scalation: Moderately stout; head fairly distinct, but long, pointed and slender. *Eyes very small and beadlike.* Scales strongly keeled.

Coloration: Uniform brown to grayish brown above; yellowish white beneath. In absence of pale dorsal band, lack of pink or red beneath, and in having slender, pointed head with relatively very small eyes, this species is distinct from the Brown Snakes of the Genus *Storeria.*

Distribution: The southeastern United States, extending westward across the Mississippi Valley to Oklahoma and eastern Texas.

Habits: See **Brown Snake,** Chapter VIII.

Smooth-scaled Brown Snake, Virginia's Snake, Brown Snake, Worm Snake, *Virginia valeriae elegans* Kennicott

Size: Very small. An adult in my collection is 8 inches long, with diameter of ¼ inch.

Form and scalation: Moderately stout, with abruptly tapering tail. Head but little distinct, pointed. Scales appearing smooth on gross examination, but showing very faint keels posteriorly if examined with a glass.

Coloration: Grayish to brown, usually with two rows of minute black dots along the back. Abdomen yellowish white.

Distribution: Timbered regions of the Mississippi Valley, extending westward to Iowa, Kansas and Oklahoma.

Habits: See **Smooth Brown Snake,** *Virginia valeriae valeriae,* Chapter VIII.

CHAPTER XII

The Mildly Poisonous Rear-fanged Snakes

The Genera *Coniophanes, Tantilla, Oxybelis,*
Trimorphodon and *Leptodeira:*

While a few of the larger rear-fanged snakes of the tropics may be rated as possibly dangerous in the effects of their bites, the species inhabiting North America cannot be listed as specifically "poisonous." These serpents have enlarged, grooved teeth in the posterior part of the upper jaw. There is connection with a small gland secreting venom to paralyze their prey when it is grasped. In *Coniophanes* and *Tantilla,* the members are so small that their bites, if specimens are restrained, may be discounted as harmless to a human. In the larger species, included under the generic heads of *Oxybelis, Leptodeira* and *Trimorphodon,* their poisons are strong enough to benumb small lizards, but not sufficiently powerful, in laboratory experiments, to subdue mice and small rats. A bite from one of these snakes, attended with its characteristic, *chewing* grip, might induce a numbness of finger or a tender spot, but the kinds inhabiting North America cannot be listed, so far as the human is concerned, among distinctly poisonous reptiles—neither can the larger ones be considered as quite harmless. Owing to this peculiar status, however, they are listed in this chapter separate from the nonvenomous snakes.

Black-banded Snake, *Coniophanes imperialis* (Baird)
Size: Small. Total length of an adult example is 14 inches, with tail 6 inches.

Form and scalation: Rather slender, head but slightly distinct. Scales smooth.

Coloration: Pale brown with a black band on the back and a similar band on each side. Abdomen reddish, sometimes spotted. There is a black-bordered yellow band from the snout to temple.

Distribution: Mexico and southern Texas.

THE BLACK-HEADED SNAKES
Genus *Tantilla*

This is a fair-sized genus, with headquarters in the American tropics. Eight species occur in the western section. All are small, quite slender, with smooth, opalescent scales. They are pale, uniform brown, with dark or blackish head, with or without a whitish collar at base. Length in the average is under 12 inches. All are secretive. The key in Chapter X designates head markings to extent of preliminary diagnosis. The presence or absence of a narrow white collar and specific distribution figure in further deduction, as here outlined:

General coloration: Uniform brown; head much darker, or blackish
  A. *A narrow pale collar at base of head*

  Pale collar nearly touching large head shields—parietals—and followed by black border:
    Wilcox's Black-headed Snake, *Tantilla wilcoxi* Stejneger.
  Distribution: Huachuca Mountains, Arizona.

  Pale collar one to two scales to rear of large head shields—parietals:
    Günther's Black-headed Snake, *Tantilla atriceps* (Günther).
  Distribution: Oklahoma and western Texas to southeastern Arizona.

  Much like the preceding, but head is not so black nor collar so evident. Also larger. Adults of *atriceps* range from 96 to 230 mm. In the present species the range is from 128 to 297 mm.:
    Blanchard's Black-headed Snake, *Tantilla utahensis* Blanchard.
  Distribution: Southwestern Utah and west into the Sierra Nevada in California.

  Pale collar, 3 – 4 scales to rear of large head plates—parietals:
    Eisen's Black-headed Snake, *Tantilla eiseni* Stejneger.

Distribution: Southern California and northern Lower California.

Similar to *eiseni* but has a lower count of ventral plates; 134 – 140, as against 165:
>**Lower California Black-headed Snake,** *Tantilla planiceps* (Blainville).

Distribution: Southern Lower California.

B. *No pale collar at base of head*
  Head but slightly darker brown than body:
>**Slender Dark-headed Snake, Sand Snake,** *Tantilla gracilis* Baird and Girard.

Distribution: "Missouri and eastern Kansas (except in the north) south to extreme southern Texas, west to about the ninety-eighth meridian." (Blanchard.)

Top of head dark brown extending backward to the 3rd scale behind the parietals:
>**Kirn's Dark-headed Snake,** *Tantilla kirnia* Blanchard.

Distribution: "Comanche County, Oklahoma, southward through Texas nearly to Brownsville, westward to San Antonio." (Blanchard.)

Head black, the black pointing backward about four scale lengths beyond the parietal shields:
>**Kennicott's Black-headed Snake,** *Tantilla nigriceps* Kennicott.

Distribution: Western Kansas to eastern Colorado and southward through Oklahoma and Texas to New Mexico and Arizona.

Habits: Little is known about the habits of these secretive reptiles. Strecker and Williams in notes on the reptiles of Bowie County, Texas, refer to *Tantilla gracilis:* "All these specimens were found under logs in woods in the neighborhood of water." Burt in records of Ecology and Distribution of Amphibians and Reptiles in the Middle West, says about the same species: "In the prairie the sand snake is usually found under rocks in ledges either where there are no trees or in glades, but farther east it occurs in rockless woods, where specimens may be removed from decaying stumps and logs."

Long-headed Snake, Arizona Vine Snake, *Oxybelis micropthalmus* Barbour and Amaral

Size: The type specimen is approximately 30 inches long, the tail more than 21 inches in length.

Form and scalation: Extremely slender, particularly the tapering anterior portion and the tail. The excessive length of tail may be noted in the preceding paragraph. Diameter of body at the thickest part should not exceed ½ inch. The scales are smooth with satiny luster.

Head extremely long and slender, with pointed snout, its form (in miniature) like that of a pickerel. Owing to the long, thin and wiry neck, the head is fairly distinct.

Coloration: In the original description coloration is given as "reddish above; throat and upper lip white, the white area on head and neck bounded above by a dark brown line; belly dusky red with a few dark spots."

Distribution: But few specimens are known. The species was a surprise discovery in a comparatively recent year—1926—when it was announced that Dr. C. T. Vorhies had collected in southern Arizona two specimens representing the Genus *Oxybelis*. This had formerly been considered a strictly tropical genus, not extending farther north than the humid parts of central Mexico.

When the new species was first described, it was explained that the range was indicated as covering the Calabasas Cañon, extending from the Santa Cruz Valley, about fifty miles south of Tucson, to and across the International Boundary west of Nogales, in the Tumacacori Mountains. The range also includes the area about Tucson. The type was taken about four miles north of the boundary, and a second specimen was captured in the outskirts of the city of Tucson. Here is another of the rarities to be sought by the reptile student.

Habits: The tropical species of *Oxybelis* are persistently arboreal, living in low trees or thick bushes. Resting in the foliage, in extended undulations they so resemble vines or twisted branches that they are extremely difficult to detect. With all of my Central and South American specimens—and I have noted the actions of many—their favorite food consisted of lizards, which they grasped and by chewing motions imbedded the posterior, grooved fangs. Within a few minutes the prey is paralyzed by the poison, when it is swallowed. In frequent instances I have seen the prey swallowed while still alive, but it was almost inert. Thus the poison does not appear to be quickly lethal as with elapine and crotaline snakes. While they are not ordinarily inclined to bite when handled, I regard any species of *Oxybelis* as warranting caution, though not dangerously poisonous.

THE LYRE SNAKES
Genus *Trimorphodon*

These are moderate-sized, rather slow-moving snakes, of moderate thickness, but tapering to slender neck, on which the head is broad and very distinct, swollen at the temples, with large eyes having *elliptic pupils*. From this latter character the snakes of this genus and the succeeding one may be distinguished from other North American colubrine serpents—excepting the little Rock Snake, *Hypsiglena,* and Leaf-nosed Snakes, *Phyllorhynchus,* which are not rear-fanged. The members of this and the succeeding genus are similar in form, but differ in arrangement of head shields. With *Trimorphodon,* there are two loreal plates, on each side of the head. These are the small shields between the oculars, bordering the eye anteriorly, and rear nasal shield. With *Leptodeira* (succeeding) there is one loreal plate or shield. The three species of *Trimorphodon* are characterized by a lyre-shaped blotch at top of the head.

The snakes of both genera feed mostly upon lizards, which are overcome by poison from the posterior, grooved fangs.

Arizona Lyre Snake, *Trimorphodon lyrophanes* (Cope)

Size: 2½ –3 feet. The following dimensions are of an adult: Total length 30 inches; length of tail 6 inches; diameter at middle ⅝ inch; width of head ⅞ inch.

Form and scalation: Body sharply tapering towards neck and tail. The head is broader than diameter of body. Pupil elliptic. Scales smooth.

Coloration: Pale gray, with about twenty pairs of dark brown blotches along back and an irregular row of smaller blotches on each side. Abdomen whitish, with dark spots along the edges of the shields. *A large, dark brown, lyre-shaped blotch at top of the head.*

Distribution: Arizona and southern Utah.

Habits: Collected in boulder-strewn areas. These snakes sometimes climb into low bushes. As captives they feed upon small lizards, grasping them, thence advancing the jaws in chewing motions until the fangs are imbedded. Lizards appear to die within five minutes or so of retained hold.

Cowles and Bogert have studied the effects of the poison and produced an article on their observations (*Copeia,* 1935, No. 2, pp. 80 – 85). They demonstrate that the bite of these rear-fanged snakes, while capable of killing small lizards, was not lethal to small mammals—such as mice.

Van Denburgh's Lyre Snake, *Trimorphodon vandenburghi* Klauber

Size, form and scalation similar to preceding, but the anal plate is usually entire—that of *T. lyrophanes* usually divided.

Coloration: The blotches are more regularly disposed than with with *T. lyrophanes.*

Distribution: Southern Nevada and southern California. It is the only species of *Trimorphodon* recorded from California.

Wilkinson's Lyre Snake, *Trimorphodon vilkinsoni* Cope

Size and form similar to the two preceding species.

Coloration: The pairs of dorsal blotches are quite widely separated as compared with the more western species (preceding). The lyre-shaped blotch of the preceding may be represented by three dark spots on the head.

Distribution: Mexico, extending into extreme western Texas.

Habits: All three species appear to be similar.

Annulated Snake, Bush Snake, *Leptodeira septentrionalis* (Kennicott)

Size: Average adult length about 30 inches; tail about one fifth of total length.

Form and scalation: Body of moderate thickness, tapering to slender neck. Head flat, swollen at temples and much wider than neck. One loreal plate. Scales smooth. Pupil elliptic. Form similar to *Trimorphodon.*

Coloration: Greenish to yellowish gray, with large black or dark brown blotches, 6 – 8 scales in width of extension along the back and extending downward nearly to margins of abdominal shields; abdomen yellowish. A pale band across rear of head.

Distribution: Northeastern Mexico, extending into southern Texas.

Habits: Captive specimens are inclined to hide under stones or bark, and from this it would seem that when wild this snake is secretive, or, judging from its catlike eye pupils, is nocturnal. One specimen laid a dozen eggs, yellowish white, with leathery integument, but they were infertile. They were hidden under a flat stone, in a cavity scooped in some sand. My specimens preferred small lizards, but also took young mice and small frogs. I would not recommend too close familiarity with rear-fanged snakes. While the action of the poison of this snake may be as mild as that of the members of *Trimorphodon,* it has not been closely studied, and there is possibility of after-effects from a bite, though but mildly poisonous, becoming susceptible to bacterial invasion. Tissue may be weakened, producing areas that are planting grounds for septic conditions.

CHAPTER XIII

The Poisonous Snakes of Western North America

THE DANGEROUSLY POISONOUS snakes of the western section of this field book fit into three divisions of classification, as follows:

1. The *Elapidae;* **Elapine Snakes:**

The New World representatives are the Coral Snakes. This is a large family with its headquarters in the Old World. It contains the Cobras, Kraits, Mambas and variety of kinds in Australia. Its members as a rule, in outline, do not typify the common idea of poisonous snakes. They are relatively slender-bodied, with but moderately distinct heads as with the average harmless snakes. Their poisons are largely neurotoxic—attacking the nerve centers. The New World Coral Snakes, all brilliantly ringed with scarlet, yellow and black, are numerously represented in the tropics—with two occurring in the southern United States. One enters the southeastern portion of the western section, hence is included among the western reptiles. It is described among the southeastern snakes. The other poisonous Coral Snake occurs in southern New Mexico, southern Arizona and on one island in the Gulf of California. Owing to secretive habits and short fangs, accidental bites from these snakes are infrequent. The body is slender and maximum length about a yard.

2. The *Hydrophidae;* **Sea Snakes:**

This is a large family inhabiting the tropical oceans of the eastern hemisphere. One species occurs commonly in the southern Gulf of California, thence southward to northern South America. It does not occur on the Atlantic side of tropical America. The Sea Snakes are characteristic in having a vertically compressed body and much compressed (vertically) paddlelike tail. The species inhabiting the waters of southwestern North America is from two to three feet long.

3. The *Crotalidae;* Pit Vipers, Rattlesnakes, Water Moccasin and Copperhead Snakes:

The term Pit Viper comes from a deep pit between eye and nostril. This is largely a New World family, with headquarters of its rattlesnakes in North America and dwindling species through Mexico, and but two inhabiting South America—only one of the latter with broad distribution. South America, however, has an imposing number of pit vipers without rattles, among them the Bushmaster (*Lachesis*), the world's longest viperine snake.

Over a vast area of western North America the only poisonous serpents are rattlesnakes. The Copperhead Snake, so numerous in the East, extends as far westward as Oklahoma and central Texas. The Water Moccasin crosses the Mississippi into Missouri and Arkansas, thence ranges southward into eastern Texas.

Descriptions follow in continuity of family outlines:

Texas Coral Snake, *Micrurus fulvius tenere* (Baird and Girard)

Size: Seldom as long as a yard. Average length about 24 inches, with diameter of ½ inch.

Form and scalation: Slender and cylindrical, with but little taper the entire length. Head blunt and barely distinct from the neck. Scales smooth and lustrous. Pupil round.

Coloration: Broad rings of deep scarlet and blue black, separated by narrower rings of yellow. Snout black; a wide band of yellow crossing middle of head, and behind this *the first black ring* of the body pattern. The red rings are usually speckled with black. The dorsal colors are carried across the abdomen.

Distribution: The typical form, *Micrurus fulvius fulvius,* ranges from the Carolinas to the Gulf and crosses the Mississippi into Arkansas, extreme southeastern Oklahoma, thence extends into eastern Texas to intergrade with a form with wider yellow rings—*M. fulvius tenere.* It is indicated that this form may extend well towards central Texas. Nearer the coast it is recorded from Victoria County, and Stejneger has stated that along the Rio Grande it extends up to the mouth of the Pecos.

In July of 1938, an entirely black specimen, the first on record, was captured at Victoria, Texas. Its finding was attended by a serious bite, the symptoms and treatment attending which have been described by Dr. Howard K. Gloyd in *Herpetologica,* Vol. 1,

No. 5, 1938, with a photograph of this unusual specimen compared with one of normal pattern.

Sonoran Coral Snake, *Micruroides euryxanthus* (Kennicott)

Size: Up to a yard, but average length about 20 inches, with diameter at that length of about ½ inch.

Form and scalation: Rather slender, head blunt and not distinct. Scales smooth and polished.

Coloration: Rings of brick red or crimson and about equal rings of black, these separated by yellow rings of lesser width. Snout black, followed by a broad band of yellow, this succeeded by the first *red ring* of 'the body pattern, the species thus differing from the eastern Coral Snake, in which the headband is followed by a black ring.

The colors and pattern of this dangerous snake should be checked with the coloration of *Lampropeltis zonatus* and *L. pyromelana* (see key of Chapter X). These harmless "mimics," the latter extending into the range of the poisonous Coral Snake, have similar coloration, but the combination of ring contact is different. On flash examination both harmless and dangerous kinds may appear much alike.

Distribution: Southern New Mexico, southern Arizona, Tiburon Island, in the Gulf of California, and northern Mexico.

Habits: But two examples have been in my collection, but both acted alike and similarly to the eastern Coral Snake, *Micrurus fulvius*. This snake does not strike, but, if touched, will snap from side to side, fasten its jaws upon an offending object, retain its hold and chew in an endeavor to imbed its short fangs. From the few reports I have had regarding such bites upon humans of the similarly sized and related eastern Coral Snake, I regard this species as extremely dangerous, and particularly so because of its attractive colors and slender outlines as compared to the forbidding appearance and spectacular defense of the rattlers inhabiting its range. While of far lesser bulk than a rattlesnake, the neurotoxic secretion from its glands and wounds from its small fangs may produce as serious consequences as bites of the bulky pit vipers.

The food appears to consist of the smaller nonvenomous snakes and lizards. The species lay eggs.

Yellow-bellied Sea Snake, *Pelamydrus platurus* (Linnaeus)

Size: Dimensions of an adult follow: Total length 28 inches; tail 3½ inches.

Form and scalation: Body vertically compressed. Tail vertically flattened to be thin and paddlelike and slightly higher than the body at its thickest part. Greatest lateral thickness ¾ inch. The form is rather eellike, with elongated head. There are no enlarged abdominal shields, the body above and beneath covered with small, rounded scales.

Coloration: Upper portion dark brown or black, the lower half of body yellow. The line of demarkation is sharp and extends along the upper and lower halves of the compressed form when seen from the side. The tail is usually barred with yellow and brown or black.

Distribution: Ranging widely through the tropical Pacific and Indian oceans, this species extends into the Gulf of California at least as far north as Espiritu Santo Island, thence southward along the Pacific coasts of Mexico and Central America.

Habits: This snake is no hazard to humans unless hauled up in fish nets, when it may try to bite. It feeds upon fishes and eels, and its poison quickly subdues such prey, which are gripped by the fangs until their struggles have ceased. During visits to Panama, where these reptiles are not uncommon, I have heard of no instances of these snakes biting bathers. There was an authenticated account of a man swimming ashore from a disabled launch and unwittingly making his way through a small school of these snakes. He was terrified to find himself among them, but they parted to give him a lane of progress, and there was no indication of attack. These snakes give birth to living young, and the female seeks tide pools where the progeny may gain strength away from the roll of outside waters.

The **Pit Vipers:**

These are very different poisonous snakes from the preceding. The body is heavy and the head wide and distinct. All or the greater number of plates under the tail are in a single row. There is the pit between eye and nostril, and the pupil is elliptic. The fangs are long, folding against the roof of the mouth when the jaws are closed. The poison is hemolitic, destroying tissue and red blood cells. These snakes *strike* from a lateral, anterior loop.

Southern Copperhead Snake, *Agkistrodon mokasen mokasen* (Beauvois)

Size: 2½ to 4 feet long, the latter length exceptional. A large example may be listed as 33 inches long, with diameter of $1\frac{1}{4}$ inch at thickest part and width of head 1 inch.

Form and scalation: Rather stout; head distinct. Greater number of plates under tail in a single row. Body scales moderately keeled.

Coloration: Pale brown or pinkish brown, with a series of rich brown, hourglass-shaped crossbands along the back, $2-3$ scales wide along the dorsal area and widening so abruptly on the sides that, in profile, they appear triangular.

Distribution: The southeastern states to northeastern Texas; the Mississippi Valley states, with overlapping, related form or race, one extending into Oklahoma and well into Texas.

A geographical race of the Copperhead Snake, recently defined as *A. mokasen cupreus* (Rafinesque), has bands not so constricted on the back and defined as "spool-shaped" or $3-5$ scales wide along the dorsal area. I am not as yet convinced of the logic in splitting the Copperhead into the subspecies indicated, as pattern variants appear to crop up in separated regions. This form, the Northern Copperhead, however, is indicated as occurring as follows:

"Eastern Oklahoma and eastern Kansas; higher areas of west-central and northwestern Arkansas, Missouri (except southeastern part) . . . specimens intergrading with *mokasen*" (the typical form) "are known from northeastern Arkansas, southeastern Missouri. . . ." (Gloyd and Conant.)

Broad-banded Copperhead, *Agkistrodon mokasen laticinctus* Gloyd and Conant

Size: Smallest of the forms of the Copperhead Snake, seldom exceeding 30 inches.

Form and scalation: Similar to the preceding forms.

Coloration: Pale reddish or pinkish brown, with vividly defined, *wide* reddish-brown crossbands, which are indented along the dorsal area, but much less constricted than in the other subspecies. Tail usually yellowish or greenish, a retention from juvenile character seen with the young of all the forms of the Copperhead. Abdomen pinkish or salmon, typical of all Copperheads, and usually blotched along margins of the plates.

Distribution: This is the most western of forms of the Copperhead Snake. Its range is defined by Gloyd and Conant:

"Western and central Texas, from Jeff Davis, Reeves and Brewster counties eastward to Colorado County; north through central Oklahoma to Cowley County, Kansas. It intergrades with *cupreus* in Okmulgee, Tulsa and Key counties, Oklahoma, and probably with *mokasen* in southeastern Texas."

Habits: See **Copperhead Snake**, Chapter V.

Water Moccasin, Cotton-mouth Snake, *Agkistrodon piscivorus* (Lacépède)

Size: Large, up to 5 feet—but this is exceptional. Measurements of a quite large adult follow: Total length 4 feet; diameter $2\frac{1}{2}$ inches; width of head $1\frac{3}{4}$ inch.

Form and scalation: Stout and heavy-bodied, with wide and distinct head. Scales strongly keeled.

Coloration: Dull olive or brownish, paler on sides, on which are wide, dark bands, which enclose blotches of the body hue. Upper labials yellow, above which is a dark band from eye to angle of mouth. Abdomen yellow, with dark blotches, becoming blackish towards the tail.

Juvenile specimens are reddish, strongly banded with dark transverse blotches, margined with white. In pattern they thus resemble the Copperhead Snake, but lack the marked dorsal constriction of the bands.

Distribution: This is not to be rated as a western reptile. From the Southeast it ranges into eastern Missouri, Arkansas, eastern Oklahoma and the coastal region of Texas.

Habits: See **Water Moccasin**, Chapter IX.

THE RATTLESNAKES
The Genera *Sistrurus* and *Crotalus*

Southwestern North America is the headquarters or congregation of the species of rattlesnakes, whence they radiate northward, eastward and southward in diminution of species, though the respective kinds ranging far from the center of maximum occurrence of species retain strong occurrence in numbers.

The genera of North American rattlesnakes are readily separable by the top-head scalation. Definition of the two genera is in simple terms:

1. *Top of head with large, symmetrical shields.* Three forms in the western region, with one extending to the far western states. Genus *Sistrurus.*

2. *Top of head with small scales, or a few enlarged shields anteriorly.* Over a dozen species, and a number of subspecies, the range of the genus throughout the western region to the Pacific coast. Genus *Crotalus.*

Descriptions follow:

Strecker's Pygmy Rattlesnake; *Sistrurus miliarius streckeri* Gloyd

Size: Moderate—the smallest rattlesnake of the central-western region. Adults about 18 inches long, with diameter slightly over ½ inch.

Form and scalation: Moderately stout; head distinct. Tail slender, with *miniature rattle.* Scales keeled.

Coloration: Gray or brownish gray, with rounded, black dorsal blotches and smaller black spots on sides. There may be a reddish hue between the anterior dorsal blotches. Beneath dull white, blotched with black.

Distribution: In its Mississippi Valley range this form extends into southeastern Missouri, thence southwestward to central Oklahoma, central and southern Texas. It is a common form in Arkansas.

Habits: See **Pygmy Rattlesnake,** Chapter IX.

Massasauga, *Sistrurus catenatus catenatus* (Rafinesque)

Size: Larger than the related (preceding) species. Specimens in excess of 2½ feet are not infrequent, although such length is above the average. The length of a fair-sized adult is 26 inches, with diameter of 1⅛ inch; width of head ¾ inch.

Form and scalation: Fairly stout, tail short with well-developed rattle.

Coloration: Grayish brown, with series of rich brown or blackish saddles along the back, which may be narrowly bordered with white. Usually three series of smaller dark blotches along the sides. Posteriorly, towards the tail, the light and dark hues present a ringed appearance. Two longitudinal dark blotches at posterior top of head. A dark band from eye to angle of mouth. Dull gray beneath, marbled with black, or entirely black.

The body hue may vary to very dark brown, rendering the dark blotches very obscure. There are occasional blackish specimens.

The shielded head of this small rattlesnake serves as a strong distinguishing feature.

Distribution: The typical form occurs from western New York and Pennsylvania to Iowa, southern Minnesota and eastern Nebraska, thence southward through eastern Kansas and Oklahoma. It does not appear to occur through the lowgrounds of the Mississippi Valley.

A more western form, *S. c. edwardsii* (Baird and Girard), with paler ground hue, smaller dorsal spots and less evidence of blotches on the sides, carries the range of this species to southeastern Arizona, through the greater part of Texas, thence within intervening area to meet the typical form.

Habits: While this small rattlesnake in the central West prefers damp or swampy districts, it also ranges into prairie regions. Burt records: "This small rattlesnake was found under a rock in a prairie ledge, one mile northeast of Otto, Cowley County, Kansas. . . ."

Like its smaller ally, *S. miliarius,* the Massasauga will take both cold- and warm-blooded prey. Specimens in my collection have eaten frogs. This is at variance with species of the typical rattlesnake genus, *Crotalus,* which almost invariably refuse other than warm-blooded prey.

The Genus *Crotalus:*

The typical rattlesnakes range from very large to rather small size, the latter not much bigger than the species of *Sistrurus.* The small kinds are Willard's Rattlesnake, of Arizona and northern Mexico, the Green or Ringed Rattlesnake, of the boundary region of Texas, New Mexico, Arizona and adjacent Mexico, and the Horned Rattlesnake or Sidewinder, of desert regions of the southwestern United States. The Florida Diamond-back Rattler and the Western Diamond-back are the giants of the genus, the heaviest-bodied snakes of North America. Closely trailing, as to length, are the Canebrake Rattlesnake and the Black-tailed Rattlesnake. No matter what the species may be, all these reptiles display their identity by presence of a rattle.

Descriptions of the western species follow, the first grouping relating to rattlesnakes with chain of rhomboid or "diamond" markings along the back:

Western Diamond Rattlesnake, *Crotalus atrox atrox* (Baird and Girard)

Size: Very large, up to 6 feet and weight of 15 pounds. The largest size is attained in Texas and northern Mexico. 4 – 5 feet is more within the average. A fair-sized adult shows a total length of 4 feet 6 inches, diameter $2\frac{1}{4}$ inches and width of head 2 inches.

Form and scalation: Stout and heavy; head very broad and distinct. Scales heavily keeled.

Coloration: Gray, yellowish gray, bluish gray, with chain of darker, rhomboid markings, margined with dull white or pale yellow. Tail white, with jet-black rings, which has produced the name, in some areas, of **Coon-tailed Rattlesnake.**

Distribution: Mountains of western Arkansas, extending northeastward to southeastern Missouri, southwestward to Texas (generally), thence ranging to southern Colorado and the region westward to the Sierra Nevada; southward to the boundary and into northern Mexico; southeastern California, with related forms in Lower California.

Coupled with this wide distribution, subspecies extend the range to islands adjacent to Lower California. Subspecies are outlined:

Reddish brown, the pale margins of the rhombs incomplete on the sides:
   C. atrox elegans Schmidt.
Distribution: Appears to occur only on Angel de la Guardia Island.

Reddish gray, with strongly and completely defined pale margins of the chain of rhombs:
   C. atrox lucasensis (Van Denburgh).
Distribution: Southern Lower California—and the only rattler with a symmetrical rhomboid pattern occurring in the region.

Pattern similar to preceding, but difference of head shields. Identification may be simplified by note of its resricted habitat:
   C. atrox tortugensis (Van Denburgh and Slevin).
Distribution: Tortuga Island, Lower California.

Habits: Atrox is a particularly dangerous rattlesnake, wandering in open areas and inclined to strike quickly. The species has a bad record for fatal bites, particularly in Texas, where over broad stretches it is numerous. Its striking coil is dramatic, with partially arched neck and buzzing rattle. As a captive it takes rats, rabbits, guinea pigs and birds, thus indicating its preference for warm-blooded prey, when wild. Large examples are nervous and morose and as a rule are difficult to induce to feed. While I am not advocating conservation of such reptiles in a wild state, there is no doubt about the species being a strong factor in rodent control in its native environment.

Red Diamond Rattlesnake, *Crotalus ruber* (Cope)

Size: Large—to 5 feet.

Form and scalation: Body heavy, head broad and distinct. Scales strongly keeled.

Coloration: Reddish, often of brick-red hue, with chain of darker diamond markings margined with dull white. The tail is in contrast to the body hue, being white, with black rings—similar to the "coon-tail" markings of *atrox.*

Distribution: Klauber defines the range as:

"The narrow belt in California and Lower California west of the desert to the coast, from the north line of Riverside County in California to north central Lower California, but excluding the coastal plains of Los Angeles and Orange counties. It also occurs on Cedros and certain Gulf of California islands."

Curiously enough, this large rattler, while similar in body bulk and pattern to the temperamental *atrox,* is as a rule gentle, not inclined to strike or to rattle. This has been the case with most specimens I have observed. Rather incongruously, for rattlesnakes, some of my specimens declined to bite through the top of a parchment-covered glass as we sought to extract venom in the laboratory. They seemed more surprised than angry when we cautiously held them by the neck and applied their jaws to the extracting apparatus. We got to regard them in friendly spirit, and they reciprocated by feeding readily—even after being forcibly handled. As a captive this rattler will not do well unless kept very dry and warm and given opportunity of sun-basking.

Cedros Island Rattlesnake, *Crotalus exsul* Garman

Size: Smaller than *C. ruber* (the preceding).

Form and scalation: Similar to *C. ruber.*

Coloration: Reddish, with chain of rather obscure dorsal rhombs. Tail white, with black rings.

Distribution: Geographical consideration defines this species, it being recorded only from Cedros Island, west coast of Lower California. It is closely related to *C. ruber,* and its status as a full species is not strong. Geologically speaking, the islands off the coasts of Lower California may have become detached fairly recently from the mainland. Detachment from mainland fauna has resulted in change of feeding conditions, with lack of variety in prowling terrain, reducing in size, possibly otherwise physically changing these island kinds.

Mohave Diamond Rattlesnake, *Crotalus scutellatus* (Cope)

Size: 3½ – 5 feet, the latter exceptionally large.

Form and scalation: Stout and heavy in body; head wide and very distinct. Scales strongly keeled; anterior part of head, from midway between the orbital plates, with enlarged, irregular scales.

Coloration: The pattern resembles *C. atrox,* but the defining differences are as follows: The rhombs or "diamonds" are less angulate or pointed along the center of the back, not tending to produce actual contact or perfectly connected chain in the middle section. There are narrow, but not vivid, black ringlike markings on the tail. Body hue is yellowish to greenish gray.

Compared with the powdery-gray Western Diamond-back, *C. atrox,* with its vividly marked black-and-white tail ("coon-tail" markings), the Mohave Diamond Rattler is a clearly definable snake.

Distribution: Northern Mexico, with extension into southeastern California, Arizona, New Mexico and western Texas. Concerning the range in the southwestern United States, Klauber says:

"In California, the ranges of *scutellatus* and *atrox* do not coincide, as in Arizona. *Scutellatus* inhabits the Mojave Desert and Antelope Valley with a northern extension into the Indian Wells Valley. *Atrox* seems restricted to the Coachella and Imperial valleys, although it is found beyond the Chocolate Mts. in the Palo Verde Valley. In each of these areas so many specimens of the one form have been taken, with none of the other, that separate ranges are strongly indicated."

Habits: A quick-striking, nervous rattlesnake that usually throws itself into coil and rattles vigorously when approached.

Black-tailed Rattlesnake, *Crotalus molossus molossus* (Baird and Girard)

Size: Large, 3½ – 5 feet.

Form and scalation: Stout and heavy; head very distinct. Three pairs of enlarged scales on snout, the two anterior pairs the larger. Body scales strongly keeled, although the general scalation appears finer than with the other larger rattlesnakes.

Coloration: Distinct among the large rattlers of the Southwest by the uniform black tail. While the pattern approaches that of the western Diamond Rattlesnakes, the markings do not assume the form of symmetrical or connected rhombs.

Body hue is rich yellow to pale brown or olive, with a series of dark irregular, rhomblike markings, narrowly and brightly bordered with yellow and containing yellowish centers. Each of these angular blotches has a narrowed and dark extension down the side to the margin of the abdominal plates. The blotches become indistinct posteriorly. *Tail uniform black.*

Distribution: Southern portions of Arizona, New Mexico and Texas. Not uncommon in the Santa Catalina and Rincon mountains, near Tucson, Arizona. It is also fairly common in southwestern Texas. It has wide distribution through arid portions of Mexico.

Habits: Prefers elevated, ledgy country. As a captive its average behavior is quiet and less nervous than the behavior of rattlers that prowl in more open country.

Cope's Rattlesnake, *Crotalus enyo* (Cope)

Size: Not much above a yard.

Form and scalation: Typical of *Crotalus,* except that four to five of the lower rows of scales are without keels.

Coloration: Strongly marked and not dissimilar to *C. molossus.* Ground hue, grayish brown to yellowish, with dark, dorsal rhomblike markings, pale-bordered, not in contact and tending to extend to the sides or break into lateral spots. The pattern is vividly defined. It somewhat resembles that of *molossus* and *C. tigris* (later described), but *C. enyo* is remote, in habitat, from both of those species.

Distribution: Appears to be restricted to the southern portion of Lower California.

The *C. viridis* group:

From a typical form of the prairies to southern Canada, there are radiating, related forms extending to the Pacific coast and the boundary region of the Southwest.

Prairie Rattlesnake, *Crotalus viridis viridis* (Rafinesque) (formerly *Crotalus confluentus*)

Size: Large, but varying according to locality. The usual run is 3 – 4 feet and an adult before me, from Wyoming, is 40 inches long, with diameter of $1\frac{3}{4}$ inch. Exceptional specimens are close to 6 feet long, relatively much heavier-bodied than smaller examples, and are up to $2\frac{1}{2}$ inches in diameter, with indented, dorsal line indicating exceptionally good feeding grounds, hence large and heavy body.

Form and scalation: Typical rattlesnake form; scales strongly keeled. Head with uniformly small scales, except the ocular plates.

Coloration: Greenish yellow, olive or tan with series of large, rounded and well-separated brown blotches along the back, which are usually bordered with white or dull yellow. The blotches become obscure towards the tail where they form bands.

Head markings are important in distinguishing the typical form from the several subspecies. With the Prairie Rattlesnake there is a wide, dark band from beneath the eye to the labial plates, bordered at front and rear by a narrow yellow band, each about the width of one head scale. Each eye plate is marked with two white or yellow lines, which run together to form a point at the outer margin.

Distribution: The range is wide and, quoting Stejneger, may be defined:

"Broadly speaking, the Prairie Rattlesnake occupies the area bounded in the east by the 96th Meridian and the upper Missouri Valley; by the main divide of the Rocky Mountains in the West; by the 33rd Parallel in Texas and the Mexican boundary further west in the South; and by the 50th Parallel in the North. In the Northeast its distribution appears to be limited by the watershed between the Missouri and the Red River of the North, according to Dr. Coues (Bull. Goal. Surv. Terr. IV, 1878, p. 267), who collected numerous specimens along the Canadian border between this watershed and the crest of the Rockies. He also states that it is to be considered fairly common in the region of the upper Missouri and Milk River and some of their Northern tributaries; its range thus extending some distance into the British Possessions, where Mr. James M. Macoun informs me that it is most abundant from Medicine Hat, on the Saskatchewan, to the boundary."

Notation of subspecies and their distribution, to follow, encroaches on the preceding, which was outlined before *viridis* (*confluentus*) was considered to indicate subspecific forms.

Burt and Hoyle record the typical form from Kansas, South Dakota and Wyoming, and Curtiss, indicating its occurrence in western Iowa, says: ". . . This is the species (of rattlesnake) of the Great Plains, where it is often encountered in the prairie dog 'villages' where it takes toll of the rodents, some of whose deserted holes it occupies. . . ."

Habits: This is an active rattlesnake, though accidental bites, as compared to its numbers and broad range, are uncommon. It is a strong factor in rodent control, and I am averse to developing tendency of destruction of rattlesnake dens in remote areas by blasting and gassing. Such practices of elimination might follow encroachment of cultivated areas where hazard from snakes may be really indicated. Rodents are, unfortunately, a strong factor of loss to western farmers and an indicated disease menace from recent investigations, yet the natural enemies of rodents among many persons appear to be regarded with more aversion than the pests themselves.

That I am not alone in the preceding contention is indicated by M. Graham Netting, of the Carnegie Museum, in his review of Clifford H. Pope's excellent book entitled *Snakes Alive*. The review contains the following:

"The author gives some support to the proponents of poisonous snake eradication campaigns in the United States, although systematic slaughter except in populous areas is scarcely justifiable. Bubonic plague is endemic in some parts in our West and tularemia is not unknown in the East. Either of these diseases is potentially far more dangerous than the pit-vipers which prey on rodent carriers. I question whether 160 persons die annually in the United States from snake poisoning. Even if the figure is correct it can be shown that a greater number of persons have fatal accidents in their bathtubs, against which there is no campaign."

Related forms: In considering the kinds under this grouping, those occurring south of the range of the typical form will first be treated. The extreme western and Pacific forms, with their extended distribution and greater distinctness, will complete the listing. The southern forms follow:

Arizona Prairie Rattlesnake, *Crotalus viridis nuntius* (Klauber)
Size: 2½ – 3 feet.
Form and scalation: Similar to the typical *viridis,* but with inclination to be more slender than the average of the rattlesnake genus.
Coloration: Reddish brown, with dark, rounded blotches, narrowly edged with white or yellow. On the anterior third the blotches are similar to the typical form, thence are smaller, more numerous and less distinct.
Distribution: Arid sections of Arizona. Klauber defines the significance of the subspecific name: "Nuntius, the messenger. In the Hopi Snake Ceremonial, these snakes are used as messengers to the gods of the underworld."

Grand Canyon Rattlesnake, *Crotalus viridis abyssus* (Klauber)
Size: 3 – 4 feet. Body outlines like the preceding forms.
Coloration: Klauber's description reads, in part: "Adult color vermilion or salmon; body blotches obsolete in adults."
Distribution: Grand Canyon of the Colorado River, Arizona. But few specimens have been collected.

Midget Faded Rattlesnake, *Crotalus viridis concolor* (Woodbury)
Size: Smallest of the *viridis* group, with adult length appearing to be under 3 feet.
Coloration: Pale buff or straw color, with barely discernible row of rounded blotches along the back and a series of smaller, obscure blotches on the sides. The tail is faintly marked with dark rings, the last one only being evident enough to be clearly outlined, in fact the strongest marking on the body.
Distribution: Recorded from the base of the Henry Mountains, Utah. It was first defined and named in 1929, and since that time further records do not appear to indicate extension of its range outside of Utah and western Colorado.

Great Basin Rattlesnake, *Crotalus viridis lutosus* (Klauber)
Size: 3 – 5 feet. One of the larger forms of *viridis.* Body outline similar to that of the typical form.
Coloration: Light brown, buff to sage green, the tone of body hue usually quite pale, making the dark dorsal blotches particularly evident.
A series of irregularly oval, dark blotches along the back, these

blotches well separated, in fact the spaces between them little narrower than the longitudinal width of the blotches themselves, this distinct separation much different from quite close setting of the rounded blotches of the typical form, together with tendency of the blotches of *lutosus* to be narrowly margined with black. This produces a more intensely marked form than the typical Prairie Rattler.

The following differences are defining:

1. In *C. v. viridis* the blotches become dull towards the tail, where they assume rather obscure pale and darker ringlike markings. With *lutosus* the markings on about the posterior third become heavily suffused with black, and transversely ringlike, which is strongly evident towards and on the tail.

2. In typical *viridis* the body blotches are margined with white or yellow. In *lutosus* they are margined with black.

3. In typical *viridis* the two pale headbands, extending obliquely from in front of and behind the eye, are narrow and of about equal width. In *lutosus* the front pale headband is much the broader.

Distribution: Stejneger and Barbour define the range as: "Plateau region from the Rockies to the Sierras, including Utah west of the 111th Meridian, northern and central Nevada, northern California east of the Sierras, southeastern Oregon and southern Idaho."

Habits: This is a strong, alert rattler, to be found in the open under near-desert conditions, or frequenting ledges along the canyons, where in specific places it congregates to hibernate at so-called rattlesnake "dens." While it is a strong and dangerous snake, actions on the average among specimens I have seen are not nearly so irritable as those of the quick-striking, peppery *C. atrox* (*cinereous*) of further south.

The **Panamint Rattlesnake,** *Crotalus viridis stephensi,* has been defined by Klauber as a pallid, desert form of Nevada and eastern California. Its blotches are in form and separation somewhat like those of *lutosus,* though more obscure and margined with scattered white scales. It indicates approach to specimens of the Bleached Rattlesnake, *C. mitchellii,* but with more evident and symmetrical markings than average of the latter—*mitchellii* occurring in deserts to the southward.* There may be intergradation between this snake and *C. mitchellii,* hence *mitchellii* may be no more than a pronounced desert

*From some very recent studies of series of specimens, it appears that *stephensi* may be later accepted as a subspecies of *mitchellii,* which latter contention is illustrated in the classified list forming Chapter XV.

form of the *viridis* group. Its description immediately follows this grouping of the forms of *viridis*. Its arrangement of anterior head shields, however, appears to be unique.

Pacific Rattlesnake, *Crotalus viridis oreganus* (Holbrook)

Size: $3\frac{1}{2}$ – $4\frac{1}{2}$ feet; seldom longer. Average length slightly over a yard.

Form and scalation: Typical rattlesnake outlines; head large, broad and distinct. A 3-foot specimen from near San Bernardino, California, is $1\frac{1}{2}$ inch in diameter.

Coloration: Brown, grayish or olive, with row of large dark blotches along the back in close contact, the narrow spaces between them paler than on the sides, the blotches often with pale margins angulate enough on the sides to indicate a rhomboid pattern. Posteriorly the light and dark marking appear ringlike from above.

In this subspecies there is common tendency towards suffusion with black. Some specimens collected in the mountains of San Bernardino County were velvety black, with a narrow chain of whitish markings, distinctly rhomblike, and I heard them referred to as "black diamondbacks."

Distribution: This is the common and only rattlesnake (in fact the only poisonous snake) of the entire Pacific region—except southern California, where other rattlers occur. It inhabits the Pacific region from southern British Columbia to southern California, ranging through variety of terrain, from low altitudes to elevations in the Sierras of 8,000 feet. Its distribution extends eastward to Nevada and Idaho. Southward the range extends well into Lower California, and there are dwarfed or stunted races on some of the islands off the west coast of California and northern Lower California, particularly Santa Catalina Island and Los Coronados. I have had such specimens, with string of uniform rattle segments, showing full maturity, which were less than 2 feet long.

During my collecting trips the Pacific Rattlesnake was observed in the high timber of the California mountains, and we came across a fine large specimen at a "well" in desert country east of the divide in the Sierras. The largest skins I have seen, slightly topping 4 feet, were at a little roadside stand a bit north from Ensenada, in Lower California. They were strongly blotched. The district was bleak and desertlike, and close behind it were barren hills with rocky ledges. I was told that these snakes were common enough among the hills.

Habits: Collecting trips and talks with a number of persons, both to the west and east of the Pacific mountain chain, indicate to me that the habits of this snake, particularly in the more northern parts of its range, are similar to those of *Crotalus horridus* (see Chapter VI). Encountered on open ground, it may assume a striking coil and rattle vigorously, but if near rock shelter its disposition is to seek to escape from intrusion, gliding under shelving stones—or almost throwing itself into a fissure. If coiled under the edge of a shelving rock, it may remain motionless and quiet, even though closely approached, such tendency indicating that immobility of body may escape the eye of the intruder at its lair. All of my captive specimens have soon become tame and quiet and were readily induced to feed, which is different from the habits of some of the more nervous rattlers. Mice, rats and young rabbits have been the favorite food.

There can be no doubt about the importance of this snake as a factor in rodent control, and while rattlers are dangerous in districts frequented by humans and domestic animals, I consider more far-fetched than practical the energy expended in destroying their dens or places where they congregate for hibernation if such are remote from human contact.

In southern parts of California I could find no definite evidence of these snakes congregating at dens. At elevations, of course, there may be such tendency. From data acquired farther north, in the Cascades, I heard of extensive rattlesnake dens, crevices or great rock slides to which the reptiles returned each year as the weather grew cool.

My most interesting specimens came from islands off the coast of southern California. They were stunted or dwarfed, less than 2 feet long and no thicker than my finger. That they were fully grown and mature was shown by their long rattles, with segments of uniform size. These snakes were unafraid, quiet and could not be induced to rattle. While I didn't try it, as I have strong ideas against taking risks with poisonous snakes, I am convinced they could have been freely handled without their showing resentment. Unlike most rattlers, they would feed at any time and under conditions that would be very disturbing to the average crotaline snake. They did not strike their prey, but glided to it, seized and held it. They would immediately take dead mice offered to them on pair of long forceps, and I once surprised some friends who were interested in reptiles by placing two of them on my open desk, offering each a dead mouse, which was immediately seized and swallowed.

White Rattlesnake, Bleached Rattlesnake, Mitchell's Rattlesnake, *Crotalus mitchellii mitchellii* (Cope)

Size: Compared to the average among the larger rattlesnakes, this species is of but moderate size. An adult is $3 - 3\frac{1}{2}$ feet long.

Form and scalation: Form and width of head typical of the larger western rattlers. The scales are rather more coarsely keeled than the other western species. A difference in the extreme anterior head scalation is important in identification. The large plate in front of the nostril is separated from the plate on the snout—the rostral—by small scales. With other rattlesnakes the anterior nasal and rostral are in contact.

Coloration: Pinkish, pale yellowish gray to bluish gray or almost white, with sprinkling or speckling of dark dots, which on the back are crowded into a series of blotches, not in contact and sometimes angular enough in outline to suggest rhomblike markings. The markings become ringlike towards the tail. While some more strongly marked examples might be mistaken for *C. atrox,* it should be noted that there is not a connected rhomboid chain.

The author has seen specimens of this desert snake so pale that they could quite properly be called "white rattlesnakes."

Distribution: Desert hills and lower mountains of southern Arizona, southern California, Lower California and northwestern Mexico.

Habits: I have not collected or studied this snake in its native environment. As a captive it is timid and quiet, as far as my specimens have shown, requiring to be kept warm and very dry, or it is extremely reticent in feeding.

The **Speckled Rattlesnake, Bleached Rattlesnake, Granite Rattlesnake,** *Crotalus mitchellii pyrrhus* (Cope), is a form occurring in desert parts of San Diego County, California, and close to the eastward. It is defined by more contrasty though irregular markings than the typical *mitchellii.* The pale body is strongly speckled or marked with broken bands of reddish or reddish gray. The body hue may be very pale gray, pale tan or even pink.

Tiger Rattlesnake, *Crotalus tigris* Kennicott

Size: Moderate for the genus—usual length $2\frac{1}{2} - 3$ feet; seldom in excess of a yard.

Form and scalation: Body moderately stout, but head relatively smaller than with other species of *Crotalus.*

Coloration: Yellow, gray or tawny, with numerous, dark, rather narrow crossbands, particularly barred or ringlike on the posterior half. The tail is usually uniform dark—sometimes obscurely ringed.

Definition of markings varies from rather obscure to quite strong pattern. With occasional specimens, a smoky darkening extending from the transverse bands obscures so much of the ground hue that this appears only as dull gray or brownish bars along the posterior part of the body along the sides.

Distribution: Desert mountains of Arizona (possibly southeastern Nevada and extreme southeastern California) ; northwestern Mexico.

Habits: I have found this to be a quiet, lethargic snake as a captive, mostly indifferent to the type of food taken by other rattlers. It is possible that with abundance of sunshine and air-conditioning of its quarters in simulation of desert environment, it might thrive as a captive. Experiments are shaping along these lines in maintenance of various desert types. Here is a field for the reptile student interested in solving unusual problems.

Banded Rattlesnake, Timber Rattlesnake, *Crotalus horridus horridus* (Linnaeus)

Size: Large—to 6 feet (exceptional). Dimensions of a fair-sized specimen follow: Total length 3 feet 8 inches; diameter $1\frac{5}{8}$ inch.

Form and scalation: Stout and heavy; head wide and distinct. Scales strongly keeled.

Coloration: Yellow to brown, sometimes blackish, with wide, dark crossbands, usually angulate at the rear. The bands are sometimes broken into three series of blotches, the larger ones along the back. Head usually unmarked ; tail black.

Distribution: An eastern rattler, with but moderate extension into the central-western regions of the United States, being recorded in southeastern Wisconsin, southeastern Minnesota, Iowa, southeastern Nebraska, eastern Kansas, eastern Oklahoma and as far westward in Texas as Victoria County. The typical form occurs in hilly, moun-tainous and ledgy country. Burt, in "Records of Kansas Reptiles," says :*

*Transactions Kansas Academy of Science, Vol. 36, 1933.

"According to a report of M. J. Harbaugh, he observed a den of about 25 of these timber rattlesnakes on October 1, 1932, at a place known as the 'Devil's Backbone,' which is located on a slope about 75 feet above a creek at a point $3\frac{1}{2}$ miles northwest of Irving, Marshal County. There were many rock crevices in the numerous boulders of this vicinity, and at one place the den of buzzing rattlers was located. Due to protection afforded by their habitat, only 5 of these snakes could be captured."

Curtiss, in *The Snakes of Iowa,** states:

"Of our three rattlesnakes, the only venomous snakes found within our borders, this is the most common. This form probably maintains its numbers more readily than does the Massasauga because of its preference for rocky places in timbered regions where ordinary farming operations and the grass fires do not imperil it so often and where it may more readily escape from its one arch-enemy —man."

In the region immediately west of the Mississippi, in Missouri, Arkansas, western Louisiana and coastal Texas, the form recognized as the **Canebrake Rattlesnake** or **Velvet-tail,** *Crotalus horridus atricaudatus* (Latreille), takes the place of the typical *horridus.* The body hue is gray to pinkish gray, the crossbands quite intense black and chevron-shaped, or pointed at the rear, while there is a rusty-red, yellowish or brownish band along the back, more prominent anteriorly. There is a dark band from the eye to angle of mouth. As a rule *atricaudatus* attains an average larger size than the typical form.

Habits: See **Canebrake Rattlesnake,** Chapter IX.

Willard's Rattlesnake, *Crotalus willardi* Meek

Size: Smallest among the species of *Crotalus.* Appears not to grow much longer than 15 inches.

Form and scalation: Body relatively stout, but with rattle slender and small as compared to body size. Head, large, wide and distinct.

Coloration: This is a very distinct species of *Crotalus,* particularly because of its unique head markings. The body hue is grayish, with large dark blotches separated by narrow crossbands (almost linelike) of paler hue.

*Iowa State College of Agriculture, Bulletin 239, 1926.

The head is dark, with two whitish or yellow stripes beneath the eye, in strong contrast. The upper of these stripes extends obliquely downward from the snout backward to cover the rear labial plates; the lower extends from the margin of the snout plate (rostral) along the front labial plates. There is a vertical pale bar on the snout (rostral plate).

Distribution: Whether this curious rattler is rare or collectors have not located its lurking places among the mountain ledges remains to be seen and should be a lure in seeking further knowledge of the species. So far as is known, its range is into the Santa Rita Mountain region of Arizona from northern Mexico.

Habits: These remain to be elucidated from search and observation.

Spotted Rattlesnake, *Crotalus triseriatus pricei* (Van Denburgh)

Size: Small. Following are measurements of an adult: Total length 21 inches; diameter ½ inch.

Form and scalation: Relatively stout. Head more narrow and oval than with the larger rattlesnakes; less wide and bulging at the neck. Rattle, as compared to body size, well developed.

Coloration: Brown to grayish, with two or three series of closely set, small brown blotches along the back, narrowly—usually faintly—bordered with white. The usual tendency is for the blotches to fuse transversely on the posterior portion and assume ringlike markings on the tail.

The head has a V-shaped blotch at its base, usually a broad dark band from behind the eye and through the temporal area, and beneath this a whitish and intensifying margin.

Distribution: Northern Mexico, extending into southern Arizona.

Habits: Beyond a disposition to frequent mountainous places and considerable elevations, its habits remain to be noted.

Green Rattlesnake, *Crotalus lepidus lepidus* (Kennicott)

Size: Next to the smallest of the genus—but exceeding *C. willardi.* Following are dimensions of an adult, with rattle of uniform segments: Total length 23 inches; diameter ¾ inch; width of head ¾ inch.

Form and scalation: In comparison with other rattlesnakes this species is rather slender, though its head is flat and distinct.

Coloration: Among the rattlesnakes its pattern is unique. Body hue is olive to greenish gray, with widely separated, narrow black ringlike bands. These bands or semirings are usually (narrowly) bordered with a paler hue. The abdomen is pale and unmarked.

The first black marking is immediately behind the head in the form of a black collar or blotch bluntly forked in front. There are seldom any definite head markings. Some of the body scales between the black half-rings may be tipped with black.

Distribution: Two subspecies have been recognized, the differences not of a nature to produce confusion with other rattlesnakes. *C. lepidus lepidus* ranges along the boundary region at least as far eastward as Eagle Pass, Texas, and is not uncommon. From southwestern Texas, from about the region of El Paso, the form *C. lepidus klauberi* extends through New Mexico to southeastern Arizona. The broader range is within northern Mexico.

Habits: Has been collected at elevations in the mountains, as well as in the plains. I have received specimens that prowled into the outskirts of towns in Texas. As a captive the species appears timid and quiet.

Horned Rattlesnake, Sidewinder, *Crotalus cerastes* Hallowell

Size: Among the smallest of the rattlesnakes. The maximum length is about 30 inches, which is exceptional. Adults commonly range from 18 to 24 inches.

Form and scalation: Quite stout, with flattened and distinct head. Rattle well developed for a snake of its size. Scales coarsely keeled, the central dorsal rows particularly rough, as the keels stand out in knobby fashion.

Distinct among all rattlesnakes in having a blunt but prominent horn over each eye, this being an elongated development of the upper eye shield (the supraocular).

Coloration: Pallid, in keeping with desert habitat. Body hue is yellowish, pale brown, pale gray or pinkish, with rather symmetrical series of darker blotches along the back, with whitish separations. Usually a few black bars on the tail, irregular with average examples, or broken.

Distribution: Found only in desert places, the range including southern Nevada, southwestern Utah, western Arizona and southeastern California.

Habits: The name Sidewinder is appropriate, owing to unique locomotion among rattlesnakes, in fact among all North American snakes, in its pronounced specialization for rapid progress over yielding sand. While able to glide in a fashion normal among rattlesnakes, its motions, when speeded, are by series of loops thrown forward, one loop following another, which moves the reptile at an angle oblique to the direction its head is pointing. Its ability during such travel is grotesque. While on desert reconnoiter east of the southern California mountains, I came upon two of these little rattlers, which rushed off, almost side by side, for the shelter of a clump of sage. A friend in the party, who had not previously seen a Sidewinder, was astonished at the snakes' actions. It had been heavy going for my party after leaving the car on hardpan. The yielding sand impeded our walking, but over this surface the rattlers rushed for the only cover near by. My friend insisted that the snakes' progress could best be described as "galloping." Early that day he had seen the swift and bewildering glide of Desert Racers (*Masticophis*) and, compared to the graceful get-away of such slender reptiles, his designation of the progress of the Sidewinders fitted their specialized antics. About a year later, when in northern Africa, I saw some small vipers go parading across sand in the same way. Quite a few African and Arabian vipers are so fitted for a desert life. Here is impressing demonstration of parallelism, without relationship, among widely separated kinds.

If kept warm and dry and given access to sunlight (though not through glass), the little Sidewinder can be maintained as a captive and becomes very tame. My specimens have preferred small rodents. Two were induced to take Collared Lizards (*Crotaphytus*). It is probable that lizards form a fair part of the natural food, as there is a variety of such species in the desert regions.

Summary of the Rattlesnakes: The key in Chapter X and descriptions in the present chapter illustrate the scope and importance of the main rattlesnake genus (*Crotalus*) and the great range in size of its members from the heavy and powerful *C. atrox* (*cinereous*) to the miniature *C. willardi.* Also, that the headquarters or concentration of species is in southwestern North America.

When reference has been made to snakes having segments of the rattle of uniform width, showing cessation of growth and indicating full maturity, the structure, outline and growth of the rattle may be further elucidated.

Rattlesnakes are born with a single segment or "button"—a knob-like projection at the tail tip. A developing segment awaits uncovering with each shedding of the skin. The button is not dried or loose enough to produce a buzzing sound. Infant rattlers, born in late summer or in early autumn, may develop fast enough to grow the first segment, shed the second skin following birth, and thus before hibernating so dry out or complete hollow attachment or looseness between the first segment and the terminal "button" that they produce audible buzz from the yet miniature caudal appendage. Such examples, the coming warm season, with average three successive sheddings of the skin, will thus acquire a pointed rattle of five "joints"—four segments and the terminal button. Three segments the year are the usual addition, although there may be four and in the extreme southern states as many as five. As the snake grows, the segments or joints increase in size. A pointed rattle, with increasing size of segments, means a growing snake, and if terminated with a "button"—meaning that the rattle has remained perfect and unbroken—may be used as a figuration as to the age of the snake if in a region where there are cold months requiring hibernation. Three segments may be allowed for each year. This is, of course, gross reckoning, but fairly accurate in estimating the age of a snake having a perfect rattle.

The tail of a rattlesnake is carried at an angle oblique to the ground, and the chain of segments forming the rattle sag in crescentic curvature. A rattle of twelve segments or over is inclined to trail the ground at its terminal portion, hence is broken or worn away and the terminal joints are lost. Snakes with a greater number of segments or joints are rare. I regard 16 to 18 joints to be the maximum carried, and few such rattles are to be seen. When the terminal segments of youth (or increasing growth) are thus worn away and lost, and the rattle is of uniform width, the snake observed has ceased growth during possession of such a rattle and for a period that is indeterminate.

Thus the only possibility in figuring the age of a rattlesnake is in noting an example with pointed rattle, or "button," and if the latter and its early attachments are missing, to figure the loss of early segments from the shape of the appendage. My longest observation of rattlesnake longevity was with a Florida Diamond Rattler, which lived for fifteen years and was unfortunately injured and thus died from accidental cause.

PART FIVE

CHAPTER XIV

Treatment of Snake Bites

(*In Humans and Domestic Animals*)

In an illustration among the plates of the head of a venomous snake it is indicated that a bite is attended by relatively deep penetration of a pair of hollow teeth injecting a powerful poison. The Rattlesnakes, Copperhead and Water Moccasin have teeth of this kind to implant their poisons, which produce destructive effect upon the blood and disintegrate tissue. The proportionately small and slender Coral Snakes, having very short fangs, retain their hold in biting and chew with venom-injecting teeth, moderately imbedding a powerful neurotoxin. The latter poison is highly dangerous in progressively paralyzing effect upon nerve centers, without marked damage to blood and tissue. In injuries from both types, remedial measures consist of extraction or mechanical drainage of poison from the bitten area, plus neutralization of what poison may have entered the body circulation. Treatment of snake bite is not complicated but should be performed with a clear picture of what may occur, the strength or development of symptoms, plus understanding of the relative gravity from bites of different kinds of snakes.

The strike of any of the Pit Vipers or Crotalids (Rattlesnakes, Copperhead and Water Moccasin) consists of a forward thrust of the head from a lateral loop. The average stroke is about one third the reptile's length, but may be as much as half the length. With the lunge the jaws are thrown wide open and the fangs project forward. As the fangs reach the offending object, they are driven in by the force of the lunge, and at the instant of penetration there is a biting action, with contraction of muscles against the temporal poison glands, this forcing venom forward and out of the fangs. The whole operation is performed like a flash, with head as quickly returning, and is actually a stabbing stroke aided by a bite and resulting in injection of poison. If the snake is large the injection is relatively deep; also, if the action is well directed, a proportionately large amount of poison may be imbedded. While toxicity of venom among the Crotalids differs to some extent, the danger from snake bite in North America may mostly be rated upon the size of the snake. A Copperhead of average size—about two and half feet long—will produce fang penetration of about a quarter of an inch, a rattler of about five feet will have fangs about half an inch long, while with the big Diamond-backs of the southern and southwestern regions there may be fang length of nearly an inch. The larger rattlers may inject four to five times as much venom as a Copperhead, hence a figuration of relative danger in comparing snakes and injuries inflicted.

Circulation of snake venom into the body is much slower than commonly surmised. A rapid swelling follows the bite. This tightens surrounding tissue and constricts channels of absorption. There is rush of serous fluid to the affected parts, this diluting and producing a certain neutralizing effect on the poison in its extension. The larger the body bulk or blood content of the victim, the less the danger, although the amount of venom injected by a big snake may overwhelm the largest victim unless remedial measures are prompt and thorough.

Two such measures are available. Life or grave and permanent injury may be saved with one or the other. It is far better to employ both.

As has been noted, the bite results in the injection of a powerful toxin, rather slowly absorbed or circulated; hence prompt drainage of the poisoned area is of great importance. This may be effected by a simple device, a small cupping outfit of a type well known and produced by several of the larger surgical concerns. It is inexpensive, but highly efficacious. Small incisions are made into the fang wounds and poisoned blood is drawn away. While *prompt* treatment points to the probability of great reduction of grave symptoms, suction is worth while even though several hours have elapsed. Considerable venom may be dammed in the serum-flooded swelling surrounding the wound. If suction is quickly resorted to, a moderately tight ligature should be applied to the bitten limb to retard circulation into the body. Such ligature should be removed about every fifteen minutes and left off for a couple of minutes, to re-establish circulation. This treatment should intermittently continue for an hour, and much longer with elimination of ligature, if the swelling invades a large area. Surgical advice points to additional drainage incisions following the margin of large and progressive swelling.

The associated remedial measure is the injection of neutralizing anti-venin. This is a sterile horse serum, from animals immunized against the poisons of North American snakes. The serum is provided in hypodermic syringe-tubes, with attachable needle and plunger. The tube contains 10 cc. of the neutralizing serum, each cc. of which neutralizes 3 milligrams of snake poison—the total neutralizing power of a tube thus acting upon 30 mgm. of poison that may be injected by the bite of a snake.

It is important to estimate what a bite may amount to, how much poison may have been injected into a bitten part, hence dosage of serum to be indicated.

Antivenomous serum is expensive. It costs from $10 to $12 the 10-cc. tube, but against this is consideration of grave necrotic damage, or even death, that may be the hazard from a snake bite.

While it is difficult to figure accurately the amount of poison in-jected by the bites of snakes of different sizes, the carrying capacity of the venom glands is known through "milking" operation in the labora-tory. These amounts are from 50 to 75 mgm. with a snake the size of a Copperhead, 100 to 125 mgm. from a fair-sized Water Moccasin, up to 150 mgm. from a large Timber Rattlesnake, with average of 250 to 400 mgm. from the big Diamond-back Rattlesnakes, *Crotalus adamanteus* and *C. atrox*.

"Milking" operation in the laboratory, when venom is obtained for immunizing horses, consists of first controlling the snake, thence seizing it by the neck and applying its jaws to a glass with parchment tied over the top. As the snake bites and the fangs pierce the parchment, its poison glands are compressed by the operator's thumb and forefinger. Several more drops of poison are thus obtained than through mere angry biting during which there has been contraction of the temporal muscles over the glands. There is sometimes not much difference in the quantity obtained from a grasping bite *into a parchment* and the quantity obtained from finger compression over the glands.

An angry snake, thus held, bites more deliberately than one which strikes from a coil. My experiments show that the poison glands are but moderately emptied at a natural stroke, there possibly being barely half the amount thus ejected, or injected, than during forceful "milking" in the laboratory. The striking operation is performed in a flash; the head darts forward, the fangs stabbing and, at the instant of penetration, more firmly imbedded by a biting motion. During these almost simultaneous actions there has been included the contraction and compression of muscles to squeeze the poison glands—but the train of action is so quick that the human eye can detect little more than a dart and return of the serpent's head.

With deduction of the snake's stroke as against venom obtained in laboratory extraction, it is thus fair theory to estimate *at barely half* the amount injected by striking as compared with the amount obtained during the "milking" process. Hence amounts to be counteracted per milligram in accidental snake bite against cubic centimeters of serum stand thus: Approximately 35 mgm. for a Copperhead Snake, as much as 60 mgm. for a fair-sized Water Moccasin, 75 mgm. for a large Timber Rattlesnake, with possibility of up to 200 mgm. for the big and long-fanged Diamond Rattlers. As already mentioned, the syringe-tube of antivenomous serum for human use contains 10 cc. of neutralizing serum, and in the human of average weight this amount appears to reduce the destructive effect of up to 30 mgm. of snake poison. This would indicate the injection of least one tube of serum for a Copperhead bite for a human adult *and more for a child of much less body bulk,* and six to eight tubes for an adult in case of bites from the big rattlers, the administration of these successive injections to be guided or governed by gravity of symptoms and possibly disturbing serum reaction of the patient.

Before administering such large doses of serum, it is important to resort to prompt and continued suction treatment. Such treatment means the lesser destruction of tissue and shock to the organism if the bulk of the venom, while localized, is promptly reduced.

Moderate ligation, incision of fang punctures and suction are not dangerous procedures, and, as noted, are highly efficacious. One or two initial, protective injections of serum may be made in the field, although intolerance of certain persons to horse serum should be borne in mind. Packages of antivenomous serum contain clear instructions, but I would rather see the victim of snake bite headed toward a doctor—suction being steadily maintained—before large doses of serum are administered. There are now few parts of the North American continent, with its radial penetration of automobile roads or trails, where medical advice is not available within a few hours.

Dr. Dudley Jackson, of San Antonio, Texas, has demonstrated that much of the poison remains localized in the area of the wound for hours, sometimes for days. His findings show that a lethal dose for dogs, with no treatment, is one mgm. of venom to the pound of body weight. A laboratory subject was injected wtih rattlesnake poison much in excess of the lethal dose, and after swelling took place suction was applied and the bloody serum recovered was injected into four other dogs. Two of these died, and the other two suffered such sloughs that they were killed. The dog from which the serum was extracted by suction recovered.

Other points of care should be noted. The bitten person should exert himself as little as possible. If it is necessary to walk, he should maintain a slow or moderate gait. The wounds should never be cauterized, as such destruction of tissue interferes with drainage, adds to the breakdown of poisoned tissue and is the reverse of proper treatment. While in recent years the use of potassium permanganate has been derided as useless, even dangerous, I still recommend it, provided that understanding and common sense are used in its application. Its oxidizing effect in *mild* fluid form reduces the toxicity of venom with which it comes in contact. While this action may be superficial as compared to the high efficiency of suction treatment, I continue to recommend potassium permanganate as an oxidizing agent to reduce bacteria that may have been carried into the fang wounds from the snake's mouth— and highly pathogenic forms may thus be transmitted, among them *B. welchi,* the gas bacillus; hence washing of wounds with permanganate is well worth while to reduce the danger of infection from microorganisms. I recommend permanganate to be carried in a field kit as one of the most practical germicides to be stowed in small space. A vial no thicker than a penholder and a couple of inches long, containing compressed tablets or dry crystals, will make several quarts of solution when but a small portion of the contents is simply dropped into water. The word of caution about such solution is that it will damage tissue if applied too strong. Color may grossly define it as good for use or injurious. It should look like heavy red wine, not deeply purple. A mild solution will not induce necrosis; a strong solution is injurious to tissue; and to rub pure crystals into a wound is utterly rash and as reprehensible as cauterization.

It should be understood, so that precautions shall be unrelaxed, that one effect of snake poison is to reduce resistance to germ or bacterial multiplication and spread; hence the danger of possible infection, other than from microorganisms from the snake's mouth, unless the wounds are protected and kept clean. The wound areas should be covered with mild antiseptic wet dressings for about a week after marked symptoms have been alleviated. A saturated solution of boric acid is a good wet dressing. Such moistening and softening of wound areas also induces serous drainage, which may continue for some time.

Whisky has no effect in neutralizing snake poison. In mildly stimulating doses to a depressed or frightened victim it may be of benefit. In larger quantities it may do considerable harm.

The manifestations of snake-bite poisoning vary according to amount of venom injected, which largely depends upon the size of the snake, or even, with larger snakes, the character of a bite. In the latter case there may be penetration from but one fang, or the co-ordination of fang penetration and discharge of venom may function a split second out of kilter, with little injection of venom. Mr. George P. Meade, of Grammercy, Louisiana, recently told me about a man in his neighborhood who was struck by the fangs of a large Water Moccasin and suffered nothing beyond soreness from the perforations. Such a mild effect following bites from the larger snakes, however, is rare. Symptoms following bites of poisonous snakes include burning pain and quick, puffy swelling. Severity of poisoning is soon indicated by profuse perspiration, reflex nausea, extension and continuation of swelling.

Persons going into regions where poisonous snakes are known to be frequently encountered should carry a suction outfit, at least. It is inexpensive and may be stowed in one's pocket. Doctors in regions of indicated hazard should be stocked with antivenomous serum, and this should apply to ranches, extensive farms and field contacts of organizations employing linemen or other such workers.

Leather leggings (puttees) or high, thick boots are good protection. The majority of bites are on the lower limbs. Care should be taken in descending steep places, as in such instances bites have been recorded above the knees. It is rash to use one's hands in climbing ledgy places unless the hold has been scrutinized as safe.

A good point to remember is that a "dead" snake is not safe. I have heard of several accidents—indicating that there may be more—where snakes have been killed and the heads chopped off and the slayer attempted to pick up the severed neck and head. Enough reflex muscular stimulus remained to activate the head in turning and biting. A recent, nearly fatal case was of this kind.

SNAKE BITES AMONG DOMESTIC ANIMALS

Poisonous snake bites occur among bovines, equines and more frequently among dogs, particularly of the more valuable, hunting types. The greater number of injuries to large stock occur in the West and Southwest and among canines in the southeastern United States. Consideration of injuries among canines reverts to what has been said in regard to bitten humans—the lesser danger with large body and blood bulk. In considering the administration of antivenin to bitten dogs, we check back to amounts of poison injected by different kinds of snakes. On this subject I am indebted to Dr. Thomas S. Githens, of the Mulford Biological Laboratories, at Glenolden, Pennsylvania, where antivenin is produced. Dr. Githens has written me:

"In order to make antivenin available for use in domestic animals at a price lower than that of the syringe package for human use, we put up unconcentrated antivenin in 50 cc. bottles. Of this 1 cc. neutralizes 1 mgm. of standard venom, so that the total immunizing power is greater than that of the 10 cc. syringe, each cc. of which neutralizes 3 mgm. This unconcentrated serum is available only for the Nearactic Crotalidic Antivenin, used in North America. . . . As to dosage we have not much information, but it is certain that dogs, probably on account of their smaller size, require relatively larger doses than adult humans, while cattle and horses seem to be more relatively protected. We have only 18 reports of cows and horses treated by antivenin, and all recovered. On the other hand, reports received here of 164 dogs bitten by native pit vipers" (Rattlesnakes, Copperhead and Water Moccasin) "show that 45 died in spite of treatment. In most of these the 'human' concentrated form was used. The figures for each species of snake are as follows; 29 bites by 'rattlesnake' in Florida being ascribed to *C. adamanteus*:

"SPECIES				RECOVER	DIE
Copperhead Snake	*Agkistrodon*		*mokasen*	19	1
Water Moccasin	"		*piscivorus*	4	2
Diamond Rattlesnake	*Crotalus*		*adamanteus*	33	29
Western	"	"	*atrox*	9	3
Timber	"	"	*horridus*	17	3
Prairie	"	"	*viridis*	2	0
Pacific	"	"	*v. oreganus*	21	4
Horned	"	"	*cerastes*	2	0
Pygmy	"	*Sistrurus*	*miliarius*	0	2
Species unknown				12	1"

In elucidation of the column of species, it may be noted that *Crotalus adamanteus,* of the southeastern United States, and *C. atrox,* ranging westward, are the largest, hence most dangerous, poisonous snakes of North America. The Pygmy Rattlesnake, *Sistrurus miliarius,* while the smallest of the eastern rattlers, appears to have the highest toxicity of venom, drop for drop, among the North American pit vipers.

The treatment of bitten animals should be checked against explanation of human treatment as previously outlined, with reference to amounts of venom injected by snakes of different sizes and to body bulk of the victim. The problem differs somewhat from human treatment in there being lesser probability of bites upon limbs (particularly with canines), hence impossibility of ligation. Even with bovines and equines the more frequent bites are upon some part of the head as the animal browses—with dogs upon the head or shoulders. Also, the bite may be received sometime before the victim is in contact for treatment, and considerable swelling may have taken place, with spread or dissemination of poison, before the animal comes under observation; hence there may be difficulty in locating the site of the injury and inducing efficient drainage.* Such conditions indicate large doses of neutralizing serum.

Referring to Dr. Githens' figures of 50 mgm. neutralizing power of 50 cc. veterinary package, it will be seen that the smallest amounts to be injected for the bites of the smaller snakes would be the full 50

---

*Injuries to hunting dogs, however, have occurred almost under the eyes of their owners; hence importance of an available suction kit.

cc. bottle and as much as 200 cc. for the big rattlers, or successively four bottles, according to gravity of symptoms. The smaller the animal, the relatively larger dose of serum required; hence animals the size of an average dog should initially receive 100 cc. If treatment has been delayed, the serum may be administered intravenously. With large animals, when symptoms are not of an alarming nature the initial dose may be as low as 50 cc., provided that the subject be kept under observation for development of symptoms which might indicate further injections. As in human treatment, valuable stock should be watched for infection in wound areas, owing to reduced resistance to bacterial invasion, and if the bitten animal is of particularly high value, combined prophylaxis against *B. welchi* and tetanus may be considered, as the presence of both organisms occasionally accompanies severe snakebite poisoning. With such stock there are also remedial measures in the form of intravenous salt solutions and blood transfusions to counteract particularly severe cases discovered after organic disturbance has resulted in great destruction of red blood cells.

As a summary concerning accidents to domestic animals it may be noted: That dogs are most frequently bitten by poisonous snakes and the fatality rate is fairly high. Fatalities among bovines and equines are low, but such animals may suffer necrotic sloughs. Suction treatment in early discovered cases is simple, with inexpensive and specifically designed outfit which is readily available. Neutralization of absorbed poison is effected by veterinary antivenin injected intramuscularly or intravenously, the latter treatment with advanced or grave symptoms. The combination of both suction and injection of serum is advisable. There should be surveillance of valuable range stock in order to give one or both treatments before symptoms of poisoning have progressed to a dangerous extent. Hunting dogs should be kept under better control in retarding their prowling into thick places associated with the lairs of venomous snakes. Antivenomous serum should be available on stock ranches and carried by riders; also, hunters who value their dogs should carry suction kit and neutralizing serum.

CHAPTER XV

Classified List of the North American Snakes

THE FOLLOWING LIST, with condensed range definitions, shows the scope of the Suborder Serpentes in North America.*

FAMILY *LEPTOTYPHLOPIDAE*
Genus *Leptotyphlops*

	REGION
Texas Blind Snake	Central, Southwestern
California Blind Snake	"
Desert Blind Snake	"
Sleven's Blind Snake	"
Mexican Blind Snake	"

Leptotyphlops dulcis
" *humilis humilis*
" " *cahuilae*
" " *sleveni*
" *myopica*

FAMILY *BOIDAE*
Genus *Lichanura*

Rosy Boa	"
Desert Rosy Boa	"
Three-lined Boa	"

Lichanura roseofusca roseofusca
" " *gracia*
" *trivirgata*

Genus *Charina*

Rubber Boa, Silver Snake   Western

Charina bottae

*This list represents the latest résumé from various publications, before the field book goes to press. A few subspecies, not appearing in the descriptive chapters, are indicated. Their status is, as yet, not generally accepted.

FAMILY COLUBRIDAE

Genus *Carphophis*

Carphophis amoena amoena	Eastern Worm Snake	Eastern
" " *helenae*	" " "	Eastern, Central
" " *vermis*	Western " "	Central

Genus *Abastor*

Abastor erythrogrammus	Rainbow Snake	Eastern

Genus *Farancia*

Farancia abacura abacura	Horn Snake	"
" " *reinwardtii*	" "	Eastern, Central

Genus *Diadophis*

Diadophis amabilis amabilis	Pacific Ring-necked Snake	Western
" " *modestus*	San Bernardino Ring-necked Snake	"
" " *occidentalis*	Northwestern Ring-necked Snake	"
" " *pulchellus*	Coral-bellied Ring-necked Snake	"
" " *similis*	Southern California Ring-necked Snake	"
" " *vandenburghi*	Van Denburgh's Ring-necked Snake	"
" " *anthonyi*	Anthony's Ring-necked Snake	Lower California

		REGION
Diadophis punctatus punctatus	Southern Ring-necked Snake	Southeastern
" " *arnyi*	Prairie Ring-necked Snake	Central
" " *edwardsii*	Eastern Ring-necked Snake	Northeastern
" " *strictogenys*	Mississippi Ring-necked Snake	Central
" *regalis regalis*	Southwestern Ring-necked Snake	Southwestern
" " *arizonae*	Arizona Ring-necked Snake	"
	Genus *Heterodon*	
Heterodon browni	Brown's Hog-nosed Snake	Southeastern
" *contortrix*	Eastern Hog-nosed Snake	Eastern, Central
" *nasicus nasicus*	Western Hog-nosed Snake	Central, Western
" " *kennerlyi*	Kennerly's Hog-nosed Snake	Southwestern
" *simus*	Southern Hog-nosed Snake	Southeastern
	Genus *Liopeltis*	
Liopeltis vernalis	Smooth Green Snake	Eastern to Central
	Genus *Opheodrys*	
Opheodrys aestivus	Keeled Green Snake	" " "
	Genus *Drymobius*	
Drymobius margaritiferus	Green-Spotted Racer	South-Central to Tropics

278

Genus *Drymarchon*

Drymarchon corais couperi	Indigo Snake, Gopher Snake	Southeastern
" " melanurus	Texas Gopher Snake, Blue Bull Snake	South-Central to Tropics

Genus *Coluber*

Coluber constrictor constrictor	Blacksnake	Eastern to Central
" " flaviventris	Blue Racer	Central, Southwestern
" " mormon	Pacific Blue Racer	Western

Genus *Masticophis*

Masticophis aurigulus	Lower California Whip Snake	So. Lower California
" barbouri	Barbour's Whip Snake	Islands of Lower Calif.
" flagellum flagellum	Coachwhip Snake	Southeastern, Central
" " flavigularis	Western Coachwhip Snake	Central
" " frenatus	Red Racer	Western, Southwestern
" lateralis	Banded Racer	Southwestern
" piceus	Pink-bellied Racer	"
" semilineatus	Half-striped Racer	"
" taeniatus taeniatus	Striped Racer	"
" " girardi	Ornate Racer	"
" " ruthveni	Ruthven's Racer	"
" " schotti	Schott's Racer	South-Central

279

Genus *Salvadora*

		Region
Salvadora grahamiae grahamiae	Banded Flat-nosed Snake	South-Central, Western
" " *hexalepis*	Arizona Flat-nosed Snake	Southwestern
" " *virgultea*	California Flat-nosed Snake	"

Genus *Phyllorhynchus*

Phyllorhynchus browni	Brown's Leaf-nosed Snake	"
" *decurtatus decurtatus*	Leaf-nosed Snake	"
" " *perkinsi*	Perkins' Leaf-nosed Snake	"

Genus *Elaphe*

Elaphe bairdi	Baird's Rat Snake	"
" *chlorosoma*	Green Rat Snake	"
" *guttata*	Corn Snake, Red Rat Snake	Eastern
" *laeta*	Prairie Rat Snake	Central
" *obsoleta obsoleta*	Pilot Blacksnake, Black Chicken Snake	Eastern, Central
" *confinis*	Gray Rat Snake	Eastern, Central
" *lindheimeri*	Texas Rat Snake	South-Central
" *quadrivittata quadrivittata*	Chicken Snake, Magnolia Snake, Banded Rat Snake	Eastern
" " *deckerti*	Deckert's Rat Snake	"
" *rosacea*	Pink Rat Snake	"
" *rosaliae*	Peninsula Rat Snake	Lower Calif.

" *subocularis*	Davis Mountain Rat Snake	Southwestern
" *vulpina*	Fox Snake	Central

Genus *Arizona*

Arizona elegans elegans	Slender Gopher Snake	South-Central, Southwestern
" " *occidentalis*	Southwestern Slender Gopher Snake	Southwestern

Genus *Pituophis*

Pituophis catenifer catenifer	Pacific Bull Snake, Gopher Snake	Western
" " *annectens*	Coastal Bull Snake, Gopher Snake	Southwestern
" " *deserticola*	Desert Gopher Snake	"
deppei deppei	Mexican Gopher Snake	"
melanoleucus melanoleucus	Pine Snake	Eastern
" " *lödingi*	Black Pine Snake	"
" " *mugitus*	Florida Pine Snake	"
" " *ruthveni*	Ruthven's Pine Snake	"
sayi sayi	Bull Snake, Western Gopher Snake	Central, Western
" " *affinis*	Arizona Gopher Snake	Southwestern
" " *vertebralis*	San Lucan Gopher Snake	"

Genus *Rhadinaea*

Rhadinaea flavilata	Yellow-lipped Snake	Eastern

281

Genus *Lampropeltis*

		REGION
Lampropeltis alterna	Davis Mountain King Snake	Southwestern
" *calligaster*	Prairie King Snake	Central
" *catalinensis*	Santa Catalina King Snake	Santa Catalina Island, Gulf of Calif.
" *elapsoides elapsoides*	Scarlet King Snake	Eastern
" " *virginiana*	Blanchard's Scarlet King Snake	"
" *getulus getulus*	King Snake, Chain Snake	"
" " *brooksi*	Brook's King Snake	"
" " *californiae*	California King Snake	Western, Southwestern
" " *floridana*	Florida King Snake	Eastern
" " *holbrooki*	Spotted King Snake	"
" " *nigra*	Black King Snake	"
" " *splendida.*	Mexican King Snake	South-Central, Southwestern
" " *yumensis*	Arizona King Snake	Southwestern
" *pyromelana*	Arizona Coral King Snake	Southwestern
" *rhombomaculata*	Mole Snake, Brown King Snake	Eastern
" *triangulum triangulum*	"Milk" Snake, House Snake	"
" " *amaura*	Cope's "Milk" Snake	Eastern, Central
" " *annulata*	Ringed "Milk" Snake	South-Central

" " *gentilis*	Western "Milk" Snake	Central-Western, Southwestern
" " *syspila*	Red "Milk" Snake	Central
" " *zonatus*	California "Coral" Snake, Coral King Snake	Western, Southwestern
	Genus *Stilosoma*	
Stilosoma extenuatum	Short-tailed Snake	Eastern
	Genus *Contia*	
Contia tenuis	Pacific Brown Snake	Western
	Genus *Cemophora*	
Cemophora coccinea	Scarlet Snake	Eastern
	Genus *Rhinocheilus*	
Rhinocheilus lecontei	LeConte's Snake	Western
	Genus *Sonora*	
Sonora episcopa	Variable Ground Snake	Central
" *miniata miniata*	Reddish Ground Snake	Southwestern
" " *linearis*	Striped Ground Snake	"
" *mosaueri*	Mosauer's Ground Snake	Lower Calif.
" *occipitalis*	Ringed Ground Snake, Desert Ground Snake	Southwestern
" *semiannulata semiannulata*	Banded Ground Snake	Southwestern
" " *blanchardi*	Blanchard's Ground Snake	South-Central, Southwestern
" *gloydi*	Gloyd's Ground Snake	Southwestern
" *taylori*	Taylor's Ground Snake	South-Central

		REGION
Genus *Ficimia*		
Ficimia cana	Hook-nosed Snake	Southwestern
" *streckeri*	Strecker's Hook-nosed Snake	South-Central
Genus *Hypsiglena*		
Hypsiglena torquata ochrorhyncha	Spotted Night Snake	Central, Western, Southwestern
Genus *Chilomeniscus*		
Chilomeniscus cinctus	Red and Black Ground Snake	Southwestern
" *punctatissimus*	Island Ground Snake	"
" *stramineus*	Straw-colored Snake	"
Genus *Natrix*		
Natrix clarkii	Clark's Water Snake	Eastern
" *compressicauda*	Flat-tailed Water Snake	Southeastern
" *cyclopion cyclopion*	Green Water Snake	"
" " *floridana*	Florida Green Water Snake	"
" *erythrogaster erythrogaster*	Red-bellied Water Snake	Central, Southeastern
" " *transversa*	Yellow-bellied Water Snake	Central, Southwestern
" *grahamii*	Graham's Water Snake	Eastern
" *kirtlandii*	Kirtland's Water Snake	"

" rhombifera rhombifera	Diamond-back Water Snake	South-Central
" rigida	Striped Water Snake	Eastern
" septemvittata	Queen Snake	"
" sipedon sipedon	Common Water Snake	Eastern, Central
" " confluens	Blanchard's Water Snake	" "
" " fasciata	Banded Water Snake	" "
" " insularum	Lake Water Snake	Eastern
" " pictiventris	Cope's Water Snake	Southeastern
" " pleuralis	Mississippi Water Snake	Central
" taxispilota	Brown Water Snake	Eastern
" valida	Western Water Snake	Southwestern

Genus *Seminatrix*

Seminatrix pygaea	Black Swamp Snake	Eastern

Genus *Storeria*

Storeria dekayi	DeKay's Snake, Brown Snake	Eastern, Central
" occipitomaculata	Storer's Snake, Red-bellied Snake	" "
" victa	Florida Brown Snake	Southeastern

Genus *Virginia*

Virginia valeriae valeriae	Smooth Brown Snake	Eastern
" " elegans	Smooth Brown Snake	Central

285

Genus *Haldea*		
		REGION
Haldea striatula	Small-eyed Brown Snake	Eastern, Central
Genus *Tropidoclonion*		
Tropidoclonion lineatum	Striped Swamp Snake	" "
Genus *Liodytes*		
Liodytes alleni	Allen's Mud Snake	Southeastern
Genus *Thamnophis*		
Thamnophis angustirostris	Long-headed Garter Snake	Southwestern
" *butleri*	Butler's Garter Snake	Eastern, Central
" *eques*	Brown Garter Snake	South-Central, Southwestern
" *marcianus*	Marcy's Garter Snake	South-Central, Southwestern
" *megalops*	Mexican Garter Snake	Southwestern
" *ordinoides ordinoides*	Pacific Garter Snake	Western
" " *atratus*	Black Garter Snake	"
" " *biscutatus*	Northwestern Garter Snake	"
" *couchii*	Couch's Garter Snake	"
" *elegans*	California Garter Snake	"
" *hammondii*	Hammond's Garter Snake	Southwestern
" *hueyi*	Lower California Garter Snake	Southwestern

" " hydrophila	Southern California Garter Snake	" "
" " vagrans	Gray Garter Snake	Western, Southwestern
radix	Plains Garter Snake	Central, Western
sauritus sauritus	Eastern Ribbon Snake	Eastern
" " proximus	Western Ribbon Snake	Central
" " sackenii	Southern Ribbon Snake	Southeastern
sirtalis sirtalis	Common Garter Snake	Eastern, Central
" " concinnus	Red-spotted Garter Snake	Western
" " infernalis	One-striped Garter Snake	" "
" " parietalis	Red-barred Garter Snake	Central, Western

Genus *Coniophanes*

Coniophanes imperialis imperialis	Black-banded Snake	Southwestern

Genus *Oxybelis*

Oxybelis micropthalmus	Long-headed Snake, Vine Snake	" "

Genus *Leptodeira*

Leptodeira septentrionalis septentrionalis	Bush Snake	South-Central

Genus *Trimorphodon*

Trimorphodon lyrophanes	Arizona Lyre Snake	Southwestern
" vandenburghi	Van Denburgh's Lyre Snake	" "
" vilkinsonii	Wilkinson's Lyre Snake	" "

Genus *Tantilla*

			REGION
Tantilla atriceps		Günther's Black-headed Snake	Central, Southwestern
"	*coronata coronata*	Crowned Snake, Black-headed Snake	Eastern
"	" *wagneri*	Florida Black-headed Snake	"
"	*eiseni*	Eisen's Black-headed Snake	Southwestern
"	*gracilis*	Slender Dark-headed Snake	South-Central
"	*kirnia*	Kirn's Black-headed Snake	Southwestern
"	*nigriceps*	Kennicott's Black-headed Snake	Central, Southwestern
"	*planiceps*	Peninsula Black-headed Snake	Southwestern
"	*utahensis*	Blanchard's Black-headed Snake	"
"	*wilcoxi*	Wilcox's Black-headed Snake	"

FAMILY ELAPIDAE

Genus *Micrurus*

Micrurus fulvius fulvius		Coral Snake, Harlequin Snake	Southeastern
"	" *barbouri*	Barbour's Coral Snake, Harlequin Snake	"

288

" *tenere*	Texas Coral Snake	Texas
Micruroides euryxanthus	**Genus *Micruroides*** Sonora Coral Snake	Southwestern

FAMILY HYDROPHIDAE
Genus *Pelamydrus*

Pelamydrus platurus	Yellow-bellied Sea Snake	"

FAMILY CROTALIDAE
Genus *Agkistrodon*

Agkistrodon mokasen mokasen	Southern Copperhead Snake	Eastern, Central
" " *cupreus*	Northern Copperhead Snake	" "
" " *laticinctus*	Western Copperhead Snake	South-Central
" *piscivorus*	Water Moccasin, Cotton-mouth	Southeastern

Genus *Sistrurus*

Sistrurus catenatus catenatus	Massasauga	Eastern, Central
" " *edwardsii*	Edward's Massasauga	South-Central, South-western
" *miliarius miliarius*	Eastern Pygmy Rattlesnake	Eastern
" " *barbouri*	Barbour's Pygmy Rattlesnake	"
" " *streckeri*		South-Central

Genus *Crotalus*

		REGION
Crotalus adamanteus	Diamond-back Rattlesnake	Southeastern
" *atrox atrox**	Western Diamond Rattle-snake	Central, Western, Southwestern
" *cerastes*	Horned Rattlesnake, Side-winder	Southwestern
" *enyo*	Cope's Rattlesnake	Southwestern
" *horridus horridus*	Banded Rattlesnake, Timber Rattlesnake	Eastern, Central
" " *atricaudatus*	Cane-brake Rattlesnake	"
" *lepidus lepidus*	Green Rattlesnake	South-Central
" " *klauberi*	Klauber's Green Rattlesnake	Southwestern
" *lucasensis*	Cape Rattlesnake	"
" *mitchellii mitchellii*	Bleached Rattlesnake, White Rattlesnake	"
" " *pyrrhus*	Cope's Rattlesnake	"
" " *stephensi*	Panamint Rattlesnake	"
" *molossus molossus*	Black-tailed Rattlesnake	"
" *ruber*	Red Diamond Rattlesnake	"
" *scutellatus*	Mojave Diamond Rattle-snake	"
" *tigris*	Tiger Rattlesnake	"
" *triseriatus pricei*	Spotted Rattlesnake	"

*The forms occurring on islands off the coast of Lower California are not included in the above list. See text of Chapter XIII.

"	*viridis viridis*	Prairie Rattlesnake	Central, Western
"	" *abyssus*	Grand Canyon Rattlesnake	Western
"	" *concolor*	Midget Faded Rattlesnake	"
"	" *lutosus*	Great Basin Rattlesnake	"
"	" *nuntius*	Arizona Prairie Rattlesnake	Southwestern
"	" *oreganus*	Pacific Rattlesnake	Western
"	*willardi*	Willard's Rattlesnake	Southwestern

BIBLIOGRAPHY

THE FOLLOWING LIST of publications will be found of interest and value if the reader wishes to extend studies beyond the range of the field book. The list is representative, with no attempt to make it complete in enumeration of many excellent publications treating with North American reptiles. The works listed, however, contain numerous references to other publications. Two serial publications should be noted as highly important in dealing with North American reptiles generally. These are *Copeia,* published by the American Society of Ichthyologists and Herpetologists, and *Herpetologica,* published at the Chicago Academy of Sciences.

BLANCHARD, FRANK N. *A Key to the Snakes of the United States, Canada and Lower California.* Papers of the Michigan Academy of Science, Arts and Letters, Vol. IV, 1924, pp. 1 – 65.
Technical, with many cuts showing scalation of heads.

BLANCHARD, FRANK N. *A Revision of the King Snakes; Genus Lampropeltis.* Bulletin of the U.S. National Museum, No. 114, 1921, pp. 1 – 260.
Technical. A particularly complete study from standpoint of variation of patterns, definition of subspecies and their distribution. Contains maps, cuts and drawings of patterns.

COPE, EDWARD DRINKER. *The Crocodilians, Lizards and Snakes of North America.* Annual Report of the U.S. National Museum, 1898, pp. 155 – 1294.
Technical. The most comprehensive scientific work on the North American reptiles that has ever been prepared. There have been many changes in the recognition of species since this work was published, but its keys and extensive treatment form a volume of classic permanence.

DITMARS, RAYMOND L. *The Reptiles of North America.* Doubleday, Doran and Company, Inc. Garden City, N.Y. 1936. 465 pages, with 8 plates in color and more than 400 photographs from life.
A review of the Crocodilians, Lizards, Snakes, Turtles and Tortoises inhabiting the United States and northern Mexico, with extensive details for identification and much readable text relating to habits. (Large plates.)

DITMARS, RAYMOND L. *Snakes of the World*. The Macmillan Company, New York City. 1931. 207 pages, with 84 plates.

A readable, large-sized book imparting prominence and detail among the photographic plates. The species are treated according to continental areas of the world.

KLAUBER, LAURENCE M. *New and Renamed Subspecies of Crotalus Confluentus Say, With Remarks on Related Species*. Transactions of the San Diego Society of Natural History, Vol. VI, No. 3, pp. 95 – 144, plates 9 – 12 and map.

Technical and readable descriptions relating to the western rattlesnakes.

ORTENBURGER, ARTHUR IRVING. *The Whip Snakes and Racers. Genera Masticophis and Coluber*. Memoirs of the University of Michigan Museums, Vol. I, 1928, pp. 1 – 247, with 36 plates and numerous maps.

Technical. A highly expanded study of a comparatively small group. The full-page plates figure the species separately and photographed from life.

POPE, CLIFFORD H. *Snakes Alive*. The Viking Press, New York. 226 pages and numerous illustrations.

An excellent readable section relating to habits, which are treated with great detail. The book also contains a technical key to snakes of the United States.

RUTHVEN, A. G. *Variations and Genetic Relationships of the Garter Snakes*. Bulletin of the U.S. National Museum, 1908, No. 81, pp. 1 – 201, figures 1 – 82.

Technical and readable. A thorough review of an important and broadly distributed genus.

SCHMIDT, KARL P. *The Amphibians and Reptiles of Lower California and the Neighboring Islands*. Bulletin of the American Museum of Natural History, 1922, pp. 607 – 707, plates 47 – 57.

Technical. A valuable article in reviewing the rather detached fauna of the peninsula and its islands.

STEJNEGER, LEONHARD, and THOMAS BARBOUR. *A Check List of North American Amphibians and Reptiles*. Harvard University Press, third edition, 1933. (Another edition in 1939.)

Technical. An indispensable work for the student of herpetology. Of particular value in checking the source of original descriptions and other references.

STEJNEGER, LEONHARD. *The Poisonous Snakes of North America*. Report of the United States National Museum for 1893, pp. 337 – 487, plates 1 – 19, figures 1 – 70.

A readable exposition of great detail and permanent value. Long out of print, but in the files of the libraries of the larger museums.

VAN DENBURGH, JOHN. *The Reptiles of Western North America*. Vol.
2 (Snakes and Turtles), California Academy of Sciences, 1922; numerous plates.
  Technical. A work of ultra-detail in considering the variations of
  extreme western reptiles. The region treated includes Oregon, Washington, Idaho, Utah, Nevada, Arizona, British Columbia, Sonora and
  Lower California.

WRIGHT, A. H., and BISHOP, S. C. A. *A Biological Reconnaissance of the
Okefinokee Swamp in Georgia*. Sec. 2, Snakes. Proceedings of the
Academy of Natural Sciences of Philadelphia, 1915, pp. 139 – 192, 3
plates, figures 1 – 7.
  Both readable and technical. A summarization of observations in a
  very interesting area.

*(A number of excellent articles, some published as separate, illustrated
booklets, have been issued to cover the reptiles of separate states. Some of
these contain very helpful keys. Some have appeared among the general
pages of Copeia. Reviews of the more detailed lists of the snakes of
separate states will also be found in Copeia. A checking of the reviews in
the more recent numbers of that publication and inquiry at state sources
whence such publications may be issued are suggested for acquiring very
helpful and inexpensive literature.)*

INDEX

Abastor erythrogrammus, 76, 119, 124
"Adder," Checkered, 43, 102, 201
  Flat-headed, 28, 34, 91, 178
  Hissing, 28, 34, 36, 82, 91, 158,
    177–79
  Puffing, 34, 91, 178
  Sand, 29, 36, 82
  Spreading, 34, 91, 158, 178
Agkistrodon mokasen cupreus, 29, 63,
    243
  mokasen laticinctus, 161, 243
    mokasen, 85, 128, 161, 242
    piscivorus, 30, 59, 66, 86, 120, 161,
    244
Allen's Snake, 76, 118
Animals, domestic, bites among, and
    treatment, 273
Annulated Snake, 237
Aquatic snakes. *See* Water Snakes
Arboreal types, 13
Arizona, 194–95
Arizona "Coral" Snake, 147
  Coral King Snake, 204
Arizona elegans elegans, 147, 194
  elegans occidentalis, 194
Arizona Flat-nosed Snake, 147, 188
  King Snake, 149, 208
  Lyre Snake, 152, 237
  Patch-nosed Snake, 188
  Prairie Rattlesnake, 253
  Vine Snake, 148, 235
  Whipsnake, 183

Baird's Rat Snake, 154, 192
Banded Burrowing Snake, 145
  Chicken Snake, 79, 97
  Flat-nosed Snake, 147, 187
  Ground Snake, 145, 212
  Racer, 150, 183
  Rattlesnake, 30, 67, 86, **132, 165,**
    258
  Sand Snake, 216

Swamp Snake, 118
Water Snake, 47, 83
  Southern, 111
  Whipsnake, 183, 185
Barbour's Whipsnake, 186
Bibliography, 293
Bites, treatment, 267–75
Black Chicken Snake, 41, 78, 96, **154,**
    191
  King Snake, 45, 77
  Pine Snake, 84, 101
  Racer, 25, 38, 78, 94, 149, 180
  Rat Snake, 96
  Swamp Snake, 75, 116
Black-banded Snake, 146, 232
Black-headed Snakes, 125, 233–36
  Blanchard's, 143, 233
  Eisen's, 143, 233
  Günther's, 143, 233
  Kennicott's, 142, 234
  Lower California, 143, 234
  Wilcox's, 143, 233
Black-tailed Rattlesnake, 249
Blacksnake, 25, 38, 78, 94, 149, 180
  Mountain, 26, 40, 78, 96
  Pilot, 26, 40, 78, 96, 191
Blanchard's Black-headed Snake,
    143, 233
  Ground Snake, 213
  Water Snake, 84, 112, 158, 219
Bleached Rattlesnake, 164, 257
Blind Snake, California, 142, 171
  Desert, 172
  Mexican, 142, 171
  Texas, 141, 170
  Western, 170–72
Blotched Coachwhip Snake, 150, 182
  King Snake, 148, 205
Blue Bull Snake, 151, 186
  Gopher Snake, 151
  Racer, 25, 38, 78, 94, 149, 180
    Western, 149, 181

Boas, Dwarf Western, 172–74
California Rosy, 153
Desert Rosy, 153
Rubber, 153
Silver, 153
Three-lined, 153
Boidae, 172–74
Boundary King Snake, 148, 208
Broad-banded Copperhead, 161, 243
Brook's King Snake, 77
Brown Garter Snake, 157, 227
King Snake, 76, 105
Snakes, 52, 117, 142, 155, 229, 230
Florida, 80, 118
Red-bellied, 53, 117
Small, 228–30
Small-eyed, 26, 53, 80, 118, 155, 230
Smooth, 54, 74, 116
Smooth-scaled, 230
Southern, 118
Water Snake, 82, 113
Brown's Flat-nosed Snake, 188
Hog-nosed Snake, 82, 92
Leaf-nosed Snake, 152
Bull Snakes, 29, 43, 159, 195–200
Blue, 186
Pacific, 159, 198
Burrowing Snakes, 12
Banded, 145
Island, 145
Straw-colored, 145
Bush Snake, 153, 237
Butler's Garter Snake, 27, 56

California Blind Snake, 142, 171
"Coral" Snake, 147
Coral King Snake, 203
Garter Snake, 225
King Snake, 149, 208
Rosy Boa, 153
Canebrake Rattlesnake, 30, 86, 132, 259
Cape San Lucan Whipsnake, 185
Captivity, keeping snakes in, 62
Carphophis, 54, 117
amoena amoena, 24, 33, 74, 90

helenae, 33, 90
vermis, 91, 142, 174
Cedros Island Diamond Rattlesnake, 165, 248
Cemophora coccinea, 24, 46, 75, 104, 107, 146
Chain Snake, 25, 44, 77, 106
Chaparral Patch-nosed Snake, 188
Charina bottae, 153, 173
Checkered "Adder," 24, 43, 102, 201
Chicken Snake, 79, 97
Banded, 79, 97
Black, 41, 78, 96, 154, 191
Gray, 78, 97, 192
Yellow, 97
Chilomeniscus, 216
cinctus, 145, 216
punctatissimus, 145, 216
stramineus, 45, 217
Chunkhead, 63, 85, 128, 161
Clarion Island Whipsnake, 185
Clark's Water Snake, 81, 109
Classified list of snakes, 276
Coachwhip Snakes, 95, 150, 181
Blotched, 150, 182
Eastern, 78
Colors and patterns, 19, 87–9
Coluber constrictor constrictor, 25, 38, 78, 94, 149, 180
constrictor flaviventris, 25, 38, 78, 94, 149, 180
constrictor mormon, 149, 181
Colubridae, 174
Common Garter Snake, 27, 55, 81, 121, 157, 223, 224
Water Snake, 28, 47, 83, 110, 158, 218
Coniophanes, 232
imperialis, 146, 232
Constrictors, 14
and non-constrictors, 61–2
Contia tenuis, 142, 210
Coon-tailed Rattlesnake, 247
Cope's "Milk" Snake, 103, 104, 202
Rattlesnake, 165, 250
Water Snake, 83, 111
Copper-bellied "Moccasin," 112

Copperheads, 7, 8, 85, 161, 240
Broad-banded, 161, 243
Northern, 29, 63
Southern, 128, 242
Coral King Snake, 147
Arizona, 204
California, 203
Coral Snakes, 7, 8, 75, 85, 105, 126, 239
Eastern, 160
Sonoran, 160, 241
Texas, 240
"Coral" Snakes, 75, 103, 104, 146, 202
Arizona, 147
California, 147
Coral-bellied Ring-necked Snake, 176
Corn Snake, 25, 41, 79, 99
Cotton-mouth Snake, 66, 86, 129, 161, 244
Couch's Garter Snake, 226
Crotaline Snakes, 8, 63, 128, 240, 244–64
Crotalus adamanteus, 86, 133
atrox atrox, 164, 247
(cinereous), 133, 139, 254
elegans, 247
lucasensis, 247
tortugensis, 247
cerastes, 163, 261
confluentus, 251
enyo, 250
exsul, 165, 248
horridus atricaudatus, 30, 86, 132, 259
horridus, 30, 67, 86, 132, 165, 258
lepidus lepidus, 163, 260
klauberi, 261
mitchellii mitchellii, 164, 257
pyrrhus, 257
molossus molossus, 165, 249
ruber, 164, 248
scutellatus, 164, 249
tigris, 163, 257
triseriatus pricei, 163, 260
viridis, 250
abyssus, 164, 253
concolor, 164, 253

lutosus, 163, 253
nuntius, 253
oreganus, 164, 255
stephensi, 254
viridis, 163, 251
willardi, 162, 259
Crowned Snake, 74, 125

Dark-headed Snake, Kirn's, 142, 234
Slender, 142, 234
Davis Mountain King Snake, 147, 205
Rat Snake, 154, 193
Deckert's Rat Snake, 79, 98
DeKay's Snake, 26, 52, 79, 117, 155, 229
Dens, 11
Desert Blind Snake, 172
Ground Snake, 145
Rosy Boa, 153, 173
Development and length of life, 14
Diadophis, 175–77
amabilis amabilis, 143, 176
modestus, 176
occidentalis, 176
pulchellus, 176
vandenburghi, 176
punctatus arnyi, 143, 175, 213
edwardsii, 24, 34, 91, 175
punctatus, 74, 91
stictogenys, 91, 175
regalis regalis, 144, 177
Diamond Rattlesnake, Cedros Island, 165
Mohave, 164, 249
Red, 164, 248
Western, 164, 247
Diamond-back Rattlesnake, 86, 133
Western, 133, 139
Diamond-back Water Snake, 28, 49, 84, 115, 159, 220
Distribution, 3–5, 23, 58–60, 139–41
Domestic animals, bites among, 273
Drymarchon, 186–89
corais couperi, 77, 99, 187
corais melanurus, 151, 186
Drymobius margaritiferus, 147, 186

Eastern Coachwhip Snake, 78
Coral Snake, 160
Hog-nosed Snake, 178
Ribbon Snake, 26, 80
Ring-necked Snake, 175
Economic value, 62
Edwards' Massasauga, 162
Egg-laying snakes, 12, 60
Eisen's Black-headed Snake, 143, 233
Elaphe bairdi, 154, 192
chlorosoma, 155, 193
guttata, 25, 41, 79, 99
laeta, 154, 190
obsoleta confinis, 78, 97, 192
lindheimeri, 154, 192
obsoleta, 26, 40, 78, 96, 154, 191
quadrivittata deckerti, 79, 98
quadrivittata, 79, 97
rosacea, 79, 98
rosaliae, 155, 194
subocularis, 154, 193
vulpina, 25, 41, 154, 190
Emory's Rat Snake, 154, 190

Faded Rattlesnake, Midget, 164, 253
Faded Snake, 194
Fangs, poison, 8
Farancia abacura abacura, 76, 122
abacura reinwardtii, 23, 76, 122, 151
Ficimia, 213–16
cana, 145, 214
streckeri, 145, 214
Flat-headed "Adder," 28, 34, 91, 178
Flat-nosed Snake, Arizona, 147, 188
Banded, 147, 187
Brown's, 188
Flat-tailed Water Snake, 82, 115
Florida Brown Snake, 80, 118
Green Water Snake, 84
King Snake, 77
Food, snakes', 14
Fox Snake, 25, 42, 154, 190

Garter Snakes, 221–28
Black, 226
Brown, 157, 227
Butler's, 27, 56

California, 225
Common, 27, 55, 81, 121, 157, 223, 224
Couch's, 226
Gray, 226
Hammond's, 226
Long-headed, 157, 227
Marcy's, 157, 226
Mexican, 156, 222
Northwestern, 226
One-striped, 225
Pacific, 225
Plains, 27, 57, 156, 222
Red-barred, 224
Red-spotted, 224
Slender, 120
Western, 156, 225
Getulus, 206–10
Girard's Whipsnake, 184
Gloyd's Ground Snake, 213
Gopher Snakes, 77, 99, 195
Lower California, 199
Mexican, 160, 199
San Lucan, 160
Sharp-nosed, 194
Slender, 147, 194
Southwestern Slender, 194
Western, 29, 43, 195–200
White, 100
Yellow, 159, 195, 198
Graham's Water Snake, 27, 51, 81, 108, 157, 218
Grand Canyon Rattlesnake, 164, 253
Granite Rattlesnake, 257
Gray Chicken Snake, 78, 97, 192
Garter Snake, 226
Rat Snake, 78, 97, 192
Great Basin Rattlesnake, 163, 253
Green Snakes, 24, 179–80
Keeled, 26, 37, 80, 93, 157
Racer, 94, 180
Rat Snake, 155, 193
Rattlesnake, 163, 260
Smooth, 36, 74, 92, 179
Smooth-scaled, 144
Spotted Racer, 147, 186
Water Snake, 28, 50, 84, 114
Florida, 84

Ground Snakes, 80, 111, 118, 142, 211, 230
  Banded, 145, 212
  Blanchard's, 213
  Desert, 145
  Gloyd's, 213
  Mosauer's, 144, 212
  Pacific, 142, 210
  Pinkish, 144, 212
  Ringed, 145, 213
  Sharp-snouted, 231
  Striped, 144, 211, 212
  Taylor's, 144
Günther's Black-headed Snake, 143, 233

Habits, 10–15
Haldea, 228–30
  striatula, 26, 53, 80, 118, 155, 230
Half-striped Racer, 151, 183
Hammond's Garter Snake, 226
Harlequin Snake, 85, 105, 126
Heads, shape, 16
Heterodon, 177–79
  browni, 82, 92
  contortrix, 28, 34, 82, 91, 158, 178
  nasicus nasicus, 158, 178
  simus, 29, 36, 82, 92
Hibernation, 11
Highland Moccasin, 63, 85, 128, 161
Hissing "Adder," 28, 34, 36, 82, 91, 158, 177–79
  Southern, 29, 82
Hog-nosed Snakes, 28, 29, 34, 82, 91, 158, 177–79
  Brown's, 82, 92
  Eastern, 178
  Southern, 36, 92
  Western, 158, 178
Holbrook's King Snake, 77, 148, 207
Hook-nosed Snake, 145, 214
  Strecker's, 145, 214
"Hoop" Snakes, 76, 122, 151
Horn Snakes, 23, 76, 122, 151
Horned Rattlesnake, 163, 261
House Snakes, 24, 43, 75, 79, 102, 201
  Red, 99
  Striped, 97

Hydrophidae, 239
Hypsiglena torquata ochrorhyncha, 152, 215

Identification, 16–20, 30–2
Indigo Snake, 77, 99, 151
Island Burrowing Snake, 145
  Sand Snake, 216

Keeled Green Snake, 26, 37, 80, 93, 157, 179
Keel-scaled Green Snakes, 13
Keeping in captivity, 62
Kennicott's Black-headed Snake, 142, 234
King Snakes, 25, 44, 77, 106, 200–10
  Arizona, 149, 208
    Coral, 204
  Black, 45, 77
  Blotched, 148, 205
  Boundary, 148, 208
  Brook's, 77
  Brown, 105
  California, 149, 208
    Coral, 203
  Coral, 147
  Davis Mountain, 147, 205
  Florida, 77
  Holbrook's, 77, 148, 207
  Prairie, 148, 205
  Ringed, 202
  Santa Catalina Island, 149, 209
  Scarlet, 75, 103, 104, 146, 202
  Yellow-bellied, 25, 45, 105, 148, 205
Kirn's Dark-headed Snake, 142, 234
Kirtland's Water Snake, 27, 48

Lake Water Snake, 28, 48
Lampropeltis alterna, 147, 205
  calligaster, 25, 45, 105, 148, 205
  catalinensis, 149, 209
  elapsoides elapsoides, 75, 103, 104, 107
    virginiana, 104, 107
  getulus californiae, 149, 207, 208
    brooksi, 77, 106
    floridana, 77, 106

Lampropeltis—Cont'd
  getulus, 25, 44, 77, 106, 207
  holbrooki, 77, 106, 148, 207
  nigra, 45, 77, 106
  splendida, 148, 208
  yumensis, 149, 208
  pyromelana pyromelana, 147, 204, 241
  rhombomaculata, 76, 105
  triangulum amaura, 76, 103, 104, 107, 146, 202
    annulata, 202
    gentilis, 202
    syspila, 44, 201
    triangulum, 24, 43, 75, 102, 146, 201
  zonatus, 147, 203, 241
Leaf-nosed Snake, 188
  Brown's, 152
  Southwestern, 152, 189
Le Conte's Snake, 148, 210
Length of life, 14
Leptodeira, 232
  septentrionalis, 143, 237
Leptotyphlops dulcis, 141, 170
  humilis cahuilae, 172
    humilis, 141, 170
    slevini, 172
  myopica, 142, 171
Lichanura roseofusca gracia, 153, 173
  roseofusca roseofusca, 153, 173
  trivirgata, 153, 173
Lindheimer's Rat Snake, 154, 192
Liodytes alleni, 76, 118
Liopeltis, 179–80
  vernalis, 24, 36, 74, 93, 144, 179
List, classified, 276
Living young (viviparous), 60–61
Long-headed Garter Snake, 157, 227
  Snake, 235
Lower California Black-headed Snake, 143, 234
  Gopher Snake, 199
  Water Snake, 159, 221
  Whipsnakes, 185
Lyre Snakes, 236–38
  Arizona, 152, 236

Van Denburgh's, 152, 237
Wilkinson's, 237

Marcy's Garter Snake, 157, 226
Massasauga, 30, 60, 66, 162, 245
  Edwards', 162
Masticophis anthonyi, 185
  aurigulus, 185
  barbouri, 186
  flagellum flagellum, 78, 95, 150, 181
    flavigularis, 150, 182
    frenatum, 150, 182
  lateralis, 150, 183
  piceus, 150, 182
  semilineatus, 151, 183
  taeniatus girardi, 184
    ruthveni, 151, 184
    schotti, 150, 185
    taeniatus, 151, 183
Mexican Blind Snake, 142, **171**
  Garter Snake, 156, 222
  Gopher Snake, 160, **199**
  Rat Snake, 186
  Ringed "Milk" Snake, 202
Micruroides euryxanthus, 160, 241
Micrurus fulvius, 75
  fulvius barbouri, 105, 127
    fulvius, 85, 105, 107, 126, 160, 240
    tenere, 240
Midget Faded Rattlesnake, 164, 253
"Milk" Snakes, 10, 24, 43, 75, 102, 146, 200–03
  Cope's, 103, 104, 202
  Mexican Ringed, 202
  Red, 201
  Western, 202
Mississippi Ring-necked Snake, **175**
  Water Snake, 158
Mitchell's Rattlesnake, 164, 257
Miter Snake, 74, 125
  Wagner's, 75
"Moccasin," 47, 158
  Copper-bellied, 112
  Water, 218
Moccasin, Highland, 85, **128**, 161
  Water, 59, 86, 129, 161, 240, 244

Mohave Diamond Rattlesnake, 164, 249
Mole Snake, 76, 105
Mosauer's Ground Snake, 144, 212
Mountain Blacksnake, 26, 40, 78, 96
Rattlesnake, 132
Mud Snakes, 12, 76, 118, 122

Natrix, 217–21
clarkii, 81, 109
compressicauda, 82, 115
cyclopion, 28, 50
cyclopion, 84, 114
cyclopion floridana, 84, 115
erythrogaster erythrogaster, 28, 48, 83, 112, 220
transversa, 83, 112, 159, 220
grahamii, 27, 51, 81, 108, 157, 218
kirtlandii, 27, 48
rhombifera, 28, 49, 220
rhombifera, 84, 115, 159
rigida, 81, 109
septemvittata, 27, 50, 81, 108
sipedon confluens, 83, 112, 159, 219
fasciata, 83, 111
insularum, 28, 48
pictiventris, 83, 111
pleuralis, 111, 158, 218
sipedon, 28, 47, 83, 110, 158, 218
taxispilota, 82, 113
valida, 159, 220, 221
Night Snake, Spotted, 152, 215
Nonconstrictors and constrictors, 61–2
Northern Copperhead Snake, 29, 63
Ring-necked Snake, 34
Northwestern Garter Snake, 226
Ring-necked Snake, 176

One-striped Garter Snake, 225
Opheodrys, 179–80
aestivus, 26, 37, 80, 93, 157, 179
Oviparous snakes, 60
Oviparous and viviparous snakes, 12
Ovoviviparous snakes, 60–1
Oxybelis, 232
micropthalmus, 148, 235

Pacific Bull Snake, 159, 198
Garter Snake, 225
Ground Snake, 142, 210
Rattlesnake, 164, 255
Ring-necked Snake, 143, 176
Panamint Rattlesnake, 254
Patch-nosed Snake, 187
Arizona, 188
Chaparral, 188
Patterns and colors, 19, 87–9
Pelamydrus platurus, 161, 241
Peninsula Rat Snake, 155, 194
Phyllorhynchus, 186–89
browni, 152, 188
decurtatus decurtatus, 152, 189
perkinsi, 152, 189
Pilot Blacksnake, 26, 40, 78, 96, 154, 191
Snake, 63, 85, 128
Pine Snakes, 29, 42, 84, 100
Black, 84, 101
Ruthven's, 84, 101
Southern, 84, 101
Pink Rat Snake, 79, 98
Pink-bellied Racer, 150, 182
Whipsnake, 182
Pinkish Ground Snake, 144, 212
Pit Vipers, 8, 128, 240, 242
Pituophis, 195–200
catenifer annectens, 198
catenifer, 159, 198
deserticola, 198
deppei deppei, 160, 199
melanoleucus lödingi, 84, 101
melanoleucus, 29, 42, 84, 100
mugitus, 84, 101
ruthveni, 84, 101
sayi, 43
affinis, 196
sayi, 29, 43, 159, 195
vertebralis, 160, 199
Plains Garter Snake, 27, 57, 156, 222
Poison, analysis, 9
fangs, 8
Prairie King Snake, 148, 205
Rat Snake, 190
Rattlesnake, 163, 251
Arizona, 253

Prairie King Snake—*Cont'd*
  Ring-necked Snake, 143, 175
  Whipsnake, 182
Prey, subduing, 14
Puffing "Adder," 34, 91, 178
Pygmy Rattlesnake, 86, 131, 162
  Strecker's, 245

Queen Snake, 27, 50, 81, 108

Racers, 180–86
  Banded, 150, 183
  Black, 38, 94, 149, 180
  Blue, 38, 78, 94, 149, 180
  Green, 94, 180
  Green-spotted, 147, 186
  Half-striped, 151, 183
  Pink-bellied, 150, 182
  Red, 150, 182
  Ruthven's, 151, 184
  Schott's, 150, 185
  Striped, 151, 183
  Western Blue, 149, 181
  Yellow-bellied, 94, 149, 180
Rainbow Snake, 76, 119, 124
Rat Snakes, 96–9, 190–95
  Baird's, 154, 192
  Black, 96
  Davis Mountain, 154, 193
  Deckert's, 79, 99
  Emory's, 154, 190
  Gray, 78, 97, 192
  Green, 193
  Lindheimer's, 154, 192
  Mexican, 186
  Peninsula, 194
  Pink, 79, 98
  Prairie, 190
  Red, 41, 79, 99
  Texas, 192
  Yellow, 79, 97
Rattlesnakes, 8, 131, 240, 244–64
  Arizona Prairie, 253
  Banded, 30, 67, 86, 132, 165, 258
  Black-tailed, 249
  Bleached, 164, 257
  Canebrake, 30, 86, 132, 259
  Cedros Island, 248
  Diamond, 165
  Coon-tailed, 247
  Cope's, 165, 250
  Diamond-back, 86, 133
  Grand Canyon, 164, 253
  Granite, 257
  Great Basin, 163, 253
  Green, 155, 163, 260
  Horned, 163, 261
  Midget Faded, 164, 253
  Mitchell's, 164, 257
  Mohave Diamond, 164, 249
  Mountain, 132
  Pacific, 164, 255
  Panamint, 254
  Peninsula, 155
  Pilot, 63
  Prairie, 163, 251
  Pygmy, 86, 162
  Red Diamond, 164, 248
  Speckled, 257
  Spotted, 163, 260
  Strecker's, Pygmy, 245
  Swamp, 30, 66
  "Texas," 164
  Tiger, 163, 257
  Timber, 30, 67, 86, 132, 165, 258
  Western Diamond, 164
  Western Diamond-back, 133, 139
  White, 164, 257
  Willard's, 162, 259
Rattling, tail, 38–9
Rear-fanged Snakes, 231–38
Red Diamond Rattlesnake, 164, 248
Red House Snake, 99
  "Milk" Snake, 201
  Racer, 150, 182
  Rat Snake, 41, 79, 99
  Whipsnake, 182
Red-barred Garter Snake, 224
Red-bellied Brown Snake, 53, 117
  Snake, 155, 229
  Water Snake, 28, 48, 83, 112, 220
Red-spotted Garter Snake, 224
Rhadinaea flavilata, 75, 101
Rhinocheilus lecontei, 148, 210
Ribbon Snakes, 26, 54, 57, 120
  Eastern, 80

Southern, 81, 120
Western, 80, 120, 156, 221
Ring-necked Snakes, 24, 74, 175–77
  Arizona, 177
  Coral-bellied, 176
  Eastern, 175
  Mississippi, 175
  Northern, 34
  Northwestern, 176
  Pacific, 143, 176
  Prairie, 143, 175
  San Bernardino, 176
  Southern, 91
  Southern California, 177
  Southwestern, 144, 177
  Van Denburgh's, 176
Ringed Ground Snake, 145, 213
  King Snake, 202
  "Milk" Snake, Mexican, 202
Rock Snake, 152, 215
Rosy Boa, 173
  Desert, 153, 173
Rubber Boa, 153, 173
Ruthven's Pine Snake, 84, 101
  Racer, 151, 184

Salt and Pepper Snake, 148, 207
Salvadora, 186–89
  grahamiae grahamiae, 147, 187
    hexalepis, 147, 188
    virgultea, 188
San Bernardino Ring-necked Snake, 176
San Lucan Gopher Snake, 160
Sand "Adder," 29, 36, 82
  Snake, 234
    Banded, 216
    Island, 216
    Straw-colored, 217
Santa Catalina Island King Snake, 149, 209
Scales, 18
Scarlet King Snake, 75, 103, 104, 146, 202
  Snake, 24, 46, 75, 104, 107, 146
Schott's Racer, 150, 185
Sea snakes, 239
  Yellow-bellied, 161, 241

Semiaquatic snakes, 12–13
Seminatrix pygaea, 75, 116
Shapes, 16
Sharp-nosed Gopher Snake, 194
Sharp-snouted Ground Snake, 213
Short-tailed Snake, 76, 106
Sidewinder, 163, 261
Silver Boa, 153
  Snake, 173
Sistrurus, 244–64
  catenatus catenatus, 30, 66, 162, 245
    edwardsii, 162
  miliarius barbouri, 86, 131
    miliarius, 86, 131
    streckeri, 86, 131, 162, 245
Sizes, 5–7
Slender Dark-headed Snake, 142, 234
  Garter Snake, 120
  Gopher Snake, 147, 195
    Southwestern, 194
Small brown snakes, 228–30
Small-eyed Brown Snake, 26, 53, 80, 118, 155, 230
Smooth Brown Snake, 24, 54, 74, 116
  Green Snake, 36, 74, 93, 179
Smooth-scaled Brown Snake, 230
  Green Snake, 144
Sonora, 211
  episcopa, 144, 211
  miniata linearis, 144, 212
    miniata, 144, 212
  mosaueri, 144, 212
  occipitalis, 145, 213
  semiannulata blanchardi, 145, 213
    gloydi, 145, 213
    semiannulata, 145, 212
  taylori, 144, 211
Sonoran Coral Snake, 160, 241
Southern Banded Water Snake, 111
  Brown Snake, 118
  Copperhead Snake, 128, 242
  Hissing "Adder," 29, 82
  Hog-nosed Snake, 36, 92
  Pine Snake, 84, 101
  Ribbon Snake, 81, 120
  Ring-necked Snake, 91
  Water Snake, 83

Southern California Ring-necked Snake, 177
Southwestern Leaf-nosed Snake, 152, 189
  Ring-necked Snake, 144
  Slender Gopher Snake, 194
Species, number of, 5
Speckled Rattlesnake, 257
Spotted Green Racer, 186
Spotted Night Snake, 152, 215
Spreading "Adder," 34, 82, 91, 158, 178
Stilosoma extenuatum, 76, 106
"Stinging" Snake, 76, 122, 151
Storeria, 228–30
  dekayi, 26, 52, 79, 117, 155, 229
  occipitomaculata, 26, 53, 80, 117, 155, 229
  victa, 80, 118
Storer's Snakes, 26, 52, 53, 80, 117, 155, 229
Straw-colored Burrowing Snake, 145
  Sand Snake, 217
Strecker's Hook-nosed Snake, 145, 214
  Pygmy Rattlesnake, 245
Striped Ground Snake, 144, 211, 212
  House Snake, 97
  Racer, 151, 183
Striped Snakes, 10, 27, 55, 81, 121
  Swamp Snake, 27, 51, 155, 228
  Water Snake, 50, 81, 109
  Whipsnake, 183
Structural characteristics, 17
Swamp Rattlesnake, 30, 66
  Snake, 76
    Banded, 118
    Black, 75, 116
    Striped, 27, 51, 155, 228

Tantilla, 125, 232, 233–36
  atriceps, 143, 233
  coronata coronata, 74, 125
    wagneri, 75, 125
  eiseni, 143, 233
  gracilis, 142, 234
  kirnia, 142, 234

  nigriceps, 142, 234
  planiceps, 143, 234
  utahensis, 143, 233
  wilcoxi, 143, 233
Taylor's Ground Snake, 144
  Snake, 211
Terrestrial snakes, 12–13
Texas Blind Snake, 141, 170
  Coral Snake, 240
  Rat Snake, 192
"Texas" Rattlesnake, 164
Thamnophis, 211–28
  angustirostris, 157, 227
  butleri, 27, 56
  eques, 157, 227
  marcianus, 157, 226
  megalops, 156, 222
  ordinoides atratus, 226
    biscutatus, 226
    couchii, 226
    elegans, 225
    hammondii, 226
    ordinoides, 156, 225
    vagrans, 226
  radix, 27, 57, 156, 222
  sauritus, 57
    proximus, 80, 120, 156, 221
    sackenii, 81, 120
    sauritus, 26, 54, 80, 120
  sirtalis concinnus, 224
    infernalis, 225
    ordinatus, 55
    parietalis, 224
    sirtalis, 27, 55, 81, 121, 157, 223, 224
Three-lined Boa, 153, 173
Thunder Snake, 106
Tiger Rattlesnake, 163, 257
Timber Rattlesnake, 30, 67, 86, 132, 165, 258
  snakes, 13
Treatment of bites, 267–75
Tree snakes, 13
Trimorphodon, 232, 236–38
  lyrophanes, 152, 236
  vandenburghi, 152, 237
  vilkinsoni, 153, 237

Tropidoclonion lineatum, 27, 51, 155, 228

"Two-headed Snake, 153, 173

Van Denburgh's Lyre Snake, 152, 237
 Ring-necked Snake, 176
Varieties. *See* Species
Velvet-tail, 259
Venom, analysis, 9
 fangs, 8
Vine Snake, Arizona, 148, 235
Vipers, pit, 8, 128, 240, 242
Virginia, 228–30
 valeriae elegans, 54, 74, 117, 142, 230
 valeriae, 24, 54, 74, 116
Virginia's Snake, 230
Viviparous snakes, 60–61
 and oviparous snakes, 12

Wagner's Miter Snake, 75
Water Moccasin, 7, 8, 30, 59, 66, 86, 129, 161, 240, 244
 "Moccasin," 218
Water-Pilot, 113
Water Snakes, 10, 13, 217–21
 Banded, 47, 83
 Blanchard's, 83, 112, 158, 219
 Brown, 82, 113
 Clark's, 81, 109
 Common, 28, 47, 83, 110, 158, 218
 Cope's, 83, 111
 Diamond-back, 28, 49, 84, 115, 159, 220
 Flat-tailed, 82, 115
 Florida Green, 84
 Graham's, 27, 51, 81, 108, 157, 218
 Green, 28, 50, 84, 114
 Kirtland's, 27, 48
 Lake, 28, 48
 Lower California, 159, 221
 Mississippi, 158
 Red-bellied, 28, 48, 83, 112, 220

 Southern, 83
 Banded, 111
 Striped, 50, 81, 109
 Yellow-bellied, 83, 112, 159, 220
Western Blue Racer, 149, 181
 Diamond Rattlesnake, 164, 247
 Diamond-back Rattlesnake, 133, 139
 Garter Snake, 156, 225
 Gopher Snake, 29, 43, 195–200
 Hog-nosed Snake, 158, 178
 "Milk" Snake, 202
 Ribbon Snake, 80, 120, 156, 221
Whipsnakes, 180–86
 Arizona, 183
 Banded, 183, 185
 Barbour's, 186
 Cape San Lucan, 185
 Clarion Island, 185
 Girard's, 184
 Lower California, 185
 Pink-bellied, 182
 Prairie, 182
 Red, 182
 Striped, 183
White Gopher Snake, 100
 Rattlesnake, 164, 257
Wilcox's Black-headed Snake, 143, 233
Wilkinson's Lyre Snake, 237
 Snake, 153
Willard's Rattlesnake, 162, 259
Worm Snakes, 12, 24, 33, 54, 74, 90, 117, 142, 174, 230

Yellow Chicken Snake, 97
 Gopher Snake, 159, 195, 198
 Rat Snake, 79, 97
Yellow-bellied King Snake, 25, 45, 105, 148, 205
 Racer, 94, 149, 180
 Sea Snake, 161, 241
 Water Snake, 83, 112, 159, 220
Yellow-lipped Snake, 75, 101

Explanation of Plates

Details at relative proportions: With the first series of plates, Numbers 1 to 31 inclusive, all specimens were photographed at the same lens distance from the camera. They thus illustrate proportionate sizes among species.

In cross-examination from these plates to the keys in text, or vice versa, the following should be particularly noted as points for identification: Smooth, strongly keeled or weakly keeled scales. Head very distinct, moderately distinct or barely wider than the neck. Body pattern, whether blotched, transversely banded or striped lengthwise. Head markings and abdominal pattern (or lack of same) are important. It will be noted that some species have little or no color pattern, above or beneath.

Full figures: Following the enlarged, sectional views are full photographs from life to show variety of form. These illustrations are not of relative size, but presented to show representative points for cross-reference to the keys in the text. General deduction should relate to arrangement of patterns in relation to body length, also to comparison of body outlines. Some species will be seen to be relatively much more slender than others. Thus the significance in text descriptions which read, "stout" or "moderately stout" or "slender" may be deducted for the North American snakes generally.

All names of snakes in captions read from top to bottom.

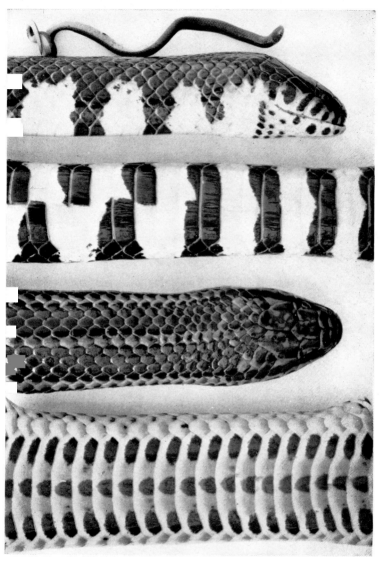

Worm Snake, *Carphophis amoena amoena*. Adult. New York
Horn Snake, *Farancia abacura abacura*. Florida
Horn Snake, *Farancia abacura abacura* (Abdominal)
Rainbow Snake, *Abastor erythrogrammus*. Florida
Rainbow Snake, *Abastor erythrogrammus* (Abdominal)

1

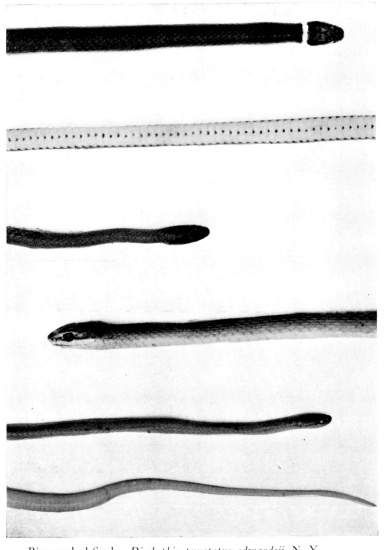

Ring-necked Snake, *Diadophis punctatus edwardsii*. N. Y.
Ring-necked Snake, *Diadophis punctatus edwardsii*. (Abdominal)
Smooth Green Snake, *Liopeltis vernalis*. New York
Keeled Green Snake, *Opheodrys aestivus*. Florida
Yellow-lipped Snake, *Rhadinaea flavilata*. Florida
Yellow-lipped Snake, *Rhadinaea flavilata*. (Abdominal)

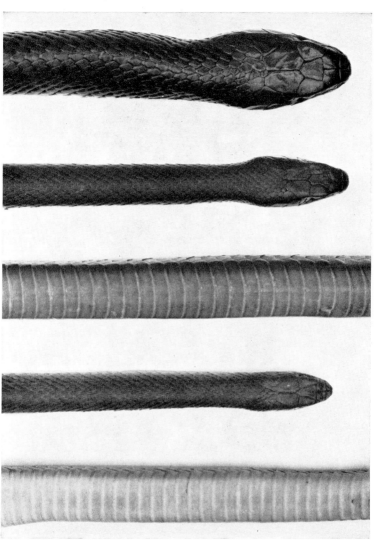

Indigo Snake, *Drymarchon corais couperi*. Florida
Blacksnake, *Coluber constrictor constrictor*. New York
Blacksnake, *Coluber constrictor constrictor*. (Abdominal)
Yellow-bellied Racer, *Coluber constrictor flaviventris*. Ohio
Yellow-bellied Racer, *Coluber constrictor flaviventris*. (Abdominal)

3

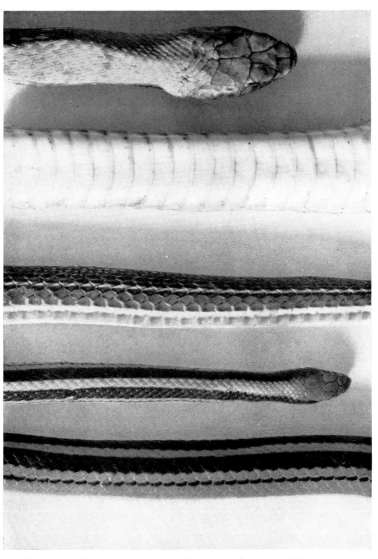

Coachwhip Snake, *Masticophis flagellum flagellum*. Texas
Coachwhip Snake, *Masticophis flagellum flagellum*. (Abdominal)
Striped Racer, *Masticophis taeniatus schotti*. Texas. (Side)
Flat-nosed Snake, *Salvadora grahamiae grahamiae*. Texas
Flat-nosed Snake, *Salvadora grahamiae grahamiae*. (From side)

4

Short-tailed Snake, *Stilosoma extenuatum*. Florida
LeConte's Snake, *Rhinocheilus lecontei*. (Tail; beneath)
LeConte's Snake, *Rhinocheilus lecontei*. (Mid-dorsal)
LeConte's Snake, *Rhinocheilus lecontei*. Texas specimen
Slender Gopher Snake, *Arizona elegans elegans*. Texas

5

Corn Snake, *Elaphe guttata*. Florida
Corn Snake, *Elaphe guttata*. (Mid-dorsal)
Corn Snake, *Elaphe guttata*. (Abdominal)
Pink Rat Snake, *Elaphe rosacea*. Florida Keys
Pink Rat Snake, *Elaphe rosacea*. (Abdominal)

Prairie Rat Snake, *Elaphe laeta*. Oklahoma
Prairie Rat Snake, *Elaphe laeta*. (Abdominal)
Fox Snake, *Elaphe vulpina*. Indiana
Fox Snake, *Elaphe vulpina*. (Abdominal)
Fox Snake, *Elaphe vulpina*. (Tail; above)

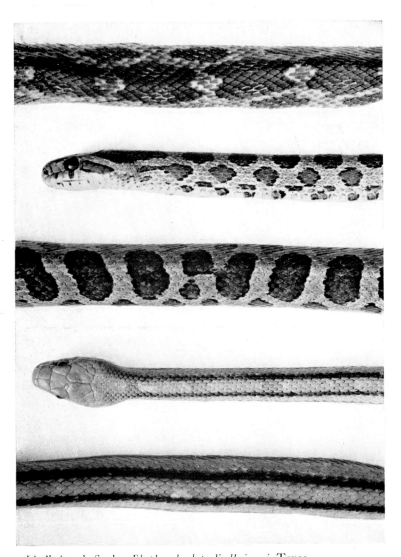

Lindheimer's Snake, *Elaphe obsoleta lindheimeri*. Texas
Prairie Rat Snake, *Elaphe laeta*. Oklahoma
Prairie Rat Snake, *Elaphe laeta*. (Mid-dorsal)
Banded Rat Snake, *Elaphe quadrivittata quadrivittata*. Florida
Banded Rat Snake, *Elaphe quadrivittata quadrivittata*. (Mid-dorsal)

8

Pine Snake, *Pituophis melanoleucus melanoleucus*. N. J.
Pine Snake, *Pituophis melanoleucus melanoleucus*. (Mid-dorsal)
Bull Snake, *Pituophis sayi sayi*. Texas
Bull Snake, *Pituophis sayi sayi*. (Mid-dorsal)

9

Scarlet Snake, *Cemophora coccinea*. Florida
Scarlet King Snake, *Lampropeltis elapsoides elapsoides*. Florida
Scarlet King Snake, *Lampropeltis elapsoides virginiana*. Va.
Red Milk Snake, *Lampropeltis triangulum amaura*. Ark.
Milk Snake, *Lampropeltis triangulum triangulum*. (Abdominal)
Milk Snake, *Lampropeltis triangulum triangulum*. N. Y.

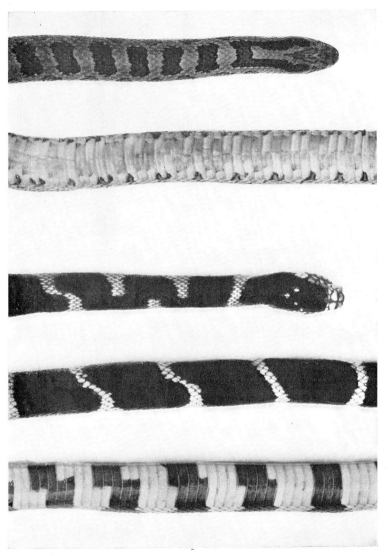

Prairie King Snake, *Lampropeltis calligaster*. Oklahoma
Prairie King Snake, *Lampropeltis calligaster*. (Abdominal)
California King Snake, *Lampropeltis getulus californiae*.
California King Snake, *Lampropeltis getulus californiae*. (Mid-
    dorsal)
California King Snake, *Lampropeltis getulus californiae*. (Abdominal)

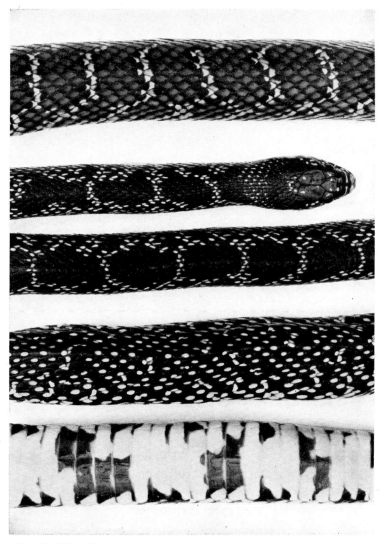

Florida King Snake, *Lampropeltis getulus floridana*
Mexican King Snake, *Lampropeltis getulus splendida*. Texas
Mexican King Snake, *Lampropeltis getulus splendida*. (Mid-dorsal)
Spotted King Snake, *Lampropeltis getulus holbrooki*. La.
Spotted King Snake, *Lampropeltis getulus holbrooki*. (Abdominal)

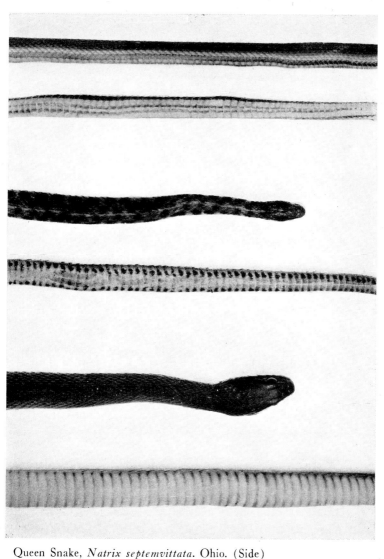

Queen Snake, *Natrix septemvittata*. Ohio. (Side)
Queen Snake, *Natrix septemvittata*. (Abdominal)
Kirtland's Water Snake, *Natrix kirtlandii*. Ohio
Kirtland's Water Snake, *Natrix kirtlandii*. (Abdominal)
Yellow-bellied Water Snake, *Natrix erythrogaster transversa*. La.
Yellow-bellied Water Snake, *Natrix erythrogaster transversa*.
  (Abdominal)

13

Green Water Snake, *Natrix cyclopion cyclopion*. La.
Green Water Snake, *Natrix cyclopion cyclopion*. (Abdominal)
Florida Green Water Snake, *Natrix cyclopion floridana*. (Side)
Florida Green Water Snake, *Natrix cyclopion floridana*. (Mid-
    dorsal)
Florida Green Water Snake, *Natrix cyclopion floridana*. (Abdominal)

14

Diamond-back Water Snake, *Natrix rhombifera rhombifera*. Ark.

Diamond-back Water Snake, *Natrix rhombifera rhombifera*. (Mid-dorsal)

Brown Water Snake, *Natrix taxispilota*. Florida

Brown Water Snake, *Natrix taxispilota*. (Mid-dorsal)

Brown Water Snake, *Natrix taxispilota*. (Side)

15

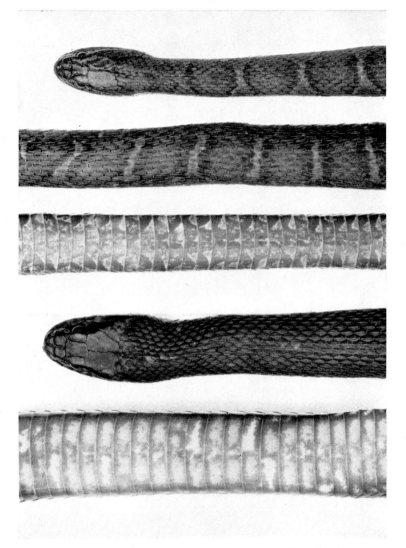

Common Water Snake, *Natrix sipedon sipedon*. New York
Common Water Snake, *Natrix sipedon sipedon*. (Mid-dorsal)
Common Water Snake, *Natrix sipedon sipedon*. (Abdominal)
Banded Water Snake, *Natrix sipedon fasciata*. Georgia
Banded Water Snake, *Natrix sipedon fasciata*. (Abdominal)

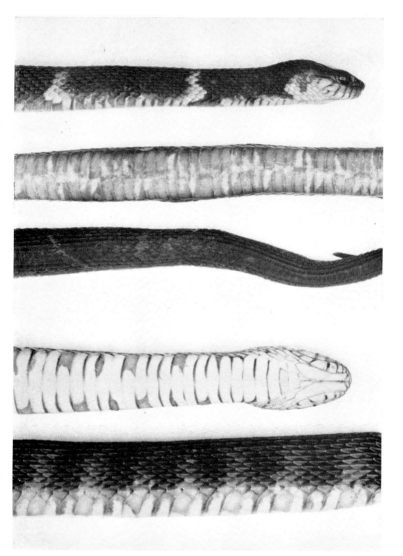

Blanchard's Water Snake, *Natrix sipedon confluens*. La.
Blanchard's Water Snake, *Natrix sipedon confluens*. (Abdominal)
Blanchard's Water Snake, *Natrix sipedon confluens*. (Dorsal)
Cope's Water Snake, *Natrix sipedon pictiventris*. Florida
Cope's Water Snake, *Natrix sipedon pictiventris*. (Side)

Lake Water Snake, *Natrix sipedon insularum*. Ohio
Lake Water Snake, *Natrix sipedon insularum*. (Abdominal)
Flat-tailed Water Snake, *Natrix compressicauda*. Florida
Flat-tailed Water Snake, *Natrix compressicauda*. (Mid-dorsal)
Flat-tailed Water Snake, *Natrix compressicauda*. (Tail)

18

Black Swamp Snake, *Seminatrix pygaea*. (From side)
Black Swamp Snake, *Seminatrix pygaea*. Florida
Allen's Mud Snake, *Liodytes alleni*. Florida
Allen's Mud Snake, *Liodytes alleni*. (Side)
Allen's Mud Snake, *Liodytes alleni*. (Tail; beneath)
Striped Swamp Snake, *Tropidoclonion lineatum*. Ohio
Striped Swamp Snake, *Tropidoclonion lineatum*. (Abdominal)

19

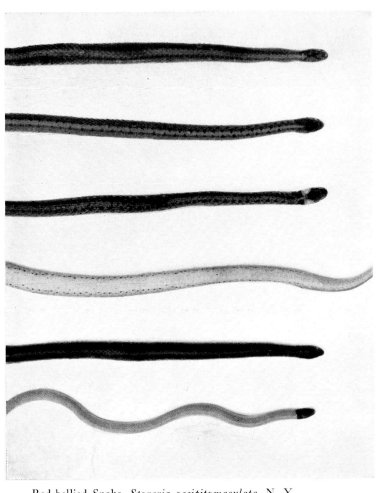

Red-bellied Snake, *Storeria occipitomaculata*. N. Y.
Storer's Snake, *Storeria dekayi*. N. Y.
Florida Brown Snake, *Storeria victa*. Fla.
Florida Brown Snake, *Storeria victa*. (Abdominal)
Smooth Brown Snake, *Virginia valeriae valeriae*. So. Carolina
Black-headed Snake, *Tantilla coronata wagneri*. Florida

20

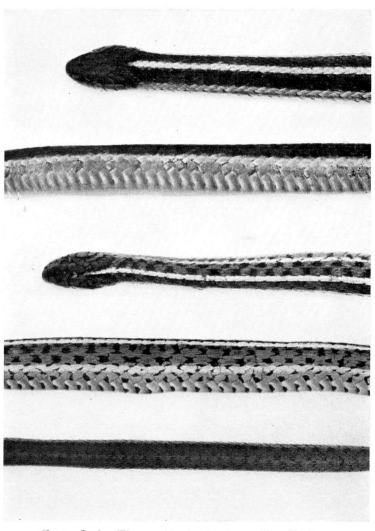

Garter Snake, *Thamnophis sirtalis sirtalis*. New York
Garter Snake, *Thamnophis sirtalis sirtalis*. (Side)
Garter Snake, *Thamnophis sirtalis sirtalis*. Florida
Garter Snake, *Thamnophis sirtalis sirtalis*. (Side)
Garter Snake, *Thamnophis sirtalis sirtalis*. N. Y. (Back)

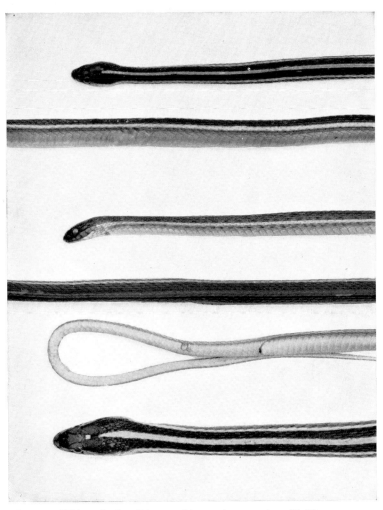

Eastern Ribbon Snake, *Thamnophis sauritus sauritus*. N. Y.
Eastern Ribbon Snake, *Thamnophis sauritus sauritus*. (Side)
Southern Ribbon Snake, *Thamnophis sauritus sackenii*. Fla.
Southern Ribbon Snake, *Thamnophis sauritus sackenii*. (Mid-dorsal)
Southern Ribbon Snake, *Thamnophis sauritus sackenii*. (Tail)
Western Ribbon Snake, *Thamnophis sauritus proximus*. Texas

Butler's Garter Snake, *Thamnophis butleri*. Ohio
Butler's Garter Snake, *Thamnophis butleri*. (Side)
Marcy's Garter Snake, *Thamnophis marcianus*. Texas
Marcy's Garter Snake, *Thamnophis marcianus*. (Side)
Marcy's Garter Snake, *Thamnophis marcianus*. (Mid-dorsal)

23

Hog-nosed Snake, *Heterodon contortrix*. Oklahoma
Hog-nosed Snake, *Heterodon contortrix*. (Mid-dorsal)
Hog-nosed Snake, *Heterodon contortrix*. New York
Hog-nosed Snake, *Heterodon contortrix*. New York
Southern Hog-nosed Snake, *Heterodon simus*. Florida
Southern Hog-nosed Snake, *Heterodon simus*. Florida

Northern   Copperhead   Snake,   *Agkistrodon   mokasen   cupreus.*
(Beneath)
Northern Copperhead Snake, *Agkistrodon mokasen cupreus.* N. J.
Southern Copperhead Snake, *Agkistrodon mokasen mokasen.* La.
Western Copperhead Snake, *Agkistrodon mokasen laticincta.* Tex.
Western Copperhead Snake, *Agkistrodon mokasen laticincta.* Tex.

25

Water Snake, *Natrix cyclopion*. Florida. (Non-venomous)
Water Moccasin, *Agkistrodon piscivorus*. Florida. (Venomous)
Water Moccasin, *Agkistrodon piscivorus*. (Mid-dorsal)
Water Moccasin, *Agkistrodon piscivorus*. (Tail; beneath)
Water Snake, *Natrix cyclopion*. (Tail beneath; double scutes)

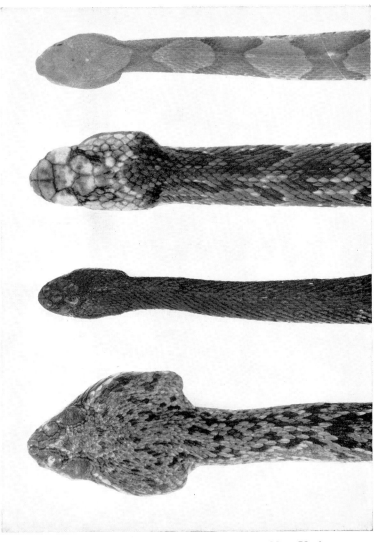

Copperhead Snake, *Agkistrodon mokasen cupreus.* New York
Water Moccasin, *Agkistrodon piscivorus.* Florida
Massasauga; Prairie Rattler, *Sistrurus catenatus catenatus.* Ohio
Diamond-back Rattlesnake, *Crotalus adamanteus.* Florida

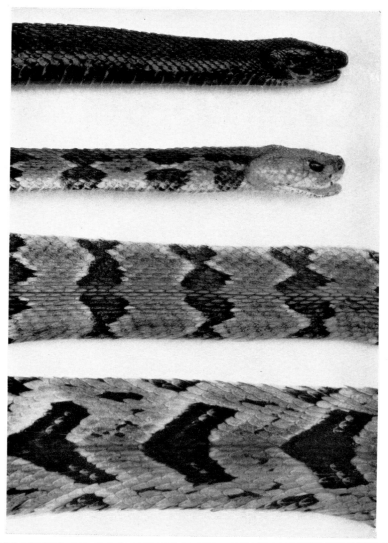

Massasauga, *Sistrurus catenatus catenatus.* Ohio. (Melanistic)
Timber Rattlesnake, *Crotalus horridus horridus.* New York
Timber Rattlesnake, *Crotalus horridus horridus.* (Mid-dorsal)
Cane-brake Rattlesnake, *Crotalus horridus atricaudatus.* Georgia

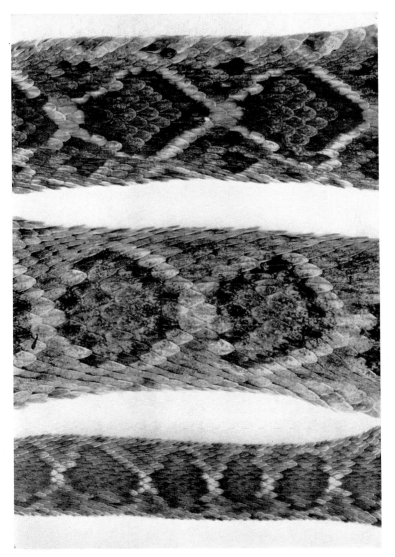

Diamond-back Rattlesnake, *Crotalus adamanteus*. Florida
Western Diamond Rattlesnake, *Crotalus atrox atrox*. Texas
Red Rattlesnake, *Crotalus ruber*. California

Diamond-back Rattlesnake, *Crotalus adamanteus*. Florida
Diamond-back Rattlesnake, *Crotalus adamanteus*. (Rattle)
Western Diamond Rattlesnake, *Crotalus atrox atrox*. Texas
Western Diamond Rattlesnake, *Crotalus atrox atrox*. (Adult rattle)
Western Diamond Rattlesnake, *Crotalus atrox atrox*. (Immature rattle)

Prairie Rattlesnake, *Crotalus viridis viridis.* Nebraska
Rattle of Cane-brake Rattlesnake, *Crotalus horridus atricaudatus*
Rattle of Diamond-back Rattlesnake, *Crotalus adamanteus*
Rattle of Red Rattlesnake, *Crotalus ruber*
Rattle of Western Diamond Rattlesnake, *Crotalus atrox atrox*
Rattle of Western Diamond Rattlesnake, *Crotalus atrox atrox.* (Young)

31

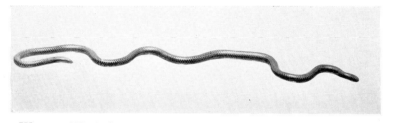

Western Blind Snake, *Leptotyphlops humilis humilis*. Calif. Size
small: 8 – 12 inches. Pale brown with darker stripes
(Permission L. M. Klauber)

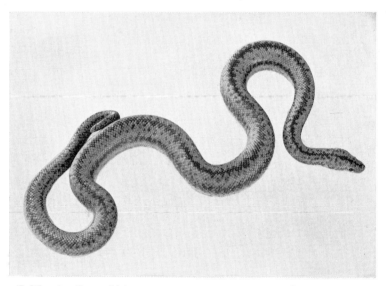

California Boa, *Lichanura roseofusca roseofusca*. Size moderate:
$2\frac{1}{2}$ – 3 feet. Brown with darker markings
(Permission L. M. Klauber)

Rubber Boa, *Charina bottae*. California. Size moderate: 15 – 24
inches. Lustrous brown or gray
(Permission N. Y. Zoological Society)

Coachwhip Snake, *Masticophis flagellum flagellum*. Georgia. Size
large: 4 – 7 feet. Gray or brown and blackish
(Permission N. Y. Zoological Society)

33

Chaparral Flat-nosed Snake, *Salvadora grahamiae virgultea*. Calif.
Size moderate: 2 – 3 feet. Brown or black; whitish bands
(Permission L. M. Klauber)

Desert Leaf-nosed Snake, *Phyllorhynchus decurtatus perkinsi*. Calif.
Size small: 12 – 15 inches. Pale yellow with dark blotches
(Permission L. M. Klauber)

Fox Snake, *Elaphe vulpina*. Ohio. Size large: 4 – 6 feet. Pale
brown; darker blotches

(Permission N. Y. Zoological Society)

Pine Snake, *Pituophis melanoleucus melanoleucus*. N. J. Size
large: 5 – 6 feet. White with black blotches

(Permission N. Y. Zoological Society)

35

Milk Snake, *Lampropeltis triangulum triangulum*. N. Y. Moderately large: 3 – 4 feet. Gray with dark blotches
(Permission N. Y. Zoological Society)

California King Snake, *Lampropeltis getulus californiae*. Moderately large: 3 – 4 feet. Black with yellow band
(Permission L. M. Klauber)

Eastern King Snake, *Lampropeltis getulus getulus*. Georgia. Size large: 4 – 6 feet. Black with white or yellow rings
(Permission N. Y. Zoological Society)

Ringed Ground Snake; Shovel-nosed Ground Snake, *Sonora occipitalis*. California. Size small: 10 – 12 inches. White, pink or yellow; black rings
(Permission L. M. Klauber)

Spotted Night Snake, *Hypsiglena torquata ochrorhyncha.* Calif. Size
small: 15 – 18 inches. Gray to yellow; darker markings
(Permission L. M. Klauber)

Red and Black Ground Snake, *Chilomeniscus cinctus.* Lower
California. Size small: 9 – 12 inches. Orange to red; black
crossbands
(Permission L. M. Klauber)

38

Common Water Snake, *Natrix sipedon sipedon*. New York. Size
large: 3½ – 4 feet. Brown with darker bands
(Permission N. Y. Zoological Society)

Red-bellied Water Snake, *Natrix erythrogaster erythrogaster*. South
Carolina. Size large: 3 – 4 feet. Brown above; red beneath
(Permission N. Y. Zoological Society)

Eastern Garter Snake, *Thamnophis sirtalis sirtalis*. N. Y. Size
moderate: 2 – 3 feet. Brown to black; yellow stripes
(Permission N. Y. Zoological Society)

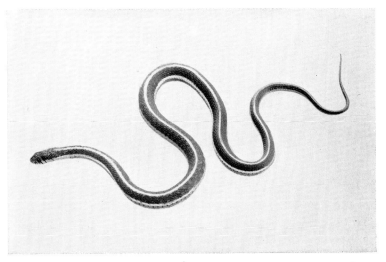

California Garter Snake, *Thamnophis ordinoides elegans*. Size
moderate: 2 – 3 feet. Brown to black; yellow stripes
(Permission L. M. Klauber)

California Black-headed Snake, *Tantilla eiseni.* Size small: 8 - 10 inches. Brown, head blackish, pale collar

(Permission L. M. Klauber)

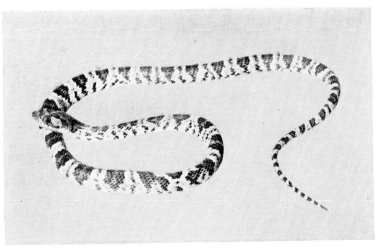

California Lyre Snake, *Trimorphodon vandenburghi.* Size moderate: 2½ – 3 feet. Gray with darker markings

(Permission L. M. Klauber)

Copperhead Snake (Venomous) showing elliptic pupil

Spreading "Adder" (Non-venomous) showing round pupil

Head of Coral Snake (*Micrurus*) showing short fangs

Head of Crotaline Snake, showing folding fangs and reserves to take
their place

Water Moccasin; Cotton-mouth, *Agkistrodon piscivorus*. Florida.
Size large: 4 – 6 feet. Dull brown or olive; darker markings
(Permission N. Y. Zoological Society)

Southern Copperhead Snake, *Agkistrodon mokasen mokasen*. Ga.
Moderately large: 2½ – 4 feet. Pale brown; darker blotches
(Permission N. Y. Zoological Society)

Massasauga, *Sistrurus catenatus catenatus.* Ohio. Size moderate:
2½ – 3 feet. Brown; darker blotches
(Permission N. Y. Zoological Society)

Diamond-back Rattlesnake, *Crotalus adamanteus.* Florida. Size large:
5 – 8 feet. Olive to brown; darker rhombs
(Permission N. Y. Zoological Society)

45

Western Diamond Rattlesnake. *Crotalus atrox atrox.* Texas. Size large: 5 – 6 feet.
Grayish; darker rhombs
(Permission N. Y. Zoological Society)

46

Prairie Rattlesnake, *Crotalus viridis viridis*. Nebraska. Size large:
$3\frac{1}{2}$ – 5 feet. Olive to tan; darker blotches
(Permission N. Y. Zoological Society)

Pacific Rattlesnake, *Crotalus viridis oreganus*. Calif. Moderately
large: 3 – $4\frac{1}{2}$ feet. Gray to tan; darker blotches
(Permission L. M. Klauber)

Tiger Rattlesnake, *Crotalus tigris*. Arizona. Moderately large:
3 – 4 feet. Yellowish-gray; darker markings
(Permission L. M. Klauber)

Horned Rattlesnake, *Crotalus cerastes*. Arizona. Size moderate:
2 – 2½ feet. Gray to yellowish; darker blotches
(Permission N. Y. Zoological Society)